SAVE HARMLESS AGREEMENT

BIOMASS TO METHANOL

A Specialists' Workshop
March 3-5, 1982
Tamarron, Durango, Colorado

Edited by: Thomas B. Reed
Michael Graboski

The Department of Chemical Engineering
The Colorado School of Mines
Golden, Colorado

Sponsored by the U.S. Department of Energy
Coordinated by the Solar Energy Research Institute

Originally issued as SERI / 234 1590 CONF-820324 UC Category 61A

ISBN: 978-1-60322-049-1

Front Row Kneeling From Left to Right:

William Stevenson, Kevin Lally, Thomas O'Connell, Joseph Haggin, Si Friedrich, Thomas Milne, Thomas Reed and Paul Danish

Standing From Left to Right:

Charles Bishop, Paul Boyd, Victor Yang, Gary Schiefelbein, Adi Guzdar , Michael Graboski Chuck Stone, Leslie Oster, (Unidentified), Pam Miles, Thomas Miles, Oliver Branden, Henry Wilson Lars Waldheim, Kamil Klier, Nils Lindman, Andrew Himmelblau, Suresh Babu, Charles Nelson, Michael Onischak Arthur Hornig, Michel Bernon, John Black, Stephen Kohan, Clayton Smith, Donald Klass and David Salisbury

v

PREFACE

In 1981 the Office of Alcohol Fuels of the U.S. Department of Energy suggested that the Solar Energy Research Institute (SERI) hold a specialists' workshop on Methanol from Biomass. Since SERI had just completed building, and was successfully testing, a one-ton/day pressurized oxygen gasifier for making methanol, we welcomed this opportunity to bring together the groups from around the world that were working in this field to share successes and problems and to learn related technology involved in biomass methanol.

These proceedings are the record of that workshop. We have tried to assemble experts on all phases of methanol manufacture from various feedstocks so that those working with biomass can take as much advantage of known technology as possible. We hope that the following papers will be useful to all others who are considering following this path to a new fuel from renewable energy.

Conventional wisdom often comes into conflict with changing conditions. Conventional wisdom suggests that synthetic fuels are most likely to be based on coal and they will be made only in very large scale, mine-mouth plants. While one can find justification for this viewpoint in history and present practice, a number of factors may make methanol from biomass, made at a much smaller scale, competitive or even more economical than coal-derived methanol. These factors are scattered through the papers presented here, and are summarized in the paper by Gage. Ultimately only time and progress can decide where biomass methanol fits into our future, but a reading of these papers will show that a number of competent scientists and engineers are convinced that this can be an important fuel source for our children.

Our thanks to the Office of Alcohol Fuels for the opportunity to hold this workshop and make the proceedings available to the wider scientific and engineering community. Our thanks to the SERI Conference Group for handling the conference details so well, allowing the participants maximum freedom for talking, listening, and thinking. Greetings to our fellow participants and we hope that in another few years a second conference on biomass methanol will be justified by the rapid progress in this field and that we and others can come together again.

Thomas B. Reed

Thomas B. Reed
Workshop Chairman
Thermochemical and Electrochemical
Research Branch

TABLE OF CONTENTS

State-of-the Art of Conventional Methanol Manufacture

STATE OF THE ART - STEAM HYDROCARBON REFORMING

P. Boyd
United Catalysts Inc.
Louisville, Kentucky

The purpose of this discussion is to cover the state of the art of steam-hydrocarbon reforming. We will cover a review of the past, a look at the present, and some thoughts as to what may be in the future.

BRIEF REVIEW OF REFORMING HISTORY

Type of Feeds

Prior to 1960, in general the feed streams have been primarily natural gas and propane which were treated at low pressures up to about 200 psig.

Feed Pretreatment

Before gas can be reformed, it is necessary to go through a pretreatment to remove sulfur compounds which would poison the reforming catalyst. This pretreatment was done using activated carbon at ambient temperature. The carbon is a cyclical operation with steam regeneration occurring every five to ten days depending on design and quantity of sulfur in the gas. In some instances, hot zinc or caustic or amine treating was used, but these were more the exception than the rule.

Type of Primary Reformers

There were a number of manufacturers of these type of furnaces. Some of the principal ones were Girdler, which used the old Hercules box type furnace, 8" tubes, 26-27 feet in the fired zone, side-fired, down flow and 10-50 psig; Chemico, which was a circular up-fired furnace, with 6" tubes with a 2" inner tube, about 30 feet in fired zone, gas flow was down the outer tube containing the catalyst and then up the center tube; Foster Wheeler and ICI also built many of the low pressure units.

Type of Secondary Reformers

In general, these are large vessels that are refractory lined and contain one big bed of catalyst. Their main purpose is to add the proper amount of nitrogen into the synthesis gas while at the same time utilizing the heat of combustion from the oxygen to complete the reforming of the residual methane present in the gas from the primary. As you can understand, the most important part of the secondary is the burner design in which the air and primary effluent gas are mixed and burned. It is the burner design that is unique in different designs

1

and is the most critical part in obtaining good combustion and distribution.

Type of Catalysts

The original reforming catalysts were silica-alumina-cement base material containing 15-30% nickel. The nickel was either compounded into the catalyst formulation or it was impregnated after the catalyst was formed or a combination of both. These catalysts were in the form of 1/2" to 1" extrudates or solid tablets. Essentially the same catalyst was used in both the primary and secondary.

As to the down-stream units, these were large vessels containing one or two beds of shift catalyst for converting the CO to more hydrogen and carbon dioxide. Also, in these early ammonia plants, copper liquid scrubbing was used to remove carbon monoxide and water scrubbing was sometimes used to remove carbon dioxide. Later the low pressure units used amine scrubbing and methanation.

PRESENT REFORMING

Type of Feeds

The major reformer feeds being used or considered are natural gas, propane, LPG, butane, naphtha, refinery off-gas and biomass. Also, another way of producing synthesis gas is by gasification units. In these partial oxidation units, a wide variety of feedstocks such as coal, oil, or wood waste are possible. The pressure of operation for current plants is 250-550 psig.

Feed Pretreatment

In preparation of these feeds, most plants either are installing or have already installed hot zinc oxide beds for sulfur removal. If the sulfur is not H_2S, then it may require installing a bed of cobalt moly catalyst ahead of the zinc oxide bed. There are also some of these plants which use only natural gas that will still use just treated activated carbon. Also for methanol and oxo-synthesis gas plants, many designs add CO_2 to the reformer feed to help get a better carbon-hydrogen balance. This CO_2 must also be sulfur free.

Type of Primary Reformers

Some of the major types of furnaces are Kellogg (down-fired); Foster Wheeler (terraced, side-fired); Selas (side-fired); and Chemico (up-fired). Some of the small furnaces are built by Hydro-Chem Co., Howe-Baker, and Girdler Corp. There are a number of additional designers and builders but the above are the ones that quickly come to mind.

In ammonia and hydrogen applications, these furnaces operate in the pressure range of 250-600 psig. The steam to carbon ratios run in the range of 3 to 6. The CO_2 is generally added to the furnace at the lower operating pressures, and at higher pressures it is added down stream.

As to the furnaces themselves, the tubes range from 2.75" to 6" in inside diameter with lengths of 32' to 44'. They are usually made of HK40 but can also be made of Inconel and/or Supertherm. The flow is generally down flow but can be up flow depending upon design. Also, furnace firing as stated above can be down, up or side fired. Most furnaces have the tubes manifolded outside the furnace at the bottom. However, the Kellogg furnaces have riser tubes and manifolded at the top.

The process steam is made either from waste heat boilers on the stack or from furnace effluent heat or both. Seldom is steam supplied or required from an outside source. The feed gas is usually heated by stack coils or furnace effluent or both, to temperatures in the range of 1000-1100°F.

With regard to gas composition exit the reformer, the ammonia plants leak about 10-15% CH_4 and the secondary exit contains about 0.2-0.5% CH_4. For hydrogen plants that want low methane, they run with 0.2-3.0% CH_4 depending on use or design. Methanol plants run with 0.5-3.0% CH_4, again depending on design.

Type of Secondary Reformers

These are large catalyst vessels with an air-gas burner in the top. The incoming air is preheated to 800-1000°F and mixed with the furnace effluent. These burners are somewhat complex in design and are produced by several companies. These burner designs, the gas distribution, and the combustion space above the catalyst are all very important in obtaining good reforming performance in the secondary.

As stated above, the air is usually heated to 1000°F which helps get additional methane reforming to occur. In earlier plants, only the heat of compression of the air was used but later and present day plants actually preheat the air either through heat exchange or a direct fired heater. Also, some secondaries add a small amount of steam to the incoming gas from the primary.

Type of Catalysts

In the early 1960's, most primary and secondary catalysts were calcium-aluminate base in the form of rings with 16-30% nickel impregnated on the carrier or compounded into the carrier or both. In the late 1960's to the current time, a ceramic base which is a high temperature fired material that may be all alumina, calcium-aluminate, or mag-alumina or possibly a combination of these or other materials is used. Nickel is still the primary active ingredient, either impregnated or compounded in concentrations of 6-20% metal. These are all supplied as rings, and in primaries the smaller the ring the greater the activity, but also the greater the pressure drop. Consequently, these two things must be balanced off against each other. In an effort to take advantage of the activity but not too much penalty in pressure drop, many furnaces are split loaded with a smaller particle in the top half and a larger particle in the bottom. Ring sizes range from 3/4" x 3/4" x 3/8" to 5/8" x 1/4" x 1/4".

In secondaries there is generally a layer of ceramic base material on top which contains about 3-4% nickel and serves as a heat shield. The remainder of the bed is the calcium-aluminate base containing 17-20% nickel. In the early high pressure plants, silica migration caused many problems until it was realized that the catalyst and refractory linings must be silica free. Therefore, it is very important that these catalysts and the vessel lining be silica free since the pressure and temperatures reached will enable silica to migrate down stream. The silica can then coat the exchanger, tubes, and the down-stream shift catalyst causing many problems, some of which are an increase in pressure drop, loss in heat transfer efficiency, or apparent loss in catalyst activity.

The units down stream are conventional catalyst vessels with beds of high and low temperature shift catalysts, heat exchanger, CO_2 removal and finally methanation in ammonia and hydrogen plants. In methanol or other synthesis gas streams, there is usually not any further catalytic processing until the synthesis loop. For some applications, there may be a small slip stream shift reactor for ratio adjustment, but again this is a matter of design.

FUTURE GAS REFORMING PLANTS

Some of the things which are being used or planned are as follows:

1. Pressure swing absorption for CO and CO_2 removal with no methanation step required.

2. Higher reforming pressures.

3. Lower synthesis loop pressures.

4. More active catalysts for the entire group, reforming through synthesis.

5. Better utilization of the energy in all of these processes.

6. Different feeds, possibly heavier stocks employing the partial oxidation or gasifier concept.

7. Treating sour gases from coal or share gasification units.

These are only a few of the things that are being considered. There are many things that have not been covered in this talk which time does not allow my discussing. I will be pleased to answer any questions now or later after the meeting.

METHANOL SYNTHESIS

K. Klier, Department of Chemistry,
Lehigh University, Bethlehem, PA 18015

ABSTRACT

The low pressure methanol synthesis is an attractive terminal stage of biomass-to-methanol flow diagram. Selection of catalysts, reaction kinetics in the presence of carbon dioxide, the preparations of the copper-zinc oxide catalysts, and mechanistic routes to low alcohols are reviewed herein to demonstrate that the operating conditions and models for methanol synthesis are well experimented out and that sound chemical principles may be used for steering the synthesis to C_2-C_4 alcohols. The latter goal has not been realized on a commercial scale, however, and requires further catalyst optimization.

INTRODUCTION

Methanol synthesis is nearly an ideal process to be combined with bio-mass gasification for the manufacture of high grade fuel and of basic chemicals from renewable resources. The processes available at the present time use catalysts that are very selective to methanol and active at mild conditions, i.e. 200-250°C and 50-100 atmospheres. The typical yields are in the range of 1.2 - 1.5 kg methanol per kg catalyst per hour, and the modern catalysts are stable for years providing no impurities such as sulphur and chlorine-containing gases are present in the synthesis gas. Since biomass-derived syngas is relatively free of these impurities, it is well suited for methanol synthesis after minimal clean-up.

The designer and operator of the combined gasifier-methanol plant may derive economic advantage from the knowledge of how the catalysts work simply by manipulating operating conditions and syngas composition. Furthermore, the requirements on the purity of fuel grade methanol are not as severe as of chemical methanol and in fact slight modifications of methanol catalysts result in catalysts and processes for a whole spectrum of low (C_1-C_4) alcohols which may be of still greater value than methanol as motor fuel. It is the purpose of this article to review the factors, including the syngas composition, that determine the yields and selectivities in methanol synthesis, and to describe chemical principles that can be used to steer the synthesis to low

5

alcohols. The maturity, advantages and disadvantages of each process will be briefly evaluated in our concluding remarks.

Stoichiometry and Thermodynamics of Alcohol Syntheses

The sources of carbon and oxygen in direct syntheses of alcohols are CO and CO_2 and the source of hydrogen is molecular hydrogen. The equilibrium conversions are dictated by the free energies of the reactions

$$CO + 2H_2 \rightleftharpoons CH_3OH \qquad \Delta H^\circ_{600K} = -100.46 \text{ kJ/mol} \qquad [1]$$
$$\Delta G^\circ_{600K} = +45.36 \text{ kJ/mol}$$

$$CO_2 + 3H_2 \rightleftharpoons CH_3OH + H_2O \qquad \Delta H^\circ_{600K} = -61.59 \text{ kJ/mol} \qquad [2]$$
$$\Delta G^\circ_{600K} = +61.80 \text{ kJ/mol}$$

$$(n+1)CO + 2(n+1)H_2 \rightleftharpoons CH_3(CH_2)_nOH + nH_2O \qquad n \geq 1 \qquad [3]$$

$$(2n+1)CO + (n+2)H_2 \rightleftharpoons CH_3(CH_2)_nOH + nCO_2 \qquad n \geq 1 \qquad [4]$$

Reactions that give rise to hydrocarbons are often side reactions in alcohol syntheses, e.g.

$$nCO + (2n+1)H_2 \rightleftharpoons C_nH_{2n+2} + nH_2O \qquad n \geq 1 \qquad [5]$$

and

$$2nCO + (n+1)H_2 \rightleftharpoons C_nH_{2n+2} + nCO_2 \qquad n \geq 1 \qquad [6]$$

Reactions [3] and [4] or [5] and [6] are related via the shift reaction

$$H_2O + CO \rightleftharpoons H_2 + CO_2 \qquad [7]$$

and in the case when alcohols or hydrocarbons are synthesized at low temperatures with the formation of CO_2 instead of water over a single catalyst, it is customary to say that the catalyst has a good "internal shift" activity. The standard Gibbs free energies of reactions [1] and [3]-[6] per carbon atom in the alcohol or hydrocarbon product are shown in Figure 1 for the temperature of 600K, near which good catalysts for alcohols work. In addition, dimethylether (DME) may be produced by dehydration of methanol

$$2CH_3OH \rightleftharpoons CH_3OCH_3 + H_2O \qquad \Delta H^\circ_{600K} = -20.59 \text{ kJ/mol} \qquad [8]$$
$$\Delta G^\circ_{600K} = -10.71 \text{ kJ/mol}$$

or in general ethers may be formed by dehydration or dehydrocondensation of higher alcohols. It is seen from Figure 1 that methanol is the least thermodynamically probable product while methane plus CO_2 are the most thermodynamically probable products of hydrogenation of CO. Hence the role of alcohol synthesis catalysts is not only to

6

promote this synthesis at a fast rate but also to control selectivity so that the more probable hydrocarbon products are not formed.

After the development involving some six decades, industry now does have a catalyst which selectively steers carbon monoxide hydrogenation to almost pure methanol. However, a viable commercial process for the C_2-C_4 alcohols that would be produced with high yields does not exist at the present time, although the chemical principles for building the carbon chain are well-known and their exploitation is documented in the literature. Yet there are many practical reasons why the synthesis of C_2-C_4 alsohols should be brought to a commercial stage: in relation to biomass processing, the implementation of small scale technology may critically depend on whether alcohols may be produced at very low pressures at which equilibrium conversion of methanol is thermodynamically restricted while that of C_2-C_4 alcohols is not. For example, at 250°C and 5 atmospheres, methanol equilibrium conversion from $CO:CO_2:H_2$ = 24:6:70 is 2.5% while that for ethanol according to equation [4] with n=1 is 99 %. Hence the incentives for making C_2-C_4 alcohols rather than methanol very much depend on the pressure range contemplated for the biomass-to-methanol plants, possibly determined by the output pressures from the biomass gasifiers.

The Low Pressure Methanol Catalysts

Although the catalysts of general composition $Cu/ZnO/Al_2O_3$ prevail in the current commercial practice, other catalysts for low pressure methanol synthesis are also known. These are metals and oxides that satisfy the following requirements:
    (i) The catalyst must not cleave the carbon-oxygen sigma bond ($\sim$360kJ/mol) in carbon monoxide. This condition prevents the synthesis of higher alcohols and hydrocarbons in which C-C bonds are formed by hydrogenolytic cleavage of C-O bond.
    (ii) The catalyst must activate the carbon monoxide molecule so that hydrogenation can occur on both ends of the molecule.
    (iii) The catalyst must be a fairly good hydrogenation catalyst which activates hydrogen molecules in a manner suitable for the above reaction.

Because the activation of carbon monoxide is undoubtedly the most difficult step, it is instructive to examine the ability of various catalysts to activate CO non-dissociatively. For metals there exists a clear-cut relationship between their position in the periodic table and their ability to chemisorb carbon monoside dissociatively. A division line has been established for ambient temperature by Brodén, Rhodin, Bruckner, Benbow, and Hurych (1) between metals that chemisorb CO dissociatively and those which have at least some crystal faces that split the CO molecule into surface carbon and oxygen. Figure 2 shows a section of the periodic table wherein elements on the right-hand-side of the borderline adsorb CO non-dissociatively and vice versa. From infrared frequencies and photoelectron energies of the residual adsorbed CO it can be predicted that the division line between non-dissociative and dissociative CO chemisorption lies, at 250°C - 300°C, between nickel and copper, rhodium and palladium, and osmium and iridium. This high temperature division line is also

7

indicated in Figure 2. Some metals on the right-hand-side of the division line, i.e. those that do not dissociate carbon monoxide, are indeed methanol synthesis catalysts. Of these the low pressure catalysts are those which lie *close* to the division line, i.e. copper (2), palladium, platinum, and iridium (3). Further factors determine whether a catalyst will be usable as a commercial catalyst: the stability of dispersion, the choice of oxide support, the oxidation state of the metal, and finally the cost. As of this writing, the copper-based catalysts are in many respects superior to the precious metal catalysts, and therefore in this article we will concentrate on these inexpensive, stable, and selective catalysts. It is demonstrated in Tables I and II that the low-pressure copper-based catalysts have invariably the composition $Cu/ZnO/Al_2O_3$ or $Cu/ZnO/Cr_2O_3$. It was further shown by the author and coworkers (4-7) that the activity for methanol resides in the Cu/ZnO system and that the Cr_2O_3 and Al_2O_3 (or $ZnAl_2O_4$ in the case of ICI catalysts) act as structural promoters.

In the Cu/ZnO system the activity is induced by interactions of the copper and zinc oxide components, as demonstrated by Figure 3. This figure shows that maxima of activity for methanol occur in the mixed catalysts while the individual components are inactive at low temperatures and pressures (8). The optimum activity exists in a catalyst of a composition $Cu/ZnO = 30/70$ when hydroxycarbonates of copper and zinc are precipitated from nitrate solution by sodium carbonate, calcined at 350°C and reduced by 250°C (4). As far as can be judged from the literature and our own results, this catalyst has properties similar to the commercial and laboratory $Cu/ZnO/Al_2O_3$ catalysts. A comparison of activities of the Cu/ZnO and $Cu/ZnO/Al_2O_3$ catalysts, their selectivities, and structural-morphologic features has been reported by this author and coworkers (4,5). These studies show that alumina is a structural promoter except for possibly inducing dehydration activity that results in DME formation, and that the Cu/ZnO catalyst performs in CO_2 atmospheres similarly as the commercial $Cu/ZnO/Al_2O_3$ catalysts. Because the effects of carbon dioxide are of particular importance in biomass processing, the kinetics of the synthesis in the presence of CO_2 is discussed in some detail below.

Reaction Kinetics in the Presence of Carbon Dioxide

It has been known for some time that small amount of carbon dioxide in the CO/H_2 synthesis gas acts as a promoter (9,4). In pursuing the effects of CO_2 further, it was found that there is an optimum CO_2/CO ratio at which the synthesis runs at maximum rate (9,10). At higher concentration, CO_2 has a gradually retarding effect on the synthesis.

The influence of the CO_2/CO ratio on the synthesis has been embedded in kinetic equations only recently. The early kinetic equations for the high pressure $ZnO-Cr_2O_3$ catalyst did not contain a CO_2-dependent term at all, perhaps because the effects of CO_2 were not significant when zinc chromite catalysts were used; Natta, Pino, Mazzanti, and Pasquon (11) proposed the rate equation for the $ZnO-Cr_2O_3$ catalyst at temperatures 300-360°C as follows:

$$r = \frac{\gamma_{CO}p_{CO}\gamma_{H_2}^2 p_{H_2}^2 - \gamma_{CH_3OH}p_{CH_3OH}/K_{eq}}{(A + B\gamma_{CO}p_{CO} + C\gamma_{H_2}p_{H_2} + D\gamma_{CH_3OH}p_{CH_3OH})^3} , \qquad [9]$$

where r is the rate of methanol synthesis, γ_i is the fugacity coefficient of species i, p_i is the partial pressure of species i, K_{eq} is the equilibrium constant of carbon monoxide hydrogenation to methanol, and A, B, C, D are empirical constants. This equation was derived under the assumption that the rate controlling step of the synthesis is the trimolecular reaction of carbon monoxide with two hydrogen molecules in the adsorbed phase. Following Natta's publication of his data and kinetic treatment, a number of empirical as well as model-derived rate equations for methanol synthesis have been proposed, some of which have demonstrated that Natta's original data could be fitted with several kinetic models. These developments were summarized by Denny and Whan (12) up to 1977.

When the synthesis was carried out with carbon dioxide-rich synthesis gas, however, the comparison of measured rates with those calculated using kinetic equation [9] or its modifications (12) showed a substantial disparity (13) and it was realized that carbon dioxide-dependent terms must be incorporated in order that the kinetic equations be useful for process design. This was accomplished by Bakemeier et al. (14) who obtained the following rate equation, once again for the $ZnO-Cr_2O_3$ catalyst:

$$r = Ae^{-\frac{E}{RT}} \frac{p_{CO}^n p_{H_2}^m [1 - p_{CH_3OH}/(p_{CO}p_{H_2}^2 K_{eq})]}{(1 + De^{F/RT}p_{CO_2}/p_{H_2})} \qquad [10]$$

In this equation, the quantities A, E, n, m, D, and F are semi-empirical parameters. It can be seen that this rate equation predicts that the methanol yield would decrease as the CO_2 partial pressure is increased, and would drop to zero for synthesis gas that contains carbon dioxide only. Hence equation [10] describes a process in which carbon dioxide is a retardant but not at all a reactant or a promoter.

In 1973, Leonov et al. (15) put forward a kinetic rate equation for the low pressure copper-zinc oxide-alumina catalyst for temperatures between 220 and 260°C. The rate equation was proposed to be:

$$r = k \left[\frac{p_{CO}^{0.5}p_{H_2}}{p_{CH_3OH}^{0.66}} - \frac{p_{CH_3OH}^{0.34}}{p_{CO}p_{H_2}^{0.5}K_{eq}} \right] , \qquad [11]$$

where k is the rate constant for the forward reaction, and K_{eq} is the equilibrium constant. Similar to the early kinetic studies with the high pressure $ZnO-Cr_2O_3$ catalysts, there are no CO_2-dependent terms in equation [11] for the low pressure synthesis.

Denny and Whan (12) also reviewed various contrasting reports on the effects of CO_2 on the synthesis, and emphasized that any complete kinetic expression should include a term involving the partial pressure of carbon dioxide. A rate equation that does contain an empirical CO_2-dependent term for the Cu-ZnO-alumina catalysts has been presented in 1980 by Andrew (9) in the form

$$r = k \, p_{CO}^{0.2 \text{ to } 0.6} \, p_{H_2}^{0.7} \, \phi_{CO_2} \qquad [12]$$

Although the function ϕ_{CO_2} was not explicitly determined, it was reported that the rate of methanol synthesis reached a maximum at the CO_2 to CO partial pressure ratio around 0.01 - 0.03, and decreased as the CO_2 pressure was further increased. It was also indicated that the methanol synthesis rate would decline at very small concentrations of CO_2. A behavior like this was also reported to be the property of the binary Cu-ZnO catalysts (4), and hence it is established that an optimum concentration of CO_2, or a ratio of CO_2 and CO concentrations, exists at which the low pressure synthesis runs at its maximum rate. A feature common to all kinetic equations summarized above is that the forward rate is proportional to a power of the product $(p_{CO} \cdot p_{H_2}^2)$.

When the reaction is carried out at low conversions, the reverse reaction is negligible and the dependence of the synthesis rate on the product $p_{CO} \cdot p_{H_2}^2$ is a strong evidence that several sites are involved in one molecular synthesis step.

Klier, Chatikavanij, Herman, and Simmons (10) presented a kinetic model based on previous observations of the physical and chemical characteristics of the binary Cu/ZnO catalysts and put forward equations that quantitatively account for the CO_2/CO-dependence of the synthesis rates. Their model has resulted in an equation

$$r = \text{const.} \left(\frac{K'x}{1+K'x} \right)^3 \frac{(p_{CO}p_{H_2}^2 - p_{MeOH}/K_{eq})}{(F + K_{CO_2}p_{CO_2})^n} \, +$$

$$+ \, k' \left(p_{CO_2} - \frac{1}{K'_{eq}} \frac{p_{MeOH}p_{H_2O}}{p_{H_2}^3} \right) \qquad [13]$$

where F is a linear function of pressures of H_2, CO, H_2O, and CH_3OH, the exponent m is close to 3, the exponent n ranges from 1 to 3 and x is the ratio p_{CO_2}/p_{CO}. K_{eq} is equilibrium constant, defined by partial pressures, for the reaction [1] and K'_{eq} for the reaction [2].

The dependence of carbon conversion on the ratio $x = p_{CO_2}/p_{CO}$ and on the temperature is shown in Figure 4. Experimental rates are marked as circles (250°C), triangles (235°C), and squares (225°C) and the theoretical curves using the integrated form of the above kinetic equation [13] with m = 3, n = 3, and $F = (1 + K_{H_2}p_{H_2} + K_{CO}p_{CO})$ are represented as solid lines passing through the experimental points. The set of constants with which the best fits were obtained is given in the original paper for three closely related models (10). At this point it suffices to say that the fits were obtained with reasonable adsorption heats for H_2 (49 kJ/mol), CO (79 kJ/mol) and CO_2 (128 kJ/mol) as well as with reasonable entropies.

The maximum of the synthesis rate in the dependence on the CO_2/CO ratio is thus produced by two countereffects: at small CO_2 concentrations, this gas brings the catalyst or some surface complex thereon into the oxidation state effective in the reaction; at large CO_2 concentrations, the synthesis is retarded by CO_2 adsorption. In addition to these rather profound effects of CO_2 on the synthesis rates, there is a change of selectivity from pure methanol production at CO_2 concentrations between zero and 10% in a syngas $CO/CO_2/H_2 = (30-x)/x/70$ to a mixed product containing methanol with small amounts of methane at CO_2 concentrations between 10 and 30%. The product compositions are compared in Figure 5 with the thermodynamic equilibrium values for methanol in dependence on the CO_2 concentration.

Although the above data permit the composition of the synthesis gas to be adjusted to optimum performance of the catalyst, it is still desirable to develop better catalysts that would be effective in higher CO_2/CO ratios. According to the author's model and estimates this could be accomplished by lowering the adsorption energy by some 10-20 kJ/mol while retaining the inherent activity for methanol unchanged. Because the primary source of adsorption heat of CO_2 is its interaction with surface basic sites, it is apparent that control of surface basicity of the zinc oxide component of the catalyst by various dopants should be considered for the optimization of the catalyst for good performance at high concentrations of CO_2.

Further Properties of the Copper-Based Catalysts

The author has reviewed the literature on the details of preparation, physical characteristics, particle size and morphology, surface composition, chemisorption of the reaction components, relative hydrogenation rates of various substrates, the role of third component in the Cu/ZnO catalysts, and the synthesis mechanism, over the Cu/ZnO as well as other metal and oxide catalysts (16). Space in this paper does not permit to go into the detail that has been covered elsewhere beyond stating that the copper-based catalysts can be prepared in high surface area porous form as well as in low surface area non-porous form, as micromonoliths such as shown in Figure 6, with dehydration component to maximize ether formation or without it, and with precious metal and alkali metal components to maximize the production of low alcohols. The latter catalysts have not been successfully optimized, however, so that the C_2-C_4 alcohols would be produced at an industrially acceptable rate. Because we are apparently enjoying an era of intensive catalyst development for the C_2-C_4 alcohols, it is deemed worthwhile to outline, in the next paragraph, the chemical principles underlying the formation of these low alcohols.

Chemical Routes to Low Alcohols

There are several existing processes that may be used for stepwise synthesis of low alcohols from carbon monoxide and hydrogen. The first stage is methanol synthesis [1] which may be followed by the carbonylation of methanol to acetic acid

$$CH_3OH + CO \xrightarrow[\text{Rh,Co}]{\text{CH}_3\text{I}} CH_3COOH \qquad [14]$$

and reduction of acetic acid to ethanol

$$CH_3COOH + 2H_2 \xrightarrow[\text{Cu/ZnO}]{} C_2H_5OH + H_2O \qquad [15]$$

or by methanol homologation

$$CH_3OH + CO + 2H_2 \xrightarrow[\text{Co}]{\text{I}^-} C_2H_5OH + H_2O \qquad [16]$$

The principal mechanistic step involved in carbon-carbon bond formation is the carbon monoxide insertion into the methyl-metal bond,

$$\qquad (M = Rh, Co) \qquad [17]$$

to form acetyl residue which is then removed as a derivative of acetic acid. The catalysts for this reaction are soluble carbonyls of rhodium or cobalt, known as homogeneous carbonylation or homologation catalysts. The reaction is promoted by halogen derivatives such as iodide which act as alkyl and acetyl transfer agents.

Attempts to combine the heterogeneous Cu/ZnO methanol synthesis catalyst with the homogeneous carbonylation catalyst dissolved in a hydrocarbon solvent and co-promoted by the iodide with the aim at ethanol synthesis in one pot will fail because halogen compounds are severe poisons for the copper-zinc oxide catalyst. If the synthesis is attempted without the halogen promoter, the carbonylation or homologation rates will not catch up with the rates of methanol synthesis and the main product will be methanol. The homologation or carbonylation catalysts may also adsorb on the surface of the copper-zinc oxide catalysts, in which case methanol is still predominant product but is synthesized at a slower rate.

Another set of reactions leading to alcohols is the Fischer-Tropsch synthesis of olefins

$$nCO + 2nH_2 \xrightarrow[Fe,Co]{} C_nH_{2n} + nH_2O \qquad [18]$$

followed by hydration

$$C_nH_{2n} + H_2O \xrightarrow[acid\ catalyst]{} C_nH_{2n+1}OH \qquad [19]$$

Fischer-Tropsch synthesis can also be optimized, particularly over iron catalysts, to produce directly a large fraction of alcohols. However, the distribution of molecular weights in Fischer-Tropsch synthesis is very broad due to the polymerization steps involved in the hydrocarbon chain growth, and major products are long chain linear alcohols which have a poor value as a motor fuel.

An important type of reaction that gives rise to C-C bonds is aldol condensation

$$RCHO + R'CH_2CHO \xrightarrow[OH^-]{} RCH\underset{|}{CH}CHCHO \qquad [20]$$

which occurs classically by a base attack at α carbon (the CH_2 group of $R'CH_2CHO$) followed by the addition of the aldehydic group of RCHO at this activated point. Since alcohols are easily dehydrogenated to aldehydes in the presence of catalysts, aldol condensation will take place where the catalyst is promoted by a base. Methanol stands alone be being dehydrogenated to formaldehyde H_2CO which does not possess α carbon; however, it is well known that closely related base-catalyzed condensations occur with the formation of hydroxy-aldehydes and hydroxy-ketones according to reactions

$$2CH_2O \longrightarrow CH_2OH.CHO \text{ (glycol-aldehyde)} \qquad [21]$$

$$HOCH_2.CHO + CH_2O \longrightarrow HOCH_2CH(OH)CHO \qquad [22]$$

$$HOCH_2CH(OH)CHO \rightleftharpoons HOCH_2COCH_2OH \text{ (dihydroxyacetone)} \qquad [23]$$

and so on down to sugars (17). The formation of glycol-aldehyde is a slow step whereas all subsequent classic aldolations are rapid. Hence if only aldol-type condensations starting from formaldehyde would be occurring, long chain highly oxygenated molecules would be the main product. However, in the presence of hydrogen glycoladehyde will be rapidly hydrogenated to a non-aldehydic intermediate which will in part decompose back to carbon monoxide and hydrogen (ethylene glycol is thermodynamically unstable at low pressures) and in part will be hydrogenated further to ethanol. Similar reactions for C_3 oxygenates will give rise to propanols etc. This then constitutes a possible pathway to alcohols on alkali-doped methanol synthesis catalysts.

The effects of alkali on the production of low alcohols over methanol synthesis catalysts have been known since early 1930's (18,19). An example is given for the high pressure catalysts Cr_2O_3/MnO doped with Li_2O, Na_2O, K_2O, Rb_2O, and Cs_2O in Table III. With the addition of alkali, methanol production decreased while greater quantities of carbon compounds were formed, e.g. with Cr_2O_3/MnO/Rb_2O = 1:0.85:0.42 the liquid product consisted of 42% methanol, 38% high alcohols, and 15% of aldehydes and acetals. Although the mechanism of these reactions has not been studied, the product composition is that expected from the above discussed aldol condensation combined with methanol synthesis.

After the advent of the low-pressure copper-based catalysts for methanol, the natural step toward achieving low alcohol synthesis appeared to promote these catalysts with alkali oxides. In a recent patent by the Institut Francais du Petrol (IFP) quaternary catalysts $Cu/Co/CrO_x$/K_2O and $Cu/Co/MnO/K_2O$ have been claimed to produce ethanol at maximum rate and the mixture of C_1-C_4 alcohols at a rate only 4-5 times lower than that of methanol production over the $Cu/ZnO/Al_2O_3$ catalysts (20). The claimed product composition over these catalysts is compared with that over selective methanol catalysts in Table IV. It is seen that indeed the alcohol mix so produced would be a very attractive motor fuel. In addition to the copper and alkali components, these catalysts contain cobalt, normally a Fischer-Tropsch catalyst that produces long chain hydrocarbons, and another oxide such as Cr_2O_3.

In order to verify the IFP patent and to test whether the cobalt component is at all useful in combination with the copper-alkali catalyst, this author and coworkers prepared several catalysts of the composition $Cu/Co/Cr_2O_3/K_2O$ and related compositions. It was found that in addition to low alcohols, undesirably high amounts of methane appeared in the product along with the typical Fischer-Tropsch distribution of olefins and paraffins. This is attributed to the presence of cobalt, which is therefore deemed a component detrimental to the synthesis of low alcohols unless cobalt can be maintained in a non-metallic form or in an ultra-finely dispersed state.

It is probable that other alkali-doped copper-based catalysts might be found effective for low alcohol synthesis in the near future. If such a development is encouraging, it is very desirable to study the aldol condensation and reaction of glycolaldehyde over these catalysts, as the mechanistic knowledge will no doubt contribute to a better control of selectivity and will result in further optimization of such catalysts.

ACKNOWLEDGEMENT

The author is grateful for DOE support grant DE-AC02-80CS83001 which enabled this work.

REFERENCES

1. Brodén, G., Rhodin, T. N., Bruckner, C., Benbow, R., and Hurych, Z., Surface Sci. 59, 593 (1976).

2. Copper must be in a special state induced by oxide supports in order to display a low-temperature activity for methanol.

3. Poutsma, M. L., Elek, L. F., Ibarbia, P. A., Risch, A. P., and Rabo, J. A., J. Catalysis 52, 151 (1978).

4. Herman, R. G., Klier, K., Simmons, G. W., Finn, B. P., Bulko, J. B., and Kobylinski, T. P., J. Catalysis 56, 407 (1979).

5. Mehta, S., Simmons, G. W., Klier, K., and Herman, R. G., J. Catalysis 57, 339 (1979).

6. Bulko, J. B., Herman, R. G., Klier, K., and Simmons, G. W., J. Phys. Chem 83, 3118 (1979).

7. Herman, R. G., Simmons, G. W., and Klier, K., Proc. 7th International Congress on Catalysis, Tokyo 1980, Elsevier 1981, p. 475.

8. Parris, G. E., Dissertation, Lehigh University, 1981.

9. Andrew, S. P. S., ICI Catalysts: The Development of Copper-Based Catalysts for Methanol Synthesis and for Water Gas Shift, Paper 12, presented as a Plenary Lecture at the Post Congress Symposium of the 7th International Congress on Catalysis, Osaka, Japan, July 1980.

10. Klier, K., Chatikavanij, V., Herman, R. G., and Simmons, G. W., J. Catalysis, submitted.

11. Natta, G., Pino, P., Mazzanti, G., and Pasquon, I., Chimica e Industria 35, 705 (1953).

12. Denny, P. J., and Whan, D. A., Catalysis - A Specialist Periodical Report, The Chemical Society London, 2, 46 (1978).

13. Wermann, J., Lukas, K., and Gelbin, D., Z. phys. Chem. 225, 234 (1964).

14. Bakemeier, H., Laurer, P. R., and Schroder, W., Chem. Eng. Prog. Symp. Ser. 66(98), 1 (1970).

15. Leonov, V. E., Karavaev, M. M., Tsybina, E. N., and Petrishcheva, G. S., Kinetics and Catalysis (English edition) 14, 848 (1973).

16. K. Klier, Advances in Catalysis 31 (1982), in press.

17. Katschmann, E.,Ber., 77B, 579-85 (1944).

18. Morgan, G. T., Hardy, D. V. N., and Procter, R. A., J. Soc. Chem. Ind. 51, 1T(1932).

www.KnowledgePublications.com

19. Morgan, G. T., and Taylor, R., *Proc. Roy. Soc.* A131, 533 (1931).

20. Sugier, A., and Freund, E., *U.S. Patent 4,122,110* (Oct. 24, 1978). Assigned to Institut Francais du Petrole (IFP); *French Patent 2,369,234* (May 26, 1978) assigned to IFP; *Ger. Offen. 2,748,097* (May 11, 1978) assigned to IFP.

21. Cornthwaite, D., *British Patent 1,296,212* (Nov. 15, 1972) assigned to ICI.

TABLE I

Cu-Zn-Al Oxide Catalysts Used in the Synthesis of Methanol

Composition[a] (wt%)	Reactants[b]	Temp. (°C)	Pressure (atm)	Space velocity (hr^{-1})	Yield (kg/liter/hr)	Company
12:62:25	2	230	200	10,000	3.290	BASF
	2	230	100	10,000	2.086	BASF
23:46:30	3	240		20,000	2.5	CCI
24:38:38	2	226	50	12,000	0.7	ICI
35:45:20	1	250				Academic
53:27:6	1	250	50			ICI
60:22:8	1	250	50	40,000	0.5	ICI
	2	226	100	9,600	0.5	ICI
64:32:4	3	250	50	10,000	0.3	Academic
	3	300	50	10,000	0.9	Academic
66:17:17	1	275	70	200[d]	4.75	DuPont
	1	250	50	10,000		Academic

[a] $CuO:ZnO:Al_2O_3$.

[b] $1 = H_2 + CO + CO_2, 2 = H_2 + CO + CO_2 + CH_4, 3 = CO + H_2, N_2$ is sometimes used as a diluent.

[c] SNM-1 catalyst.

[d] Moles per hour.

TABLE II

Cu-Zn-Cr Oxide Catalysts Used in the Synthesis of Methanol

Composition[a] (wt%)	Reactants[b]	Temp. (°C)	Pressure (atm)	Space velocity (hr^{-1})	Yield (kg/liter/hr)	Company
11:70:19	3	250		4,000		Power-Gas Corp.
15:48:37	3	270	145	10,000	1.95[c]	Jap. Gas-Chem. Co.
31:38:5	3	230	50	10,000	0.755	BASF
	4	230	50	10,000	1.275	BASF
33:31:36	3	250	150	10,000	1.1	Academic
	3	300	150	10,000	2.2	Academic
40:10:50	1	260	100	10,000	0.48[c]	T,HFA
40:40:20	2	250	40	6,000	0.26	ICI
	2	250	80	10,000	0.77	ICI
60:30:10	1	250	100	9,800	2.28	Metall-Gesell-schaft

[a] $CuO:ZnO:Cr_2O_3$.

[b] $1 = H_2 + CO + CO_2$, $2 = H_2 + CO + CO_2 + CH_4$, $3 = CO + H_2$, $4 = CO + H_2 + O_2$, N_2 is sometimes used as a diluent.

[c] Kilograms per kilogram per hour.

TABLE III

METHANOL SYNTHESIS OVER ALKALI METAL OXIDE CATALYSTS AT 400°C AND 200 ATM

Catalyst	Ratio (wt%)	Product Yield (g/hr)	% Methanol in Product	% Other Liquid Compounds in Product
$Cr_2O_3/MnO/Li_2O$	1:0.93:0.10	47	76.9	21.7
$Cr_2O_3/MnO/Na_2O$	1:0.93:0.08	43	63.9	32.9
$Cr_2O_3/MnO/K_2O$	1:0.93:0.12	39	60.8	38.4
$Cr_2O_3/MnO/Rb_2O$	1:0.93:0.00	62	80.5	13.0
	1:0.93:0.06	61	75.5	23.1
	1:0.93:0.13	62	67.2	33.1
	1:0.93:0.25	53	49.7	46.0
	1:0.85:0.42	~50	42.0	54.0
$Cr_2O_3/MnO/Cs_2O$	1:0.93:0.11	53	82.1	18.8

TABLE IV

COPPER-BASED SYNGAS CONVERSION CATALYSTS - A COMPARISON OF SELECTIVITIES

	Reactants $(H_2/CO/CO_2)$	Temp. (°C)	Pressure (atm)	Product[a] Yield	Reference
Cu/Zn(3/7)	70/24/6[b]	250	75	$1.35 CH_3OH$	4
Cu/Zn/Al (52.4/24.3/23.3 at %)	70/24/6[b]	250	75	$1.37 CH_3OH$	7
Cu/Zn/Al (60,23.3,16.7 at %)	80/10/10	250	50	$\sim99\% CH_3OH$	21
Cu/Co/Cr/K (1/1/0.8/0.09)	66/10/13[c]	250	60	$0.076 CH_3OH$ $0.125 C_2H_5OH$ $0.69\ C_3H_7OH$ $0.0045 C_4H_9OH$	20
Cu/Co/Mn/K (1/1/0.8/0.12	66/19/13[c]	250	60	$0.065\ CH_3OH$ $0.108 C_2H_5OH$ $0.064 C_3H_7OH$ $0.039 C_4H_9OH$	20

a) kg of product per kg of catalyst per hour
b) GHSV = 5000 hr^{-1}
c) GHSV = 4000 hr^{-1}

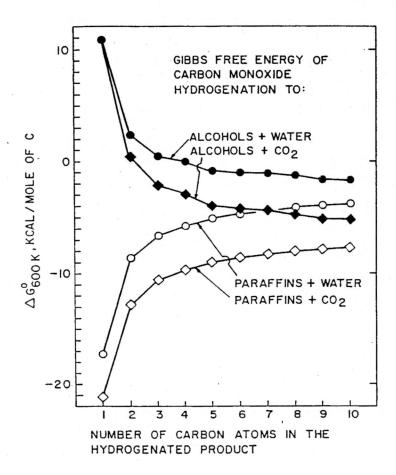

Fig. 1. Gibbs free energies $\Delta G°$ at 600 K, per gramatom of carbon, in the product alcohol or hydrocarbon, of the reactions:

$$nCO + 2nH_2 \longrightarrow CH_3(CH_2)_{n-1}OH + (n-1)H_2O \quad (\bullet)$$

$$(2n-1)CO + (n+1)H_2 \longrightarrow CH_3(CH_2)_{n-1}OH + (n-1)CO_2 \quad (\blacklozenge)$$

$$nCO + (2n+1)H_2 \longrightarrow CH_3(CH_2)_{n-2}CH_3 + nH_2O \quad (\bigcirc)$$

$$2nCO + (n+1)H_2 \longrightarrow CH_3(CH_2)_{n-2}CH_3 + nCO_2 \quad (\diamondsuit)$$

Source: D. R. Stull, E. F. Westrum, and G. C. Sinke, "The Chemical Thermodynamics of Organic Compounds," John Wiley & Sons, 1969. 1 cal = 4.184J.

CO CHEMISORPTION ON TRANSITION METALS

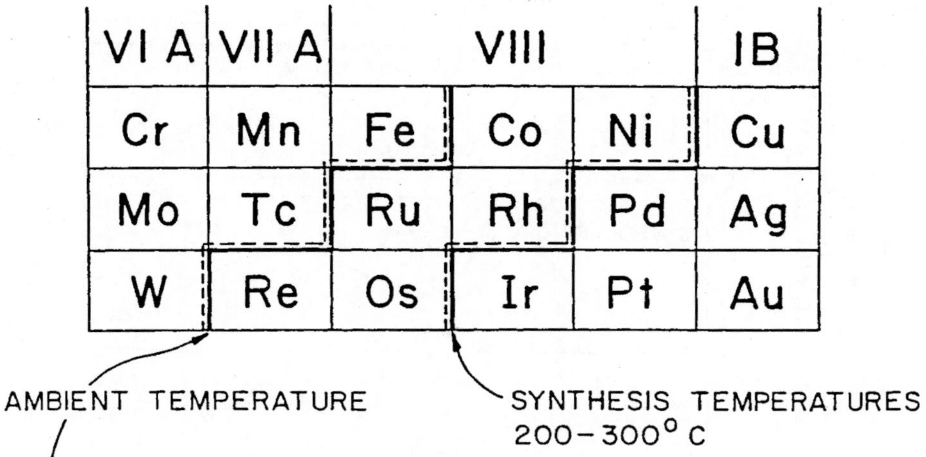
VI A
VII A
VIII
IB
Cr
Mn
Fe
Co
Ni
Cu
Mo
Tc
Ru
Rh
Pd
Ag
W
Re
Os
Ir
Pt
Au
AMBIENT TEMPERATURE
SYNTHESIS TEMPERATURES
200–300° C

G. BRODÉN, T. N. RHODIN, C. BRUCKNER, R. BENBOW, AND Z. HURYCH, <u>SURFACE SCI.</u> <u>59</u>, 593 (1976).

DIVIDING LINES SEPARATE METALS ON THE LEFT WHICH SPLIT CO FROM THOSE ON THE RIGHT WHICH ADSORB CO NON-DISSOCIATIVELY

Figure 2.

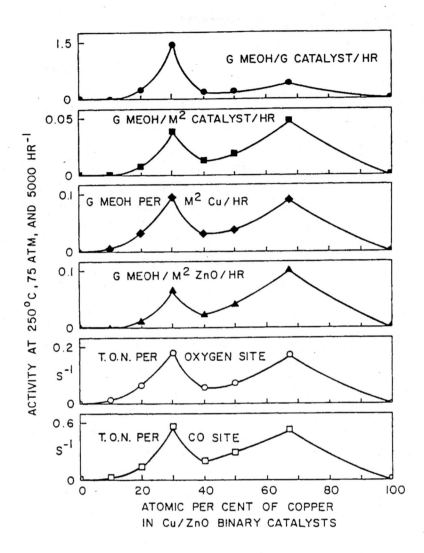

Fig. 3. Catalytic activity expressed as yield of methanol per
unit weight, per unit surface area of the Cu/ZnO
catalyst, per unit surface areas of the components
Cu and ZnO, and as turnover numbers over copper metal
sites titratable by irreversible adsorption of oxygen
and over copper/ZnO solute titratable by irreversible
adsorption of carbon monoxide.

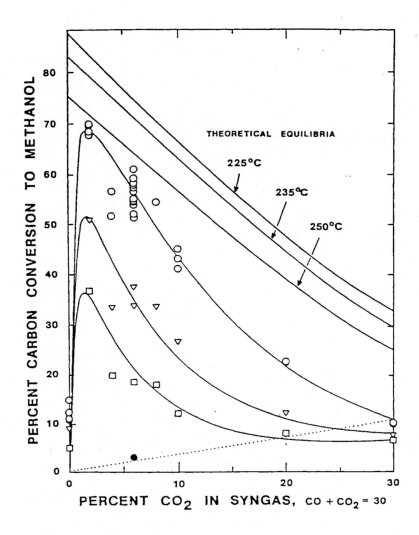

Fig. 4. The dependence of methanol synthesis rates at 225 -
250°C, 75 atm. total pressure, and GHSV 5000 hr^{-1} upon
the ratio of concentrations of CO_2 and CO. The total
hydrogen-to-carbon ratio in the feed gas was 7:3 for all
CO_2/CO ratios. Experimental data are marked as open
symbols and theoretical dependences, described by the
kinetic model in text. The full point describes an
equivalent of conversion rate when carbon dioxide in
the mixture $CO/CO_2/H_2$ = 24/6/70 was replaced by
argon (10). Reprinted with permission from J. Catalysis,
in press (1981). Copyright (1981), Academic Press, Inc.

23

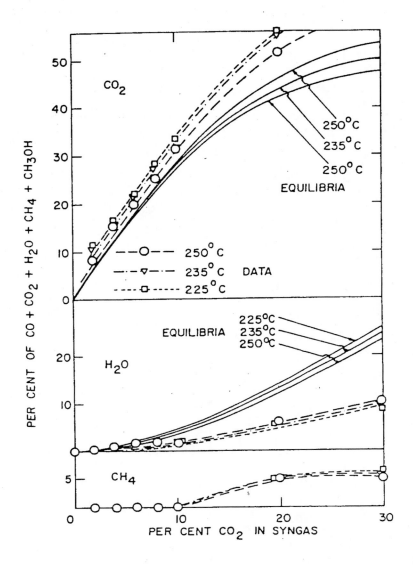

Fig. 5. The steady state concentrations of carbon dioxide (top), water (center), and methane (bottom) as functions of the CO_2/CO ratio in the feed gas at 225 - 250°C, 75 atm. total pressure, and GHSV 5000 hr^{-1} (10). Conversions to methanol are are given in Figure 4. Adapted with permission from J. Catalysis, in press (1981). Copyright (1981), Academic Press, Inc.

excess crystalline copper

0.15 µm   **ZnO Monolith with 8% Cu and 42% Al**

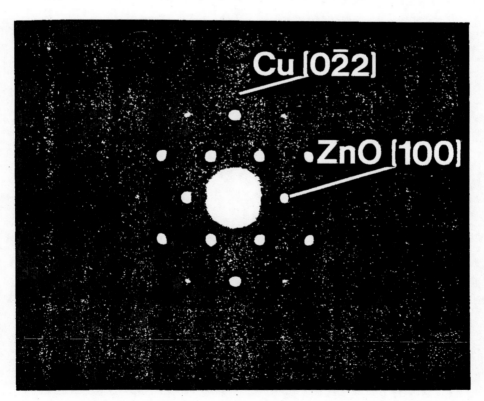

Fig. 6. a) Transmission electron micrograph and b) selected
area diffraction pattern of a single hexagonal porous
particle of the Cu/ZnO/Al$_2$O$_3$ catalyst prepared from
acetates (7). The Cu/Zn/Al ratio exclusive of
crystalline copper, which appears as dark crystallites,
was equal to 8/50/42.

CHEM SYSTEMS'
LIQUID PHASE METHANOL PROCESS

By

Marshall E. Frank
Chem Systems Inc.
747 Third Avenue
New York, NY

Abstract

Chem Systems' Liquid Phase Methanol (LPMeOH) process differs significantly from presently available technologies. This process incorporates an inert hydrocarbon liquid into the reactor in the presence of a heterogenous catalyst to effect high conversions of hydrogen and carbon monoxide to methanol. The liquid serves to control the reaction temperature by converting the sizable reaction exothermicity into a moderate temperature gain and allows maximum recovery of this reaction heat for use in the overall process. The LPMeOH process is particularly suited for coal-derived synthesis gases which are usually hydrogen deficient.

Development work has been underway for several years, initially under the sponsorship of the Electric Power Research Institute. The process is ready to move to the pilot plant stage. The Department of Energy (DOE) will provide support for this phase of the project on a cost-sharing basis with others. A skid-mounted pilot plant previously used for testing Chem Systems' Liquid Phase Methanation/Shift process will be adapted for testing the LPMeOH process. The pilot plant will be located at Air Products & Chemicals Inc.'s LaPorte, Texas synthesis gas plant. APCI will provide a major role in this program.

Introduction

Development work on the Chem Systems' Liquid Phase Methanol (LPMeOH) process started in early 1975 and continued through 1978. Most of this work has been funded by the Electric Power Research Institute (EPRI). The major areas of the development program included the following:

- Demonstration of concept feasibility

- Design and construction of a three-phase bench scale unit

- Catalyst modifications for the LPMeOH process

- Process variable studies

- Scale-up in a larger process development unit

- Long term continuous runs

- Engineering studies

Process Description

The Chem Systems liquid phase methanol process utilizes a heterogeneous catalyst in the presence of an inert hydrocarbon liquid. This liquid serves to control the reaction temperature more effiently than in gas phase processes; thereby allowing a closer approach to equilibrium and permitting maximum recovery of the heat of reaction as useable steam.

There are several ways in which to perform the

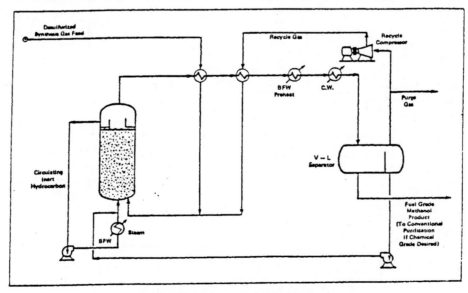

Figure 1 Chem Systems LPMeOH Process

27

three-phase reaction. Most of the work has been in a liquid-fluidized-bed reactor. Figure 1 illustrates the LPMeOH process utilizing a three-phase, fluidized-bed reactor. Synthesis gas containing CO, CO_2 and H_2 is passed upward into the reactor concurrent with the inert hydrocarbon liquid. The catalyst is fluidized by the inert hydrocarbon liquid whose presence limits the reaction temperature as it absorbs the heat liberated during reaction. Phase separation between solid, liquid and vapor occurs at the top of the reactor. The liquid-fluidized catalyst remains in the reactor. The inert hydrocarbon liquid, separated from both catalyst and vapor, is recirculated to the bottom of the reactor via a heat exchanger, where cooling occurs by steam generation. The reactor effluent gases are cooled to condense the products and any inert hydrocarbon liquid which may have been vaporized.

Methanol and inert hydrocarbon liquid are immiscible and phase separated. The methanol stream produced is suitable for fuel use directly or can be sent to a distillation system (not shown) to produce chemical grade product. Unconverted gases are recycled back to the reactor. A small purge stream is taken to limit the buildup of inerts which may be present in the synthesis gas feed.

An alternative type of three-phase reactor system that can be utilized in the LPMeOH process is termed a liquid-entrained catalyst reactor. In this type of system, the objective is to use much smaller catalyst particles and intentionally suspend the catalyst in the process liquid. The catalyst liquid slurry is circulated through the reactor. Contact with the synthesis gas is provided by feeding the gas counter current or cocurrent to the flow of the liquid-entrained catalyst solution. Figure 2 illustrates a countercurrent reactor sys-

tem. Other reactor designs are also possible. The reactor product gas is treated in the same manner as with a liquid-fluidized reactor.

While most of the development work has been accomplished in a liquid-fluidized three-phase reactor system, the work that has been done with micron size particles in a liquid-entrained system indicate that this will have economic benefits over the liquid-fluidized reactor. Furthermore, attrition of the catalyst no longer becomes a problem.

Major Accomplishments

The following discussion summarizes the major accomplishments of the early development work. For additional details, the reader is referred to EPRI report AF-1291, December, 1979. Most of the experimental work has been conducted in a 1" diameter by 6' long three-phase reactor where all process variables were investigated.

Process Liquids

Three different types of process liquids were tested: aliphatic, aromatic and oxygenated. The first two were found to be suitable for use in the LPMeOH process. The aliphatic oil used in the experiments was a mineral oil with a carbon number range predominantly of C_{14} to C_{21}. The composition was 72% paraffinic, 28% naphthenic with an ASTM boiling range of 518° to 660°F. The aromatic oil had a composition of 73% C_{10}, 18% C_{11} and some lighter and heavier aromatic components. The boiling range of the aromatic oil was 360°F to 410°F. Ethylene glycol was the oxygenated hydrocarbon tested and it underwent rapid decomposition. The mineral oil is slightly preferred over the aromatic due to its lower vapor pressure. Also, methanol is less soluble in the mineral oil than

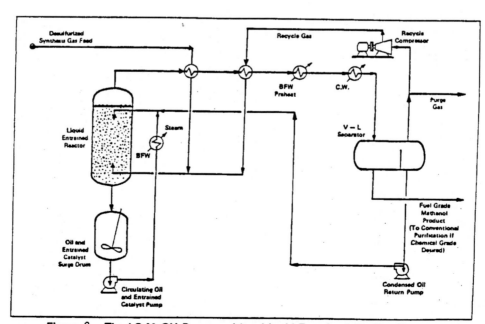

Figure 2   The LP MeOH Process with a Liquid-Entrained Catalyst Reactor

28

in the aromatic oil, which may also contribute to higher system productivities.

Synthesis Gas Composition

Most of the experimental work was done with feed gases simulating either a Koppers-Totzek coal gasifier after acid gas removal or a Lurgi coal gasifier after complete H_2S removal and partial CO_2 removal. Other feed gas compositions were examined to investigate the reactivity of both CO and CO_2. For gas compositions where equilibrium calculations indicated that only CO should react to form methanol, a minimum amount of CO_2 is required in the feed gas to the synthesis reactor. This behavior is similar to other methanol synthesis processes. The CO_2 appears to behave as a catalyst promotor, significantly boosting CO conversion levels (close approach to equilibrium) while passing through without measurably reacting itself. On the other hand, with feed gases containing high levels of CO_2 (7 to 14%) and high H_2 concentration, (ca. 75%), a substantial conversion of CO_2 to methanol is achieved; i.e., 60 to 90% of that predicted by equilibrium.

Alcohol Product Analysis

The methanol product composition produced in the Chem Systems process is slightly affected by the feed gas composition. Feed gases with a H_2 to CO ratio less than the stoichiometric 2/1 ratio tend to produce more higher alcohols. Table 1 shows typical crude methanol compositions for Lurgi and K-T feed gases.

Table 1 Product MeOH Composition[1]

Component	Lurgi Gas BSU	Koppers-Totzek Gas BSU	PDU
Methanol	96.16 wt%	91.44 wt%	89.60 wt%
Methyl Formate	0.17	0.24	0.39
Ethanol	0.32	2.55	2.46
i-Propanol	tr	tr	tr
Methyl Acetate	0.07	0.78	1.02
n-Propanol	0.14	1.23	1.31
C_4 Alcohols	0.23	1.43	2.67
C_5 Alcohols	0.33	1.40	1.14
C_6+ Alcohols	0.06	0.56	1.09
Water	2.71	0.51	0.33

(1) Oil-free basis, oil level is a function of composition (especially water concentration) and temperature.

A process development unit (PDU) built as part of the Liquid Phase Methanation development program funded at Chem Systems by DOE was used for larger scale testing of the LPMeOH process. The PDU has a 3.62" inside diameter by 7' high reactor and can handle a nominal 1,500 SCFH synthesis gas rate. Operation in the PDU represents approximately a 50-fold scale-up from the BSU. Several runs were made in January, 1977 with a Lurgi-type feed gas composition using 3/32" diameter, 5 pound crush strength catalyst mini-tablets. In two runs of 80 and 120 hours, respectively, catalyst activity, as measured by CO conversion, declined faster than an analogous BSU run being conducted at the same time. This was later attributed to nickel and iron contamination of the catalyst. A third run of 120 hours was made with crushed, commercial, vapor-

phase catalyst. Activity remained constant, indicating that trace metal impurities has been scavenged from the system.

A 645 hour PDU run was performed in October-November, 1978 concurrent with a similar run in the BSU. Feed gas for this run simulated a K-T gas with an H_2/CO ratio of 0.6. A new batch of 3/32" diameter, 5 pound crush strength mini-tablets were used. Process conditions were maintained at 250°C, 1,000 psig and 3,000 hr^{-1} space velocity. Initial results from the PDU were equivalent to BSU results. Catalyst attrition occurred throughout the PDU run indicating that the catalyst mini-tablet did not possess sufficient strength.

Long-Term Continuous Runs

Three long-term continuous runs were performed. The first one was in the BSU and lasted for 645 hours. A Lurgi feed gas composition was used with 3/32" diameter, 5 pound crush strength mini-tablets. Catalyst activity declined slowly throughout the run, from an initial CO conversion of 40% to a final value of 30%. This could have been due to trace metal contamination of the catalyst or to an operating upset that occurred between the 115th and 130th hours. A K-T type-feed gas was inadvertently used during this period, when feed gas cylinders were being switched. The CO conversion naturally dropped due to the lower H_2/CO ratio of the K-T gas. When the proper Lurgi feed gas composition was restored, the CO conversion rose but not to the level just prior to the feed gas switch. Over the next 250 hours, the CO conversion rose slightly and then slowly declined for the final 200 hours of operation.

The second and third long-term runs were concurrent runs in the BSU and PDU, respectively. Again, the 3/32" diameter, 5 pound crush strength catalyst mini-tablets were used. The feed gas composition for these runs was a K-T gas. The BSU run lasted for 720 hours. The CO conversion declined slowly from 15% initially to 11.5% at the end. The catalyst recovered from BSU reactor was 95% of that initially loaded, with only slightly reduced catalyst dimensions. Despite the use of a zinc oxide guard chamber upstream of the methanol reactor, the spent BSU catalyst contained 480 ppm nickel and 600 ppm iron, contrasted with 15 ppm and 90 ppm levels in fresh catalyst.

The PDU run lasted for 645 hours. The catalyst recovered was only 64% of that loaded. Inspection of individual recovered catalyst particles indicated that the catalyst mini-tablets used did not possess sufficient strength for the liquid-fluidized process. Additional work is required in catalyst development in order to improve attrition resistance for the liquid-fluidized mode of operation.

Spent catalyst from the PDU reactor also contained high levels of iron and nickel, indicating that some activity loss was due to contamination.

29

Work is on-going to develop a suitable attrition-resistance catalyst for use in a liquid-fluidized reaction system. Another approach to this catalyst development is to switch to a liquid-entrained reactor system where maintaining discrete particle sizes is not necessary. In addition, this alternate three-phase reactor system should significantly improve the already favorable economics of the process by using micron-sized catalyst particles. While some preliminary experimental work has been done, this concept has not been as fully developed as the liquid-fluidized system and additional laboratory development work is required before pilot plant testing.

Chem Systems has proposed to DOE a program that includes both pilot plant operation as well as supporting laboratory development work. The program is time and cost effective in that it makes use of an already existing government-owned pilot plant which will be relocated to Air Products & Chemicals' synthesis gas facility at LaPorte, Texas where the supply of synthesis gas feedstock, utilities, and operating personnel are reliably assured.

Under previous U.S. Government contracts, Chem Systems designed, constructed and operated a skid-mounted pilot plant as part of the development of its Liquid Phase Methanation/Shift (LPM/S) process. This pilot plant can be easily modified for testing the LPMeOH process and as such would provide the scale-up information required for design of commercial-sized plants.

DOE Program

The program proposed to DOE covers three and a half years and encompasses all phases of work necessary to insure the successful completion of the LPMeOH pilot plant project. The program includes laboratory development of a liquid-entrained catalyst reactor system, laboratory support for pilot plant operations, engineering design and project evaluation, as well as the installation and operation of the LPMeOH pilot plant at Air Products' LaPorte, Texas, synthesis gas plant site. The program calls for pilot plant testing of both the liquid-fluidized reactor mode and the liquid-entrained reactor mode. The latter being done after development work in the laboratory has been completed.

Air Products will be the prime contractor to DOE primarily responsible for relocation, installation, operation, and safety of the pilot plant and for supply of synthesis gas and other utilities. Chem Systems will be a subcontractor to Air Products with overall technical responsibility and for all research and development activities relating to the liquid-entrained reactor system and laboratory support work.

Air Products and EPRI will also contribute towards part of the program costs. In addition, two other companies have expressed interest in participating in the DOE program.

There are eleven major tasks designated in the DOE program as shown below:

Task	Description
1	Program Planning
2	Engineering and Design Specifications
3	Equipment Procurement
4	Pilot Plant Relocation
5	Pilot Plant Installation and Shakedown
6	Liquid-Fluidized Operation
7	Laboratory Support Program
8	Pilot Plant Modifications for Liquid-Entrained Mode
9	Shakedown for Liquid-Entrained Mode
10	Liquid Entrained Operation
11	Project Evaluation and Reporting

Most of the above are self explanatory. The LPM/S pilot plant is presently located at IGT's HYGAS pilot facility in Chicago, Illinois. It was built as a skid-mounted unit in Texas and shipped to the HYGAS site in September, 1976. It will now be dismantled and shipped back to Texas to Air Products' LaPorte, Texas site.

The new items to be added to the pilot plant for methanol operation include a feed gas blending tank, a high pressure nitrogen supply system, a methanol product storage tank and equipment for gas recycle. The design and engineering for these modifications will be done under Task 2. This task also includes the design and engineering for a separate liquid-entrained reactor which will tie into the existing unit. The initial objectives in the program are to relocate and install the pilot plant and to get it operational for testing the liquid-fluidized reaction system. Concurrently, laboratory work starts on the development of a liquid-entrained reactor system. It is expected that 18 months will be required to relocate the pilot plant, make the necessary modifications and shake-down the unit to have it ready for operation. Approximately one-year will be spent operating in the liquid-fluidized mode, testing alternative catalysts, doing process variable scans, and a short term continuous run.

The liquid-entrained reactor skid will be designed and constructed while the above is proceeding. Upon completion of the liquid-fluidized testing, projected to be at the end of month 33, the liquid entrained system will be ready for shake down and operation. A similar program will then be performed in this mode.

The proposed program has been planned to proceed in several task areas simultaneously in order to achieve maximum progress in minimal time. Chem Systems and Air Products have developed a management plan to insure successful execution of the program recognizing the complex nature of this project, which involves interaction among engineering evaluation, design, construction, laboratory development and pilot plant operations.

Economics

There is considerable interest of late in large coal-based methanol plants. Chem Systems' LPMeOH process is particularly attractive in such an application. The LPMeOH process can operate at lower pressure and in a situation where methanol is not the only product, the synthesis gas feed does not require any upstream processing other than sulfur removal. The LPMeOH Process can accept synthesis gas at any hydrogen to carbon monoxide ratio thereby eliminating the need for any water-gas shift reaction which is usually necessary for other methanol synthesis processes to increase the hydrogen concentration.

Economics have been developed for the LPMeOH process for both types of reaction systems. Two cases are considered. The first one assumes a large coal gasification complex where it is desired to convert only a fraction of the synthesis gas to methanol. Most of the synthesis gas is available for other uses; one possible application would be for fuel in an adjacent power plant. The methanol produced from the synthesis gas can be stored and used to meet peaking demands on the power plant side without oversizing the coal gasification section of the plant and accepting severe economic penalties. In this case, 3000 short tons per day of methanol are produced in a coal gasification complex using a 2nd generation coal gasification process such as Texaco or Shell-Koppers. The synthesis gas produced in the gasifier has a hydrogen to carbon monoxide ratio of approximately 0.6/1 and the gasification occurs at elevated pressure in the 500 to 1200 psia range. The only gas processing required is sulfur removal to a level amenable for copper-based methanol synthesis catalysts. This is usually less than 0.1 ppm. The Chem Systems' LPMeOH process does not require any shifting of the synthesis gas to adjust the hydrogen to carbon monoxide ratio. The synthesis gas will pass through the LPMeOH synthesis loop without any recycle with a portion of the gas being converted to methanol. Table 2 summarizes the economics for the LPMeOH process for both a liquid-fluidized reaction system and a liquid-entrained reaction system. In both cases, the operating pressure is 1000 psia and it is assumed that no feed gas compressor is required. The liquid-entrained reactor is less expensive than the liquid-fluidized reactor system due to the higher activity of the smaller catalyst particles. This results in smaller reactors and a larger CO conversion. With either system, the heat of reaction can be recovered as steam. For this evaluation, the steam pressure was 200 psig. Higher pressure steam can be generated by raising the reaction temperature. There is a trade-off however, as methanol equilibrium is adversely affected by higher temperatures.

The cost of producing methanol using the LPMeOH process depends upon the value placed on the steam export and the method of depreciation and type of financing used for the complex. In the case presented, capital related expenses have been taken at 30 percent of the total fixed capital investment. A typical breakdown for these expenses is as follows:

Depreciation	7.0 %
Maintenance	4.0
Taxes & Insurance	1.5
General Plant Overhead	2.5
Return on Investment	15.0
Total	30.0 %

Excluding the cost of the synthesis gas, the LPMeOH process produces methanol at $2.50 to $9.50 per short ton ($0.48 to $0.12 per million BTU). The liquid-entrained reactor system offers an advantage of $0.36 per million BTU over the liquid-fluidized system and this is a large part of the incentive for its further development as part of the program proposed to DOE.

The advantage of the LPMeOH process over a conventional vapor phase methanol synthesis process is considerable in the application considered here. The conventional processes require shifting of the synthesis gas to at least the stoichiometric hydrogen/carbon monoxide proportions. This also requires addition of a CO_2 removal system. Due to the heat removal limitations of the conventional vapor phase systems, the carbon monoxide conversion is limited to only 19 percent per pass or a methanol reactor effluent concentration of 5.5 mole percent. The net synthesis gas requirement is the same. The LPMeOH process has approximately a $1.00 to $1.30 per million BTU savings over the conventional processes.

Another situation regarding coal-based methanol plants is where it is desired to convert all of the synthesis gas to methanol. Table 3 summarizes the economics of the LPMeOH process for production of 5,000 short tons per day of methanol. It is assumed again that the synthesis gas is available at 1000 psia and in this case, that the hydrogen to carbon monoxide ratio is at the stoichiometric ratio of 2/1. This may require some upstream shifting depending upon the coal gasifier used. A Lurgi coal gasifier produces a synthesis gas with the hydrogen carbon monoxide proportions very close to that required for methanol synthesis and in this situation, only acid gas removal would be necessary.

This case requires recycle of unconverted synthesis gas to ensure maximum conversion to methanol. Overall conversion is a function of the level of inerts in the synthesis gas feed. Using the same economic criteria as in the previous case, methanol can be produced for $4.00 per short ton using a liquid-fluidized system.

With a liquid-entrained reactor system, the value of the exported steam more than off-sets the other costs including a return on investment and the LPMeOH process operates on essentially a cost-free basis. Again, these examples exclude the cost of synthesis gas in the analysis. However, the last case shows that the LPMeOH process has the potential for producing low cost methanol at essentially the conversion efficiency of synthesis gas to methanol.

Table 2
LPMeOH Economics
3,000 ST/D MeOH
Once-Through Operation

	LPMeOH Liquid-Fluidized Reactor	LPMeOH Liquid-Entrained Reactor
MeOH Production	3,000	3,000
CO Conversion, %	15.6	24.2
MeOH Concentration	11.1	19.8
Synthesis Gas Feed MM SCFD	817.7	511.0
Synthesis Gas Product, MM SCFD	593.8	291.5
Fixed Capital, $ MM, 1980		
Battery Limits	50.0	30.3
Associated Off-Sites	10.0	6.0
Total Fixed Capital	60.0	36.3
Annual Production Cost	**$/STon MeOH**	
Catalyst	2.3	2.1
Utilities		
Steam @ $4.40 MLbs	(11.2)	(11.5)
Boiler feed water @ $.90/MGal	0.3	0.3
Cooling Water @ $.052/MGal	0.1	0.1
Power @ $.030/KWH	0.4	0.6
Total Utilities	(10.8)	(10.5)
Capital Related Expenses @ 30%	18.0	10.8
Total Cost excluding Synthesis Gas	9.5	2.4
$/MM BTU	0.48	0.12

Table 3
Economics of the LPMeOH Process
5,000 Tons/Day
Total Conversion
of Feed Gas

	LPMeOH Liquid-Fluidized Reactor	LPMeOH Liquid-Entrained Reactor
Methanol Production, STons/Day	5,000	5,000
Methanol Concentration, %	16.3	21.7
Synthesis Gas Feed, MM SCFD		
Fixed Capital, $MM, 1980		
Battery Limits	52.0	36.6
Associated Off-Sites	10.5	7.4
Total Fixed Capital	62.5	44.0
Annual Production Cost	**$/STon MeOH**	
Catalyst	2.40	1.50
Utilities		
Steam @ $4.40/MLbs	(10.65)	(11.07)
Power @ $.030/KWH	0.49	0.54
Cooling Water @ $.052/MGal	0.13	0.10
Boiler feed water @ $.90/MGal	0.26	0.28
Total Utilities	(9.77)	(10.15)
Total Capital Related Expenses @ 30%	11.36	8.00
Total Cost excluding Synthesis Gas	3.99	(0.65)
$/MM BTU	0.20	(0.033)

Remarks by Dr. Stephen J. Gage
Vice President, Science and Technology Laboratory
International Harvester Company
to
SERI/Biomass-to-Methanol Specialists' Workshop
March 3, 1982

PACKAGED PLANTS

An analysis of the evolution to date of processing facilities in the oil refining, petrochemical, and chemical industries clearly shows the trend of ever large capacity single stream plants. This trend has been driven by the search for greater economies of scale. This has brought the benefits of scale to the point where bigger is always assumed to be better.

This thinking is typified by the rule of thumb as pomulgated by and, I might add very succesfully, the architectural and engineering firms that costs increase in proportion to plant site raised to the 0.7 power. The 0.7 rule is still undoubtedly applicable in many cases such as in facilities with high equipment and material costs or those processes with no clear limitation on size. However, a number of factors have appeared which draw into question the general validity of this conventional wisdom. These new factors have become increasingly apparent during the past decade, sometimes through sad experience of some of the major companies. These factors include:

- The economies of scale associated with large site erected plants are becoming increasingly eroded by dis-economies of scale such as increased product distribution costs, plant over-capacity (such as in the methanol industry today) and prohibitive investment costs for large projects, especially in times of high interest rates.

- The spiralling costs associated with design and engineering of large site erected facilities.

- The cost of and problems associated with the large site labor forces required for field fabrication and erection.

- The emergence of small but growing markets in developing countries accompanied by the relative market stagnation in developed countries.

An alternative concept can be envisioned, that of the packaged, modular plant.

I always hesitate to use the term "packaged plant" as one of my colleagues suggested that if I really wanted a packaged plant, I could get one at my local floral shop on my way home from the office.

What is a packaged plant? The packaged plant is a process unit based on a standard design and size, fabricated in a shop. A complete plant can

33

www.KnowledgePublications.com

thus be made up of several functional modules pre-wired, pre-piped, and pre-tested at the fabricator before being shipped to the installation site.

At the site, the erection is much simplified, requiring only the foundations, the correct positioning of the modules, and then the connecting of standard jointed piping and wiring. The design of the plant is such that additional units can be installed in parallel when increases in production capacity are required.

Such packaged plants can be skid mounted for easy handling and even for eventually changing of the installation site if factors such as feedstock availability and costs and local labor rates change significantly.

The advantages of packaged plants are manifold. They include:

1) Cost

- Historically, shop fabrication is less costly than field fabrication.
- In-shop efficiencies translate into lower cost-per-hour; hence, greater hourly productivity.
- Good modular design aims at a minimum essential capital investment.

2) Schedule -- With modular design and fabrication techniques, a schedule becomes meaningful, not a rough estimate based on long-term weather forecasting and wishful thinking:

- Modules are received and set in place as completed "equipment packages": time from delivery to start-up is minimized.
- Unanticipated delays (weather, etc.) are all but eliminated. This can be especially important for unsheltered equipment systems.
- Parallel construction/fabrication work reduces timeframe of job.

3) Quality and Operational Reliability

- Shop fabrication ensures closer in-process supervision and quality surveillance.
- Shop fabrication provides improved working conditions--improving on-the-job performance of workers.
- In-shop material control, storage, and handling techniques are far superior to those employed in the field.

4) Feasibility

- Certain projects require a schedule so limited as to demand modularization in order to meet the completion date.

- Some projects call for location of equipment in a remote or unde-veloped area where a suitable labor force does not exist. In such cases, modularization can reduce on-site manpower to an attainable level.

- Some projects, if built using conventional in-the-field methods, would require a labor force too large to be economically justi-fied. Modularization solves such a problem.

5) Material Control

- Purchasing/expediting activities are more efficient when controlled by the fabricator and handled by a centralized procurement organ-ization.

6) Risk Reduction

- Modular plants reduce the investment risk associated with under-utilization of capacity of large scale plants.

- There is a reduced investment risk associated with a large concen-tration of fixed assets in any one project ("the you bet the company" risk associated with many synfuel projects).

- The technical risk of obsolescence is reduced by permitting lower cost periodic upgrading.

- The risk associated with unexpected delays, and the operating prob-lems due to quality control exercised at the assembly area is reduced.

And last

(7) Marketing Advantages

- The possibility of establishing production units close to the end use market, and thereby reducing product distribution costs (such as transporting methanol from the gulf coast to California).

- The possibility of establishing a production unit close to a small raw material supply source.

- Avoidance of a major market disruption by sudden single, large capacity additions, permitting instead steady gradual growth tailored to customer use requirements.

- Foreign market penetration even in developing countries with a min-imum of start-up and operating problems.

I would like to elaborate a bit further on some of the cost advantages of packaged modular plants:

1) Shop Labor vs Field Labor

- Shop labor rates are less than field labor rates.

2) Productivity -- The controlled shop environment helps ensure maximum productivity.

- Work interruptions are less frequent in a shop.
- Weather-related delays are eliminated.

3) Scheduling ("Time is Money")

- Modular approach reduces overall job schedule through faster assembly: parallel site preparation/fabrication activities: in-shop equipment testing. This saves money.
- Installation and start-up time is significantly less. This saves money.
- The completed plant or system can be put into production faster. This makes money.

4) Equipment Arrangements/Space Requirement

- Good modular design leads to optimum equipment arrangements: in-field designs tend to "spread out" over available site area.
- Modules are more material efficient: require less piping, conduit, wire, and other hardware.

5) Supporting Services -- Modules require only minimal support compared to field construction:

- On site professional personnel (i.e.,: engineers and managers) are eliminated or only needed for minimal periods.
- In-field purchasing and expediting activities are minimal.
- Near site warehousing and/or in-field material inventories (and related clerical requirements) can be eliminated.
- On-site inspection personnel are limited.
- In-shop receiving inspection methods ensure components comply with specifications.
- Shop environment, with proper inventory facilities, ensures immediate availability of materials in a clean, serviceable condition.

6) Space Requirements

- Modular design most always results in a more compact system, with optimum operational convenience and accessibility for maintenance.

7) Start-up and Training

- Modules can be shop tested in various sub-assembly stages as well as given final testing as a completed unit. Field testing is thus limited to interconnecting equipment.

- The modular plant builder is usually able to provide complete training for operating and maintenance personnel--and often can conduct training right in the shop floor during pre-shipment tests.

IH has conducted a thorough investigation of the "packaged plant" concept. Based on both our internal research and the work performed by others, we have drawn some conclusions as follows:

- For an average chemical process, a "packaged plant" will have the same ROI as field erected plant three to four times its size.

- With a 20% better load factor, a packaged plant will compete in ROI with site plants five times its size.

- When the exponential scale factor on equipment is larger than 0.7, the production economies of multi-train packaged plants are similar to those conventional single train, site-erected plant of the same total capacity.

If some of you have not seen what a packaged plant might look like, I have brought a few slides of packaged plants in the delivery process.

DESIRABLE SLIDES

While these are not methanol plants or biomass-to-methanol plants, they are representative of the hardware systems. Note varying methods of transportation necessary to modularize a transport unit.

I have left until last the single most important finding in the IH research: the serial production effect. Despite our present financial condition, IH remains one of the country's main repositories of experience in serial manufacturing. We manufacture complex mobile equipment, in many cases, as complex as the chemical conversion processes discussed in these meetings this week. A good example is our axial flow combine which consists of three thousand parts and which, incidentally, does not require an engineer to operate it. We manufacture thousands of these units every year. It is interesting to speculate as to what an axial flow combine would look like and perhaps, more importantly, cost if it were designed from the beginning to be used as a single unit. In other words, we are in the business of providing production economies, not scale economies.

In our studies, we have determined that, given serial production of packaged plants at some minimum number (less than fifteen), a single packaged plant can compete in ROI with a plant at least ten times its size. Further, this conclusion is based solely on an assembly operation analysis. It does not reflect the additional production cost reductions available through system component manufacturing. The production cost savings of serially produced, skid mounted packaged plants, using numerous vendor-produced components are significant over field erected single units.

What are the disadvantages of packaged plants? Traditionally one! Operating costs of smaller plants are relatively higher per unit output than operating costs of large scale field erected facilities. We are very sensitive to this factor, and the bulk of our R&D dollars will be devoted to reducing operating costs in our biomass-to-methanol equipment system. We see much promise in this area.

Now let me address a more specific subject, the role of packaged plants in biomass-to-methanol production. In our opinion, there are two key driving forces in evaluating any biomass/methanol process: the characteristics of biomass as a feedstock and the methanol market dynamics. Biomass is unique when compared to other methanol feedstocks, natural gas, and coal. It has a relatively low geographical concentration compared to coal and natural gas. It rarely is available in any quantity in large amounts in a single concentrated location. In addition, biomass has a relatively low Btu value per unit collected compared to competitive feedstocks. This makes it more expensive to transport, thus the cost of collected biomass is highly sensitive to the collection radius. Most analysts, such as SRI, have examined biomass as a feedstock and concluded that it did not fit the scale requirements of large field erected conversion units.

On the other hand, biomass is available on a virtually unlimited basis at a very low cost, often very close to major metropolitan areas. Further, biomass has few alternative uses, and with the exception of the cash crops, a low alternative value. Thus, if collected within a relatively small local area and at relatively low tonnages, it represents a quite low cost feedstock. This is one driving force.

The dynamics within the methanol market are a second force. Time does not permit a full discussion of this market and the forces operating within it. A few key points, however, are important:

- Methanol is a commodity, and, as such, is highly sensitive to the production cost. (i.e., the market goes first to the lowest cost producer).

- The methanol market is very sensitive to demand and supply disruptions (as evidenced by the current glut caused by recession in the building industry.)

- Transportation costs from the producer to the end user add as much as 25% to the cost of purchased methanol.

- There is a growing trend to avoid the major capital investments necessary to produce the economies of scale required to produce low cost methanol from natural gas and coal.

These then are the driving forces. We at IH concluded packaged plants are a solution. Why? Packaged plants handle relatively small inputs. Biomass can be collected at a low cost if collected in small units over a relatively small area. Feedstock costs can then be competitive. Packaged plants can be produced at a capital cost competitive with large scale plants if manufactured in a single factory location. This provides competitive capital costs. Packaged plants can be placed close to the end user market. This reduces transportation costs and provides a strong incentive to the purchaser of the end product. Packaged plants are low in capital cost which reduces investment risk to the purchaser permitting a production capacity tailored to end use requirements.

The packaged plant concept thus represents a new way to provide the lowest cost product to a growing market.

Thank you!

40

Relevant Coal Technology and Recent Developments

COMPARISON OF COAL AND WOOD AS FEEDSTOCKS FOR METHANOL MANUFACTURE

Michael S. Graboski
Chemical and Petroleum-Refining Engineering Department
Colorado School of Mines
Golden, Colorado 80401

INTRODUCTION

The gasification of wood and coal for the production of fuel gas, and to some extent synthesis gas, has been widely practiced for more than 50 years. Over about the past 15 years, there has been considerable experimental work aimed at understanding the relevant properties of both feedstock types as applied to gasification. Experience using wood and coal show that there are some extreme differences between the two feeds, both chemically and physically, which tend to make wood more attractive than coal as a gasification feedstock where it is available.

Figure 1 shows a block diagram for a typical synthesis-gas gasification process with its end goal as methanol. The important steps are gasification, heat exchange and quench which cools and cleans the gas of solids and most tars, adjustment of the H_2/CO ratio by shift reaction, removal of undesirable gases including H_2S, CO_2, HCl and NH_3, final compression and methanol synthesis. The exact component in each of these steps varies depending on whether wood or coal is the plant feed.

FEEDSTOCK CHEMISTRY

The principle advantages of wood relative to coal result from the different chemical structure and composition of the materials as pertains to gasification. In the synthesis gas manufacturing process, the following general reactions take place:

1) Pyrolysis: Fuel + Heat $\longrightarrow$ Gas + Liquid + Char
2) Gasification:
$$C + H_2O \longrightarrow CO + H_2$$
$$C + 2H_2 \longrightarrow CH_4$$
$$CO + H_2O \longrightarrow CO_2 + H_2O$$
$$C + \tfrac{1}{2}O_2 \longrightarrow CO$$

In the pyrolysis process, the fuel is thermally decomposed to produce gases (CO, H_2, CH_4, C_2H_4 etc.), liquids (H_2O, tars) and a solid carbon which contains the fuel ash as well as some bound hydrogen, oxygen, nitrogen, and sulfur. Sulfur and nitrogen are evolved as hydrogen sulfide, nitrogen and ammonia. The quantity and nature of the char produced on pyrolysis is important in the subsequent carbon conversion step.

Char produced by pyrolysis must be generally removed by reaction with steam, hydrogen, carbon dioxide and oxygen. The oxygen may be eliminated and replaced by a suitable heat source which will supply the necessary energy for the endothermic carbon-steam reaction which is the main char reaction in all practical synthesis gasification processes. During gasification of char, bound heteroatoms are released producing H_2S and N_2. Ash also undergoes chemical change with certain volatile components such as sodium chloride vaporizing and being deposited in colder downstream locations.

Table 1 compares the important analytical data for typical coals and wood fuels (6). The ultimate analysis provides elemental data on the fuel including the important pollutant heteroatoms N, S, and Cl. The proximate analysis provides data on the volatility of the solid and the ash content of the fuel. The proximate analysis is important in considering pyrolysis of the fuel. The heating value of the fuel is important in considering process through-put on a Btu basis.

The coal and wood ultimate analyses reveal major differences in composition. In both fuels, the major portion is the CHO fraction. In coal, the carbon content dominates the analysis while in wood, the oxygen and carbon contents are similar on a weight basis. The greater bound oxygen content of wood is a result of the more aliphatic nature of the fuel. In wood, for example, two thirds or more of the solid is composed of cellulosic sugars (totally aliphatic) while the remainder is lignin (6). The lignin is an aromatic based binder which holds the cellulose fibers together. The most complex aromatic compound in the binder is benzene. Upon slow pyrolysis, as practiced in fixed bed gasification processes, almost all of the cellulosic material is volatilized while typically half of the lignin is converted to char. This yields 15-20% by weight char from a wood sample. For bark fuels, the char produced is somewhat higher. Flash pyrolysis as encountered in entrained gasifiers can yield less char depending on the reaction temperature and pressure. Under high heating rates and low pressure, the solid is totally volatile (3). With wood fuels, there is only a small amount of char which must be gasified away by steam and possibly oxygen. At complete devolatilization, the wood char contains about 1/3 of the original fuel heating value (7).

In the case of coal, the solid is predominately aromatic. Structural analyses of coal show ring clusters of several to tens of rings with heteroatoms bound in the ring structure and in side chains (4). Upon pyrolysis, the solid decomposes to yield a volatile fraction of about 40% and a large quantity of highly condensed (highly aromatic) charcoal. Flash pyrolysis can increase the volatile yield but cannot totally vaporize the solid (1). The heating value of the remaining charcoal exceeds 50% of the heating value of the parent coal. The greater aromatic nature of the coal charcoal makes it less reactive to steam than wood charcoals.

Wood contains little in the way of heteroatoms. Bound sulfur and nitrogen generally are present at levels less than 0.2% of the fuel weight.

In recent gasification experiments (8) sulfur gases, SO_2, H_2S and COS have been detected in a gasifier effluent at concentrations totalling 100 ppm. No ammonia has been detected. In contrast, coal synthesis gases can contain 0.5 to 1% H_2S along with possibly 0.5% NH_3 (1% = 10,000 ppm). Also in many eastern U.S. coals, high chlorine levels are observed. Volatile metals in coal ash such as arsenic can cause downstream processing problems.

The sulfur gases and ammonia are particularly important in downstream processing. In the usual coal gasification designs, selective acid gas removal processes like Rectisol or Selexol are employed to produce separate H_2S and CO_2 streams. The H_2S must be processed in a Claus plant and a tail gas cleanup plant to produce elemental sulfur. Catalyst beds must still be protected by sulfur guards. Ammonia must be concentrated in a sour water stripper and recovered, for example, using the Phosam-W process. The cost of the cleanup including acid gas removal, sulfur recovery and liquid effluent treatment for ammonia generally represents between 20 and 25% of the plant investment (2). At the low levels of sulfur in wood gas, H_2S can be economically removed by hot zinc oxide. Sulfur free CO_2 from the acid gas process can be vented directly to the atmosphere off of the regenerator or recovered for sale. The quantity of ammonia, if produced, would be small and could be handled by neutralizing the blowdown streams off of the shift converter coolers and possibly the effluent off a water wash tower. The result is a considerable savings in plant investment in gas cleanup.

KINETIC EFFECTS

Along with higher volatility, wood charcoals are more reactive in steam and CO_2 than coal chars. The relative reactivity of wood charcoals to bituminous coal chars in carbon dioxide at 900C has been determined to be 10 to 30 times as great (5). The higher volatile yield and more reactive charcoal from wood have several important effects on reactor design and process efficiency.

In order to demonstrate the effects, consider the performance of the Texaco gasifier operating on wood and coal. The Texaco unit basically consists of a burner and refractory lined chamber. Since no waterwalls exist, the refractory must be protected by thermally moderating the partial oxidation flame. The Texaco gasifier has been modelled as shown in Figure 2. In stage 1, the burner zone of the gasifier, fuel, oxygen and feed transport media are injected into the gasifier. The feedstock pyrolyzes and the volatile portion is burned to CO, CO_2, H_2 and H_2O producing a high temperature. The oxygen added is sufficient to supply heat to gasify all of the char to synthesis gas components which exit the reduction zone at an estimated 2200F. The peak temperature is important in the operability of such a gasifier. With bituminous coal, Texaco uses liquid water as a feed transport medium. The slurry technique is used to meter coal into the gasifier and to cool the burner flame. In practice, it is found that a slurry which typically might contain 1 lb H_2O/lb coal provides satisfactory gasifier performance. The water input reduces gasifier efficiency and increases oxygen consumption.

Figure 3 shows the effect of moisture content on peak gasifier temperature for coal and wood. The results show that wood can be fed with low moisture content (and no thermal moderator) while producing temperatures no higher than coals fed with liquid water. The reason for this difference in behavior is the larger mass of volatiles produced from wood which because of their greater heat capacity act as a built in thermal moderator. Figure 4 shows the oxygen demand is higher for coals than wood fuels on a MM Btu of feedstock basis. While the minimum oxygen requirement is only slightly higher for coal, Table 2 shows that the practical oxygen demand and efficiency of wood systems are improved relative to coal.

As a second example of wood system advantages, consider the fixed bed downdraft gasifier. In pilot studies on this concept (8), wood with moisture contents varying from 0 to 40% have been successfully fed. Unlike coal which requires steam to moderate and provide reaction oxygen, the oxygen in the wood plus reaction oxygen is sufficient to gasify the feedstock through in-situ generation of H_2O and CO_2. Figures 4 and 5 show predicted performance by the model for wood feed in this unit. An exit temperature of 1500F (815C), based on experimental results, has been used for these predictions. Coal system carbon-steam kinetics are exceedingly slow at temperatures 50 to 100C above this value. The model shows that the oxygen demand and thermal efficiencies are improved relative to entrained gasifiers because of the decreased exit temperature. It is doubtful that any coal except the most reactive lignites could be fed to such a gasifier without large volumes of water or steam because of over-temperature and slagging problems. Because of the ability to operate without steam, plant complexity including heat recovery and steam recycle are considerably reduced.

ECONOMIC CONSIDERATIONS

Probably the most important impact of biomass properties on plants relative to coal is scale. In terms of plant size, there is no doubt that coal is king. Methanol plants of capacities on the order of 100,000 BBld using 15,000 TPD of high rank coal are routinely proposed. Such 250 billion Btu/day plants will cost several billions of dollars, produce severe environmental and social impact on the sparsely populated western sites where they will be built, and create a hugh alcohol surplus in an undeveloped market. The largest wood processing plants today are paper mills which process several thousands of woodchips per day. A 3000 green TPD wood plant would produce about 6000 BBld of alcohol. A more realistic size plant based on crop residues or locally available wood is in the range of several hundred dry tons per day producing up to 500 BBld of alcohol. It is this aspect of size which has been used as an argument for coal and against wood.

Past trends in the economy have led us to believe that economy of scale is the most important factor in plant economics. Thus the biggest plant will yield the cheapest product. Today, however, the correct argument might be "small is beautiful". Without U.S. government financial assistance, few corporations can afford to "bet the company" on a fuel plant which may not begin to produce revenues for 5 to 10 years after its conception. With current interest rates, the cost of borrowed capital during this period could make the selling price astronomically high even with economy of scale.

Consider wood as a feedstock. Acceptable harvesting techniques are available, the fuel is non-polluting, and plants are small enough that the impact will be small around plant sites. Plant power, purchased over the fence, for a 100 TPD methanol plant will be only on the order of one to two Megawatts. The oxygen requirement of 70 TPD can be purchased over the fence. Water requirements are reasonable and waste disposal minimal with the proper technology. Acid rain will not result from such facilities and even the CO_2 produced in gasification comes from the atmosphere.

Table 3 compares the capital cost for two equal size plants based on approximate percentages for capital cost from several CF Braun studies assuming the wood gasifier to be of the downdraft type (8). Since wood will be purchased, preparation costs will be minimized. For wood, acid gas removal costs and effluent treatment will be lowered considerably because of the lack of sulfur and nitrogen in the fuel. The figures in the table reflect elimination of Claus and tail gas systems and a simpler bulk scrubbing acid gas plant. Capital for effluent treatment costs are eliminated for ammonia recovery. Because the wood plant will ultimately be small, oxygen, power and waste water treatment can be bought over the fence. A reduced plant water and steam system will exist to service heat recovery equipment and provide startup steam. General facility requirements will be minimized. A two train 250 billion Btu per day coal plant (actually for SNG) is estimated to cost $1.04 billion in 1979 dollars (total plant investment) by CF Braun (2). Assuming a 100 TPD alcohol from wood plant (1.95 billion Btu per day) and a 0.7 power for scaling, the wood plant cost would be $13.70 MM escalated to mid '81 costs. This cost includes contractor fee and contingency. Assuming startup and working capital costs, the total investment will be about $15 MM. Actually, the 0.7 scale factor is very conservative since much of the 250 billion Btu per day plant is field fabricated while the wood plant could be shop fabricated. Using the capital number for order of magnitude purposes, the plant cost has been put in the range where a consumer market is available. Shop fabrication promotes reliability and short startup time, while small size means shorter construction period. Table 4 shows a typical operating cost breakdown for the methanol plant with purchased feedstock and utilities. Using the investment and estimated operating costs, discount cash flow rates of return after taxes were computed for a variety of cases assuming 100% equity financing,

45

10 year sum of the digits depreciation and the 10% investment tax credit. Figure 7 shows rate of return as a function of methanol selling price for the base plant case. For selling prices above 70¢/gal, the rate of return falls within acceptable limits for many investors. Figure 6 also shows that if the by-product CO_2 can be recovered and sold, there is a substantial improvement on project ROI. Table 5 shows the sensitivity of the economics to investment and operating costs.

Importantly, production on the order of a hundred tons per day can be readily absorbed in local markets. Blended at the 10% level in gasoline, a 100 TPD plant could service a rather small consumer market of 6800 BBld of gasoline. The fact that such plants will not make a major impact initially on the fuel market is to their benefit. Instead they can create the market in a programmed fashion for the coal giants of the 21'st century.

CONCLUSIONS

Wood is not only a useful fuel for gasification, but offers some important advantages over coal. These include reactivity, pollution and siting, size, and marketability. The economics of small plants appear to put wood in the competitive position as a feedstock. Wood certainly has a future in the methanol production market.

46

REFERENCES

1) Anthony, D. B., Howard, J., AIChE J., $\underline{22}$ p 625, 1976.
2) Detman, R. F., "Preliminary Economic Analysis of New Gasification Processes", Proceedings of 1st International Gas Research Conference, Chicago, Illinois, June 9-12, 1980.
3) Diebold, J. P., Fast Pyrolysis Studies Under Contract to SERI, 1979.
4) Dryden, I. G. C., Chemical Constitution and Reactions of Coal", Ch. 6 in Chemistry of Coal Utilization supplementary volume (Lowry Ed)., John Wiley & Sons, 1963.
5) Graboski, M., "Kinetics of Char Gasification Reactions", in A Survey of Biomass Gasification vol II, July 1979.
6) Graboski, M. S., Bain, R., "Properties of Biomass Relevant to Gasification", Ch 3 in A Survey of Biomass Gasification vol II, SERI/TR-33-239, July 1979.
7) Herman, D., Graboski, M. S., "Pyrolysis Gasification of Densified Biomass", submitted to Fuel, 1981.
8) Reed, T. B., Graboski, M., Markson, M., "Synthesis Gas From Biomass Operating Data on a 1-Ton/Day Oxygen Gasifier", Presented at Biomass to Methanol Workshop, Tamarron, Colorado, March 3-5, 1982.

FIGURE 1   Processing Route For Coal to Methanol by Gasification

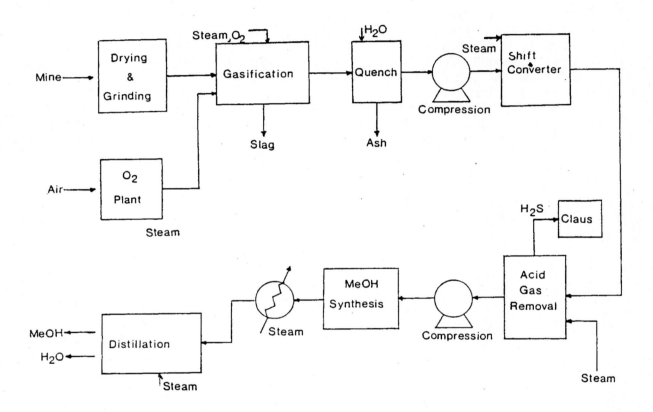

FIGURE 2

TEXACO GASIFIER MODEL

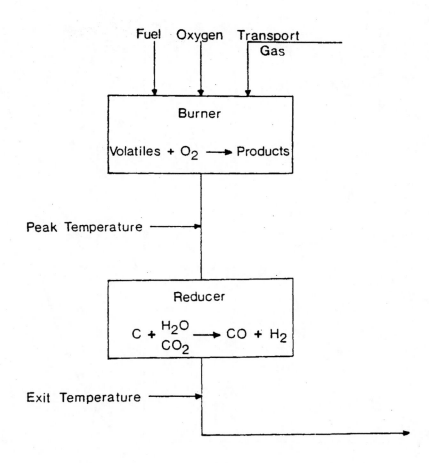

FIGURE 3   Effect of Moisture Content on Burner Temperature For Various Fuels

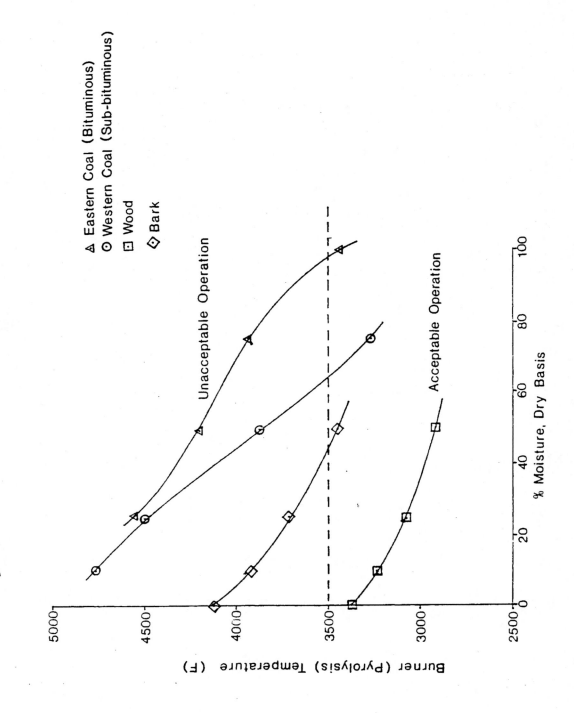

△ Eastern Coal (Bituminous)
⊙ Western Coal (Sub-bituminous)
◻ Wood
◇ Bark

50

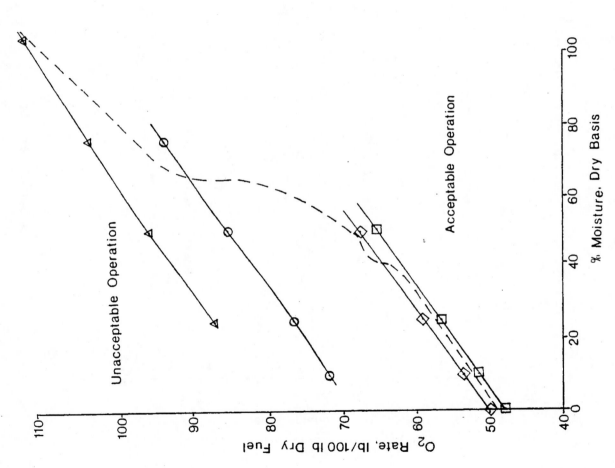

FIGURE 4

Effect of Moisture Content
on Oxygen Demand
For Various Fuels

△ Eastern Coal (Bituminous)
⊙ Western Coal (Sub-bituminous)
▣ Wood
◇ Bark

51

FIGURE 5 Fixed Bed Downdraft Results O_2 Demand

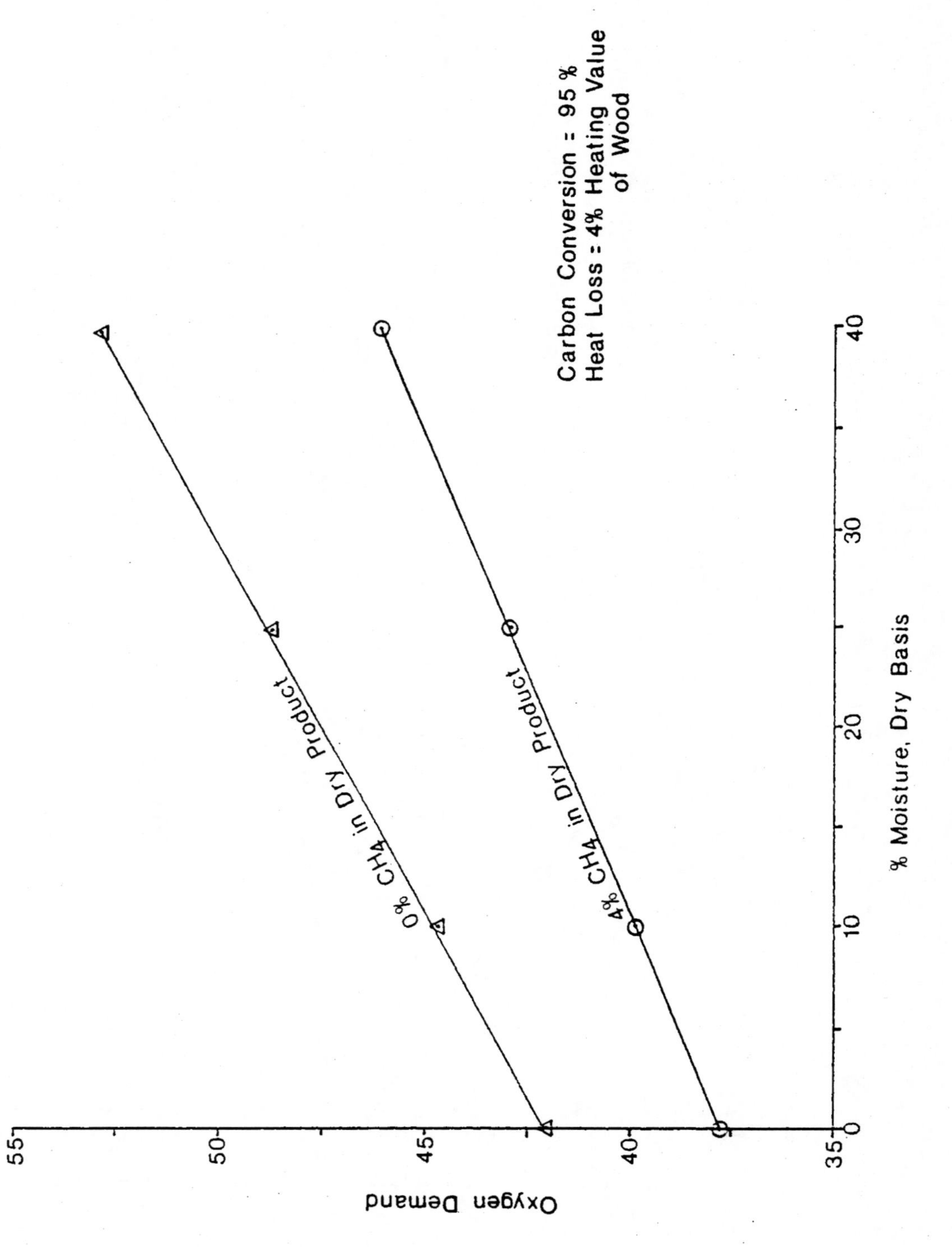

Oxygen Demand
55
50
45
40
35
0
10
20
30
40
% Moisture, Dry Basis
0% CH4 in Dry Product
4% CH4 in Dry Product
Carbon Conversion = 95 %
Heat Loss = 4% Heating Value of Wood

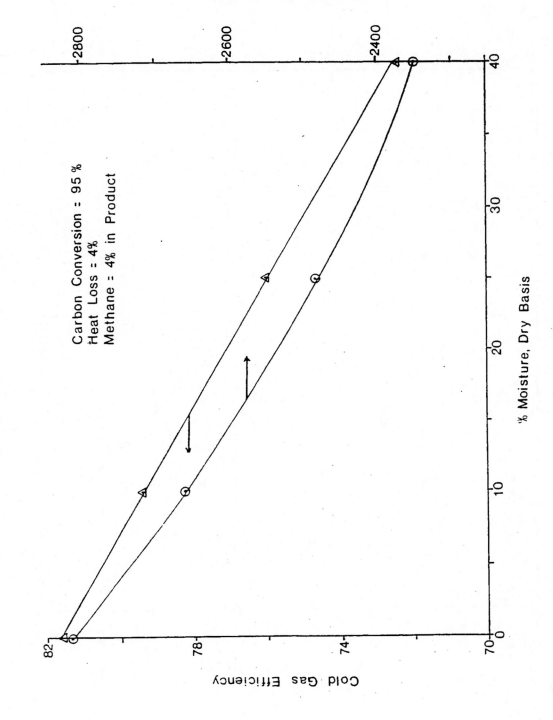

FIGURE 6   Fixed Bed Downdraft Results

Carbon Conversion = 95 %
Heat Loss = 4%
Methane = 4% in Product

Peak Reaction Temperature

% Moisture, Dry Basis

Cold Gas Efficiency

53

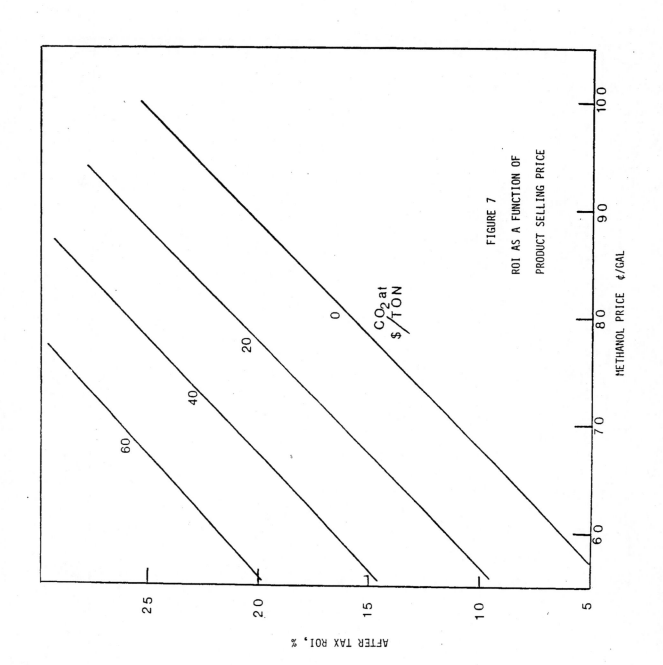

FIGURE 7

ROI AS A FUNCTION OF
PRODUCT SELLING PRICE

54

TABLE 1

SELECTED ANALYTICAL DATA
FOR WOOD AND COAL FUELS

FEEDSTOCK	ULTIMATE ANALYSIS MAF WT%						PROXIMATE ANALYSIS, MAF WT%			GROSS HEATING VALUE=BTU LB MAF
	C	H	O	N	S	CL	VM	FC	ASH	
ILLINOIS BITUMINOUS	79.6	5.4	7.6	1.8	5.3	0.3	43.2	56.8	15.1	14700
MONTANA SUB-BITUMINOUS	75.3	5.1	17.6	1.1	0.9	T	43.0	57.0	10.0	12860
PINE BARK	54.0	6.0	39.9	0.1	T	NA	74.0	26.0	3.0	9040
PONDEROSA PINE	50.3	6.0	43.6	0.1	0.05	NA	83.4	16.6	0.2	8647

TABLE 2
COMPARISON OF OXYGEN DEMAND
IN ENTRAINED GASIFICATION

O_2 DEMAND PER 10^6 $\dfrac{BTU}{MAF\ FUEL}$

	MINIMUM O_2 DEMAND	PRACTICAL O_2 DEMAND	COLD EFF.
EASTERN COAL	57	78	72.2
WOOD	55	59	79.3%

HEAT LOSS = 200 BTU/LB FEED
(2% HV OF WOOD)

TABLE 3
CAPITAL COST BREAKDOWN
FOR METHANOL PLANTS

	COAL PLANT	BIOMASS PLANT
FUEL PREPARATION	5.0	3.0[1]
GASIFICATION	16.0	16.0
SHIFT	4.0	4.0
ACID GAS REMOVAL AND SULFUR RECOVERY	22.0	5.0[2]
METHANOL SYNTHESIS	6.0	6.0
OXYGEN PLANT	14.0	0[3]
EFFLUENT TREATMENT	4.0	0[4]
PLANT WATER SYSTEM	4.0	0
STEAM PLANT	15.0	4.0[5]
GENERAL FACILITIES	10.0	2.0[6]
TOTAL	100.0	40.0

NOTES

(1) NO CRUSHING AND GRINDING COSTS
(2) NO CLAUS PLANT, BULK AND GAS REMOVAL
(3) PURCHASED O_2
(4) PURCHASED WASTE WATER TREATMENT, NO AMMONIA RECOVERY
(5) PURCHASED POWER; SOME BOILER FEED WATER PREPARATION AND PREHEATING
(6) 5% OF PLANT INVESTMENT DUE TO MINIMIZED PLANT COMPLEXITY

TABLE 4

OPERATING COST BREAKDOWN FOR A 100TPD
METHANOL PLANT FROM WOOD

BASIS: 180 Gal/Ton MeOH Yield

Raw Materials	Usage	$MM
Wood ($35/MAF ton)	174 T/D	2.00
Oxygen ($42/ton)	70 T/D	1.07
Electricity (4¢/KwH)	500 KwH/T MeOH[1]	0.66
Labor & Administration		0.40
Taxes & Insurance (1.5% Investment)		xxxx
Maintenance (3.0% Investment)		xxxx
Supplies, Chemicals, Water		0.15
TOTAL		(4.28 + 0.045I)

(1) Includes CO_2 Recovery at 167 Tons/Day

TABLE 5

SENSITIVITY OF AFTER TAX
RETURN TO COST PARAMETERS

FACTOR	EFFECT
20% Reduction in Investment	
(1) No CO_2 Credit	+ 1.7%
(2) CO_2 Credit @ $40/Ton	+ 4.8%
20% Reduction in Operating Cost	
(1) No CO_2 Credit	+ 3.9%
(2) CO_2 Credit @ $40/Ton	+ 4.8%
Elimination of 10% Investment Tax Credit - No CO_2 Credit	- 1.1%

PEAT AS A FEEDSTOCK TO
THE KBW GASIFICATION PROCESS

L. A. Oster
Project Engineer
Koppers Company, Inc.
Pittsburgh, Pennsylvania

H. J. Michaels
Manager, Marketing & Sales
KBW Gasification Systems, Inc.
Pittsburgh, Pennsylvania

ABSTRACT

The KBW Gasification process is a commercial process for converting coal to synthesis gas and subsequent methanol production. Koppers is currently conducting a feasibility study to convert North Carolina peat into methanol. Tests have been completed which show that peat can be successfully dried and pulverized to the characteristics required for the KBW gasifier. These tests coupled with logical correlations with coal gasification experience indicate that peat gasification is viable.

The KBW entrained flow gasifier and gas cooling and cleaning system will be discussed. The advantages of using the KBW gasifier for methanol synthesis will be highlighted. Finally, an overview of the North Carolina peat-to-methanol plant feasibility study will be given.

TABLE OF CONTENTS

PAGE NO.

INTRODUCTION

As conventional fuel prices generally continue to rise, several companies are starting to evaluate the use of peat as an alternate energy source. Another reason that attention has turned to peat, concerns changes in the tax laws. The alcohol tax credit passed during the Carter Administration, gives gasoline blenders a 30 to 40¢/gal. tax credit for methanol or ethanol produced from raw materials other than petroleum, natural gas or coal. It is presently believed that this tax credit would apply to the blending of methanol produced from the gasification of peat. The tax savings would offset the additional costs associated with material handling, transportation and drying of peat, (as compared to coal) and make peat gasification to produce methanol competitive with other sources of methanol.

Koppers Company, Inc. is conducting a feasibility study to convert North Carolina peat into methanol using the KBW Gasification Process. In conjunction with this study, a number of tests were conducted to dry and pulverize the peat to the requirements of the KBW gasifier.

This paper will discuss the KBW system mainly as it relates to coal gasification and conclude by an overview of the peat testing results and the peat gasification project.

KBW BACKGROUND

KBW is a relatively new name in gasification technology, however, it has over 60 years of combined experience in coal gasification behind it. KBW was formed in October 1980, and is a joint venture between Koppers Company, Inc. and the Babcock and Wilcox Company, (an operating unit of McDermott). Through licensing agreements KBW can draw on the combined staff of over 6,000 engineers and technical personnel of the parent companies.

B & W's gasification experience started early in the '40's when they constructed an entrained flow gasifier for the Bureau of Mines in Morgantown, West Virginia, and later constructed a larger pilot unit at the same site. They designed and constructed a pilot plant gasifier for E. I. DuPont at Belle, West Virginia, then in 1955 constructed a larger scale commercial (17 ton/hr.) entrained flow gasifier for DuPont. During the 60's Babcock & Wilcox operated an air blown test gasifier at their Alliance, Ohio Research Center, and in 1976, fabricated the Bigas gasifier for the Homer City pilot plant.

Koppers' experience is also in entrained flow, oxygen blow gasification. Koppers designed, constructed and operated the Bureau of Mines pilot unit in Missouri during the 40's. The first commercial installation using the process was in 1952 in Finland, and since then over 50 gasifiers were installed by others at 16 locations in Europe, Asia and Africa.

Each company also has experience in many related areas which will be successfully integrated for reliable performance of synfuel plants. Babcock and Wilcox has engineered and fabricated over 1,000 coal fired, dry-bottom and slagging boilers. They, therefore, have extensive data and expertise in coal handling, pulverizing, drying, heat transfer, fluid flow and combustion technology. Koppers has engineered and constructed over 60% of the coke plants and by-product plants in this country and two of the largest blast furnaces in the world. Koppers also manufactures a variety of material handling and pollution control equipment. In addition, Koppers owns and operates 37 chemical plants, 27 wood treating plants and has a number of subsidiaries in heavy construction and road materials.

Drawing on this background, KBW offers complete turnkey construction capabilities for synthetic fuels plants using KBW entrained flow gasifiers. This includes design, detailed design, procurement and inspection, construction, start-up and training for all areas of the plant; from coal handling and gasification through the auxiliaries.

The KBW gasifier is an atmospheric pressure, oxygen blown, slagging, entrained flow gasifier. It is not a "new" process concept. It includes all of the inherent characteristics of entrained flow gasifiers but the KBW gasifier has several distinct improvements over existing entrained flow gasifiers which will be described later.

COAL PREPARATION

The plant starts with coal received from the mine, typically 2 in. x 0. Coal is reclaimed from the stockpile and conveyed to the screening station. (See Figure 1). Over-sized material enters an impact-type crusher to crush all of the coal to minus 3/8 in. A splitter gate separates the coal for the auxiliary boiler from that for the gasifiers. Depending on the plant, 10 to 20% of the coal is used in the auxiliary boiler, and the remaining 80 to 90% is ultimately fed to the gasifier.

Crushed coal is pulverized and simultaneously dried in an air swept mill, typically to 88% minus 90 micron, and dried to between 2 and 8% moisture. Coal is classified, and pulverized product is carried overhead and separated in cyclones. The coarser material falls out and is reintroduced to the pulverizer.

Pulverized and dried coal discharges from the cyclone separator through a rotary air-lock into the product storage bin. From this point on, the material is under a nitrogen atmosphere. From the product bin, coal discharges through nitrogen "air slides" into the coal distribution box equipped with aeration pads to distribute the coal. Rotary valves discharge the coal to the pneumatic coal pumps which pneumatically convey it from the coal prep building to the coal service bins located atop the gasifier structure. (See Figure 2). There are four service bins per gasifier, one on each side. Each service bin discharges to two weigh belt feeders which measure the coal fed to the smaller gasifier feed bins below. From the gasifier feed bin, coal discharges onto variable speed screw feeders to the gasifier burner blowpipe. Coal discharges from the screw feeder and is entrained by oxygen and steam into the gasifier. The screw feeders are specially designed and fabricated by Sprout-Waldron (a subsidiary of Koppers) for this application. This design allows flexibility in feed rates and does not depend on preset clearances which change with wear.

Because the coal is pulverized to this degree of fineness, 88% minus 90 micron, the gasifiers can use 100% of the mine output. There are no problems with the percentage of fines received, as opposed to some of the problems of grate pluggage that fixed bed gasifiers encounter when less than 1/4 in. coal is fed.

KBW GASIFIER & HEAT RECOVERY BOILER

The KBW gasifier is depicted in Figure 3. The vessel is nominally 61 ft. high by 14 ft. square. The gasifier shell is fabricated of welded membrane tube wall construction. The lower 15 ft. of the gasifier is refractory lined, the upper 46 ft. is a bare tube cooling section

The coal, oxygen and steam mixtures enter the gasifier through eight burners, two per wall, one upper and one lower burner per wall. They are offset to form a vortex which promotes mixing. The gasification reactions occur at about 3100°F in the lower refractory-lined portion of the gasifier. Therefore, the products are primarily CO and H_2 with some CO_2 and traces of CH_4 (0.1 vol. %). At this temperature no phenols or tars are formed. This is attractive from an environmental standpoint. In other lower temperature processes tars and phenols are formed. When the gas is cooled, the tars and phenols condense, and must be separated from the recirculating water system. Blowdown from the system is subsequently difficult to biologically treat.

The other point is that only traces of methane are formed and therefore, no methane reforming is required downstream. This is particularly attractive if ammonia, methanol or gasoline is the ultimate product.

As the gasification reactions occur, slag impinges on the walls of the gasifier. The temperature in the gasification zone is maintained above the ash fluid temperature so the molten slag flows down the walls. Slag adhering to the walls of the bare tube section will be shed by its own weight, or be periodically removed by soot blowers located on the gasifier walls. The bottom of the gasifier has a sloped hearth floor and slag flows through the tap hole opening where it is quenched with water in the slag quench tank below. Granulated slag is removed by a drag conveyor, stabilized if required, and ultimately disposed of in a landfill.

The design of the base of the gasifier is similar to the design used in slagging boilers. This design avoids problems such as slag freezing and plugging the tap hole, or the opposite problem of having pools of molten slag form on the bottom.

As the gas passes up through the gasifier, the reactions are essentially complete as the gas exits the refractory-lined studded zone. In the 46 ft. long bare tube section above, the gas is cooled from about $3000^\circ F$ ($1650^\circ C$) to $1800^\circ F$ ($980^\circ C$) by generating high pressure steam.

The gas exits the gasifier through the cross over flue to the heat recovery boiler where it is cooled from $1800^\circ F$ ($980^\circ C$) to $450^\circ F$ ($230^\circ C$), again by generating high pressure steam. Typically, ranges of 600 psig steam can be generated for high sulfur bituminous coals to 1200 psig for low sulfur lignites. The sulfur content of the coal is one of the major constraints on the pressure and superheat temperature of the steam generated.

The obvious advantage of this system over other processes is the ability to generate usable superheated, high pressure steam. The gasifiers and heat recovery boilers can supply over 50% of the steam requirements for the entire plant. Typically, all of the large compressors are steam turbine driven. One or two of the larger turbines operate at a back pressure to supply all of the low pressure steam for the plant.

Typically, on older entrained bed gasifiers the gas exiting the gasifier is water sprayed to solidify the slag. Thus, the sensible heat is lost to the water. The KBW design does not require a water quench, and the sensible heat is recovered in the heat recovery boiler, improving the efficiency.

GASIFIER FABRICATION

The gasifier is fabricated of a membrane tube wall construction. Two and one-half inch O.D. tubes with a steel bar in between are continuously welded together on each side to form a gas-tight panel. (See Figure 4). In the lower refractory lined portion, steel studs, 3/8 in. diameter by 1/2 in. long are welded to the tubes. The refractory lining is then applied around the studs to a thickness of about 5/8 in. The studs lock the refractory in place and provide cooling for it.

Four panels are shipped in flat sections then final welds are made in the field. This construction technique has been used for 40 years in B & W's shops when fabricating boilers, including slag-tap boilers. It has proven to have long service life with minimal maintenance.

GAS COOLING AND CLEANING

From the gasifier heat recovery boiler, the gas enters a parallel cluster of cyclone separators where 90% of the entrained particulates are removed. This flyash typically contains 50% unreacted carbon and 50% ash. In cases where less reactive bituminous coals are fed and carbon conversion in the gasifier is in the range of 88 to 92%, the char collected in the cyclones may be pneumatically conveyed to the auxiliary boiler, mixed with the fresh coal mix and burned. Thus the overall carbon conversion effectively increases to 98% or better. This also reduces the quantity of solid wastes to be disposed of.

From the cyclones, the gas enters the top of the saturator-cooler and is cooled from 450°F (230°C) to 150°F (65°C) by direct water spray. The gas then enters two Theisen disintegrators arranged in series which reduce the particulate loading to 0.01 gr/dscf. The disintegrators scrub the gas with water sprays, and mechanical rotating blades remove the particulates by centrifugal force.

The gas is further cooled to 105°F (40°C) in the final cooler by countercurrent contact with water sprays.

In both the final cooler and saturator cooler the water is recirculated in each spray section. Recirculated water is indirectly cooled with cooling tower water, therefore, there is no discharge of dissolved gases to the atmosphere. All of the recirculating tanks are vented to a continuous flare to destroy the H_2S and NH_3 scrubbed from the gas.

Particulates are settled from the recirculating water in a covered clarifier which is also vented to the flare. Excess condensate from the gas cooling and cleaning system is used as make-up to the CO shift system, and the remainder, typically less than 6 gpm per gasifier, is blown down to the wastewater treatment system.

From the final cooler, the gas enters the gas blower which discharges the gas at about 20 in. W.C. A positive pressure is maintained throughout the gas cooling and cleaning train. The blower discharges the gas to an electrostatic precipitator and to the gas holder which floats on-line for compressor control. The electrostatic precipitator is a wet irrigated-type, which reduces the particulate loading in the gas to 0.0001 grains/dscf. At this point, the gas is essentially free of particulates and is suitable for a variety of different processing applications. Typical ranges in gas composition are shown below:

Gas Production:	32,000 to 45,000 SCFM/Gasifier	
Gas Composition:	Vol. % (dry)	Peat (40,000 SCFM)
CO	53 - 65	55
CO_2	8 - 11	12
H_2	25 - 35	30
Trace Compounds	1 - 2	3

APPLICATIONS

The syngas can be used for many applications as shown in Figure 5. Uses include: intermediate-BTU fuel gas, combined cycle, methanation to produce SNG, shifting to produce high purity hydrogen, or reaction to make ammonia. However, much of the current emphasis of the synfuels projects is to make a liquid fuel product such as methanol or subsequent conversion to gasoline or MTBE, in addition to CO and H_2 for the chemical and oil industry.

Since the purpose of the conference is methanol production, that is the only one of these applications which will be discussed.

METHANOL SYNTHESIS

The fact that the syngas is primarily CO, H_2 and CO_2 rather than CH_4 and long chain hydrocarbons is a distinct advantage for the production of methanol as these are the primary building blocks. First the gas is compressed to about 600 psig prior to entering the CO Shift system. The gas is split and a portion of the CO and steam is catalytically shifted to CO_2 and H_2 in a two stage process to obtain the correct H_2:CO ratio for methanol synthesis. The gas is cooled, and then enters the acid gas removal process where the H_2S and excess CO_2 are removed. CO_2 is vented to the atmosphere and the acid gas is then processed for sulfur recovery. The resultant desulfurized synthesis gas is compressed to about 1200 psig prior to entering the methanol synthesis loop. The CO, H_2 and a small amount of CO_2 are catalytically converted to methanol, and about 8 to 10 wt. % water and higher alcohols. This crude methanol is further distilled to a fuel grade product or to an anhydrous product.

In the case of gasoline synthesis, the crude methanol is catalytically converted to gasoline using the Mobil M Process, which yields about 85% gasoline and 15% LPG products.

PEAT GASIFICATION

Koppers is currently preparing a feasibility study for Peat Methanol Associates, a joint venture of Energy Transition Corporation, North Carolina Synfuels Corporation (a subsidiary of Koppers Company) and Mr. J. B. Sunderland, an independent investor.

The plant would be located in Cresswell, North Carolina, on a 40 acre site within the peat reserves of First Colony Farms. It would be a small, single gasifier plant which would produce approximately 64 million gallons per year of methanol. The total peat feed to the plant is approximately 2000 TPD @ 30% moisture (1400 TPD, dry). Peat would be mined by the shallow milled peat harvesting method. The moisture content can vary between 30 and 40%, and the peat can contain over 15% wood.

The design of the peat material handling system to provide reliable, safe, and a consistent feed to the gasifier was of primary concern.

Koppers conducted a testing program through our Research Center, and the Williams Company, a manufacturer of pulverizers and dryers. The objective of the tests was to dry peat at different moisture contents down to 8% and to pulverize to 70% minus 200 mesh.

The tests were run with raw peat between 30% and 60% moisture content, and only large pieces of wood removed. The peat was first fed through a screw feeder to a rigid hammer impact dryer mill. The peat was dried with hot air and pneumatically discharged through a velocity separator to a cyclone separator. The gases exhausted through a baghouse dust collector to the atmosphere. The material was discharged from the cyclone separator to a general purpose hammermill to a cyclone separator. The air was again exhausted through a baghouse dust collector to the atmosphere. Peat was not screened before it was fed to the unit. Inlet air temperatures to the dryer ranged in various tests from 600 to 850°F.

The results showed peat could be dried to 8% moisture, and the peat, wood and roots could be pulverized to 50% minus 200 mesh with a dryer mill and a two stage hammermill. The tests showed that power requirements and capital costs for drying and pulverizing peat will be substantially higher than for coal. It is felt that drying from 60% moisture to 8% moisture will be cost prohibitive. However, if the feed moisture content can be maintained in the 30 to 40% moisture range, drying to 8% appears feasible.

Gasification of peat, once it is dried and pulverized, is not substantially different than the gasification of coal in the KBW gasifier as previously described. It is very comparable to lignite on a moisture and ash free basis.

Gasifier Feed

	Lignite		Peat	
	Wt.% (As Fed)	Wt.% MAF Basis	Wt.% (As Fed)	Wt. % MAF Basis
C	40.34	64.98	54.33	62.01
H	3.14	5.06	5.02	5.73
N	1.24	2.00	1.28	1.46
O	15.69	25.27	26.75	30.53
S	1.67	2.69	0.24	0.27
Ash	29.92	--	4.38	--
H_2O	8.00	--	8.00	--
	100.00	100.00	100.00	100.00

Peat generally contains more volatile matter and less fixed carbon, and therefore, is somewhat more reactive than lignite. There is substantially more bound oxygen in peat which leads to a higher percentage of CO_2 in the synthesis gas rather than CO.

Peat will be dried to 8% moisture to be fed to the gasifier. At this moisture content, there is sufficient inherent moisture for the gasification reactions that steam is not added with the oxygen to entrain the peat into the gasifier as is done with most coals.

For these reasons, less CO + H_2 is generated per ton of peat fed to the gasifier than from an equivalent amount of coal.

Other differences between peat and coal are the nitrogen and ash contents. Peat tends to contain more chemically bound nitrogen which results in higher NH_3 production. The ash content of peat can vary from 3 to 25%, depending on its depth and location. The ash characteristics are similar to lignite in that they both have higher ash softening and fluid temperatures. Limestone may be added as a fluxing agent to adjust the slag fluid properties. It would also act as a binding agent for slag disposal.

The economics of the PMA project have not been finalized, however, currently the methanol cost is estimated to be 75¢/gal. at the plant gate, assuming some benefit from current tax laws.

The battery limits plant, including site preparation and some off-sites work is estimated to be $210 million (1981 dollars). The peat harvesting capital is not included. The capital estimate does reflect the results a thorough environmental analysis. PMA has submitted a PSD air discharge permit to the state of North Carolina, and has also conducted an extensive water discharge study.

Although the PMA project is a relatively small scale methanol plant, and is a single gasifier plant, which may not obtain the benefits of economies of scale, it is attractive for several reasons:

1.) The capital exposure and risks are substantially lower than those of the large scale, $1 to 2 billion plants.

2.) Construction time is nearly 2 years shorter than a large plant which minimizes the risk of escalation due to inflation and project delays.

3.) The environmental impacts of this plant are substantially lower. Once the plant is constructed, environmental data can be collected and used for permitting subsequent expansions.

4.) The plant produces a manageable quantity of methanol to try to market. Currently the marketing effort is directed toward blending the methanol in a 2 to 3% range with gasoline at an east coast refiner.

5.) The location of the plant site is in an economically depressed area, and generally there is good support from both private citizens and from the local and state government.

SUMMARY

In summary, KBW offers complete turnkey construction capabilities for synthetic fuels plants. The KBW gasifier is an entrained flow, oxygen blown, slagging gasifier which operates at atmospheric pressure. Some of the important advantages of this design include:

1.) The ability to gasify any rank of coal. The caking properties of bituminous coals do not adversely affect the gasification process.

2.) The KBW gasifier can use 100% of the coal mine output; including fines.

3.) The gasifier has a high throughput capacity, nearly twice that of other commercial entrained flow gasifiers.

4.) The KBW System has major environmental advantages as the gasifier operates at sufficiently high temperatures, and therefore, no phenols, tars, or long chain hydrocarbons are produced.

5.) The synthesis gas is primarily CO, H_2 and CO_2 and does not require methane reforming.

6.) Commercially proven, membrane tube wall construction of the gasifier shell allows production of high pressure, superheated steam.

The synthesis gas produced in the KBW gasifier can be used for a variety of applications. Those of particular interest at the present are its use for methanol as a fuel or gasoline extender; or ultimate conversion to gasoline.

The gasification of peat to produce methanol is an extension of data on the gasification of lignite. Test results show the North Carolina peat can be successfully dried and pulverized with commercially available equipment to the requirements of the KBW gasifier. On a moisture and ash free basis, the gas production will be similar to the synthesis gas produced from lignite.

The PMA peat to methanol project is unique, and may not obtain economies of scale, however, it has other economic, marketing, environmental and socio-political advantages as previously described, that make the project particularly attractive.

FIGURE 1

KBW GASIFICATION PROCESS

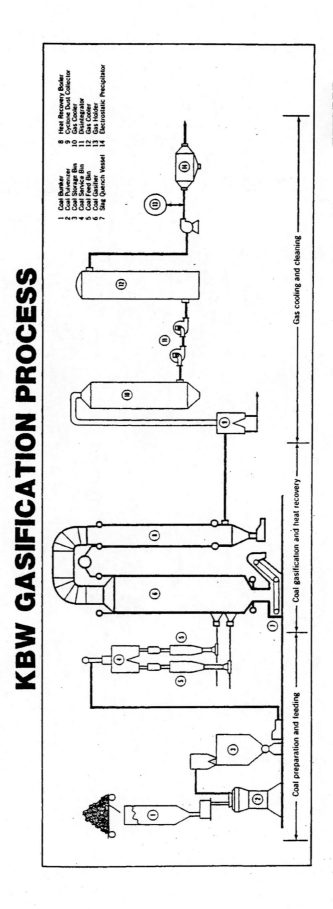

1 Coal Bunker
2 Coal Pulverizer
3 Coal Storage Bin
4 Coal Service Bin
5 Coal Feed Bin
6 Coal Gasifier
7 Slag Quench Vessel

8 Heat Recovery Boiler
9 Cyclone Dust Collector
10 Gas Cooler
11 Disintegrator
12 Gas Cooler
13 Gas Holder
14 Electrostatic Precipitator

KBW

Coal preparation and feeding — Coal gasification and heat recovery — Gas cooling and cleaning

FIGURE 2

KBW

GASIFIER & AUXILIARY EQUIPMENT

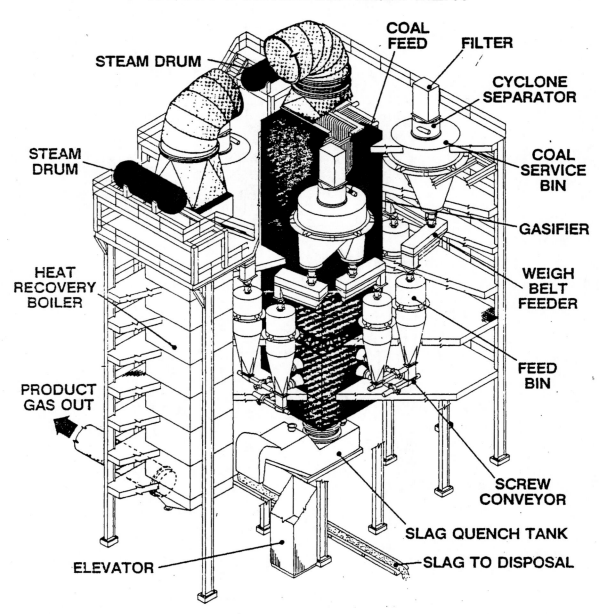

STEAM DRUM

COAL FEED

FILTER

CYCLONE SEPARATOR

STEAM DRUM

COAL SERVICE BIN

GASIFIER

HEAT RECOVERY BOILER

WEIGH BELT FEEDER

PRODUCT GAS OUT

FEED BIN

SCREW CONVEYOR

SLAG QUENCH TANK

ELEVATOR

SLAG TO DISPOSAL

FIGURE 3
KBW GASIFIER

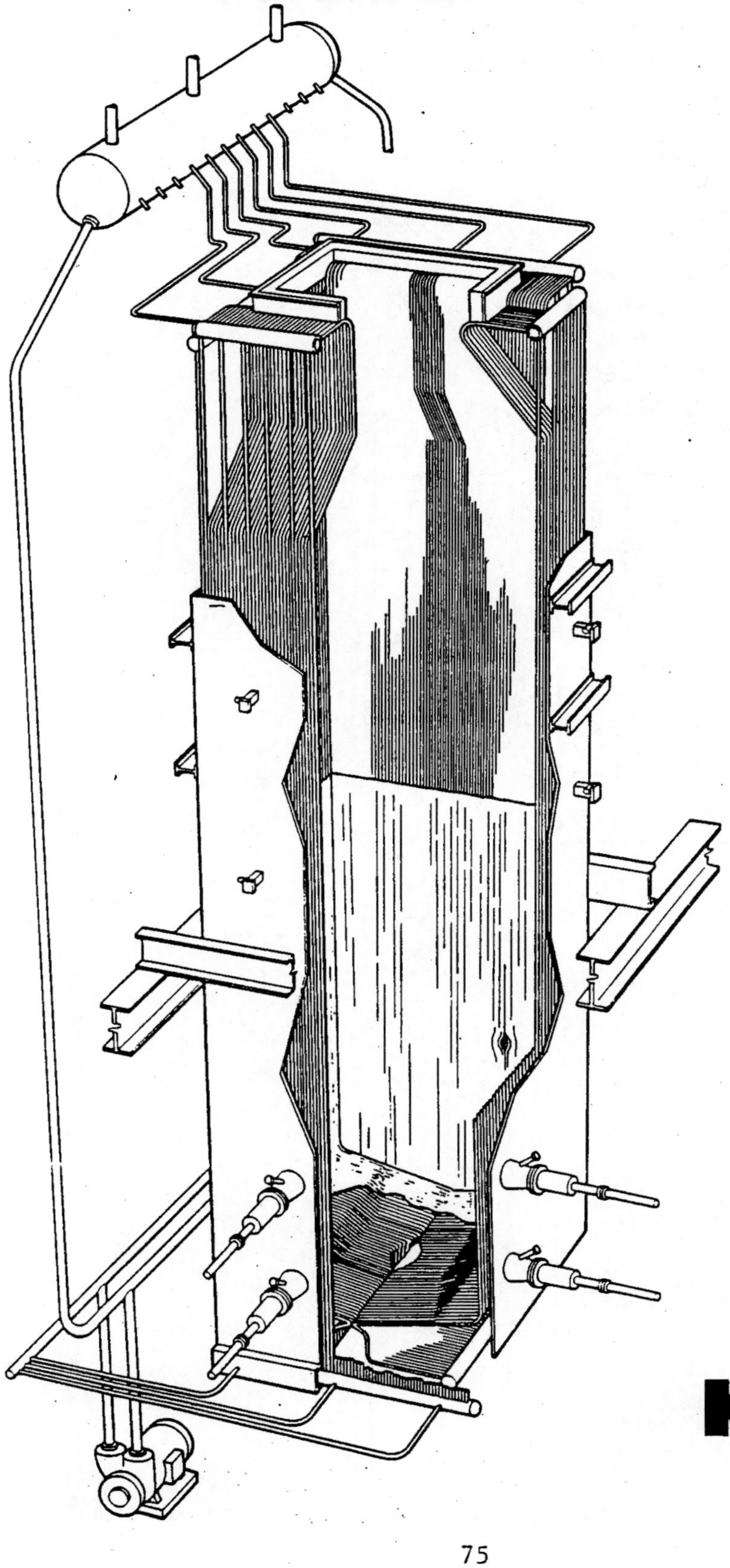

KBW

FIGURE 4

KBW GASIFIER MEMBRANE WALLS

GASIFICATION ZONE

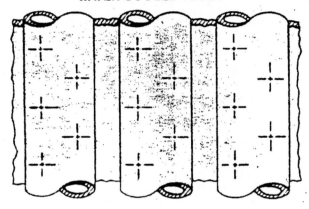

REFRACTORY   METAL STUDS

WATER COOLED TUBES

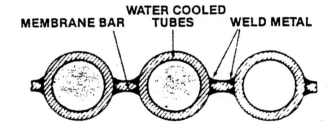

COOLING ZONE

MEMBRANE BAR   WATER COOLED TUBES   WELD METAL

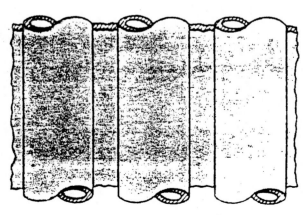

76

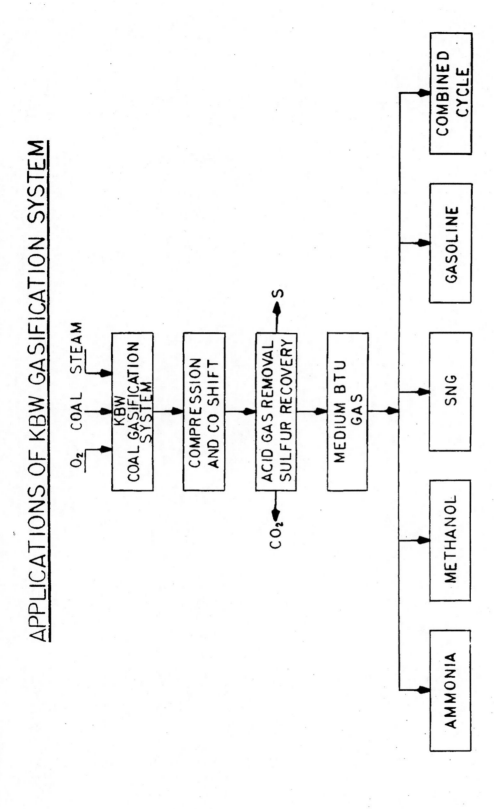

APPLICATIONS OF KBW GASIFICATION SYSTEM

77

OXYGEN PRODUCTION FOR BIOMASS GASIFICATION

Thomas B. Reed
The Solar Energy Research Institute
Golden, CO 80401

INTRODUCTION

Why is oxygen so widely used for gasification? The composition of biomass, approximately $CH_{1.4}$, $O_{0.6}$, is deficient in oxygen by 0.4 atoms relative to the gases produced in gasification, i.e., CO and H_2. The oxygen deficiency could be supplied by adding steam, H_2O, but a great deal of excess heat would have to be added, since the decomposition of water is endothermic. This would require indirect heat exchange using double fluidized beds or other means and would greatly complicate the gasification process. Although a number of these indirect processes have been developed, none has yet become commercial. The use of oxygen produces synthesis gas directly with very efficient heat exchange between the solids and the gases produced.

Oxygen production has been highly developed over the last century. The gasification of biomass, coal, and peat is greatly simplified by its use. All commercial medium Btu gas processes today now use oxygen and a number of those being developed require oxygen. This paper is a short review of current oxygen technology and the possible improvements that may be coming.

HISTORY

Oxygen is produced today primarily by the liquefaction of air, followed by distillation of the air (at -313°F) to separate the oxygen. This process was made possible by the mechanical refrigeration work in Germany of Karl Von Linde in 1877. In 1879 he founded Linde Eismachinen AG. The invention of the Dewar flask made possible storage of liquid air.

Linde Air, now a part of Union Carbide, was founded in Buffalo, NY, in 1907 to produce oxygen in the U.S. Early plants compressed oxygen in cylinders, but starting in 1949 on-site plants began to supply low cost oxygen to bulk users. Unattended on-site plants as small as 30 ton/day are now available. The development of power-vacuum insulation for large storage vessels and tank cars and trucks also greatly improved bulk oxygen distribution.

Oxygen is the second largest chemical produced in the U.S.; sulfuric acid is the first. Presently, we produce 430 billion cubic feet/yr or 17.6 million tons in the U.S. Of this, 68% is used for making steel, 11% for petrochemicals, and 9% for water treatment. The total commercial value of the oxygen produced in $525 million.

CRYOGENIC OXYGEN PRODUCTION

While there are many variations available, the low pressure cycle with reversing heat exchangers and subsequent oxygen compression provides the bulk of U.S. oxygen [1,2]. This cycle is shown in Fig. 1. Air is compressed to 90 psia and expanded to produce liquid air at -313°F. Contaminants such as water and CO_2 are removed from the air and the air is distilled to separate the oxygen, nitrogen, and argon. The gases are then brought back to room temperature through a heat exchanger, and finally the oxygen is compressed to whatever working pressure is required.

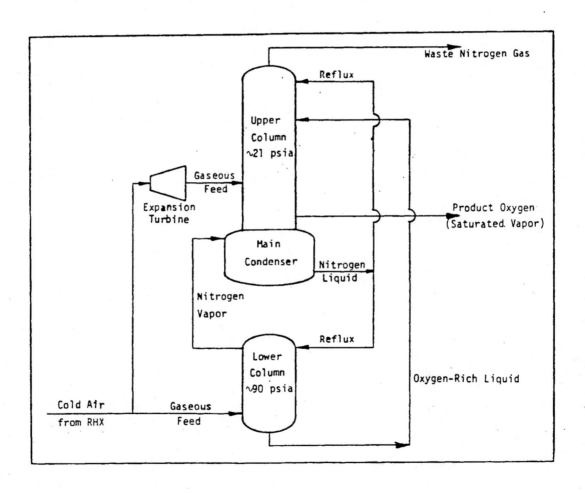

Figure 1. Simplified Double-Column Arrangement Using Air Expansion

Biomass and Peat Feedstocks for Syn-Gas Production

www.KnowledgePublications.com

The only inputs to the oxygen plant are air and electric power, so that power costs contribute 40-80% of the final oxygen costs. About 400 kWh are required for each ton of oxygen produced, depending on plant efficiencies, oxygen pressure, purity, etc. For instance, for a large 2200 ton/day plant producing 900 psig oxygen it requires 397 kWh/ton to produce 99.5% pure oxygen and 367 kWh/ton to produce 95% pure oxygen. Oxygen plants typically cost $30,000/ton-day for small 100 ton/day plants to $18,000/ton-day for 2200 ton/day plants. Because of the varying economies of scale and rapid escalation of power costs, it is impossible to give an average figure for oxygen cost which can range from $20 to $80/ton for bulk oxygen.

OTHER OXYGEN PRODUCTION METHODS

More recently oxygen has been produced by the "pressure swing absorption" method (PSA) which utilizes molecular sieves to separate O_2 and N_2 on a size basis. While this does not result in lower costs, it makes possible reasonable costs in smaller plants, from about 10 to 40 tons/day. The new PUROX plant in Chi-Chi-Bu Japan employs a 40 ton/day PSA plant.

Other methods of oxygen production are now in the development stage. Certain membranes permit differential diffusion of oxygen from nitrogen for oxygen production [3] and liquid membrane processes are showing promise. A new noncryogenic O_2-production technique uses phosphinomanganese (II) to absorb O_2 from the air [4].

Finally, although electric energy is too costly to be used to produce oxygen alone from water by electrolysis, the co-production of oxygen and hydrogen for biomass may be justified in parts of the world where surplus hydroelectric power exists.

GASIFICATION OF BIOMASS

The minimum oxygen required to gasify biomass is set by the equation:

$$CH_{1.4}O_{0.6} + 0.2\,O_2 \rightarrow CO + 0.7\,H_2$$

Unfortunately this reaction is endothermic and would require an outside heat source. We find that our SERI gasifier requires between 0.35 and 0.4 tons oxygen/ton biomass. If it requires 0.4 tons of oxygen to gasify a ton of biomass, the added direct cost of using oxygen over air for gasification of biomass would be $1.00 per MBtu of biomass gasified if oxygen is $40/ton. This represents an upper limit to the cost of oxygen, since use of oxygen increases throughput considerably and reduces gas processing costs and so results in many indirect savings.

CONCLUSION

Oxygen gasification is the simplest method for converting biomass to synthesis gas. While it contributes about $1/MBtu in direct cost to

81

the gasification process, it increases throughput and decreases gas-cleanup costs. Oxygen production is a well-developed technology and oxygen plants can be obtained in sizes from 10 to 2000 tons/day.

REFERENCES

1. Drnevich, R. F.; Ecelbargenm E. J.; Portzer, J. W. 1981 (Jan.). "Industrial Oxygen Plants - A Technology Overview for Users of Coal Gasification-Combined-Cycle Systems." EPRI AP-1674 Project 239-5.

2. Scharl, W. J. 1979. "Large Oxygen Plant Economics and Reliability." In Ammonia from Coal. Symposium, May 8-10, 1979, Tennesee Valley Authority, pp. 98-108.

3. Hwang, Sun-Tak 1981. "A Hwang Column-Cell." Presented at the AIChe Meeting. Houston, TX. April 5-9, 1981.

4. Chemical and Engineering News, July 27, 1981. p. 16.

TECHNOLOGY OF WOOD SUPPLY

J. P. Rich
J.P.R. Associates, Inc.
Stowe, Vermont

WHY AM I GIVING THIS TALK?

Where have I learned what I'm going to tell you?

J.P.R. Associates is a small forestry consulting firm in Stowe, Vermont. We started in 1965 doing surveying and forestry consulting and those functions are still carried on by the firm. In 1974, however, we began to specialize in the use of wood for energy--before it was fashionable. We see our primary job to be that of land managers.

Since 1974, we have participated in a major way in what I believe are the largest, most innovative, and far reaching wood energy projects in the Northeast.

Our first project was a feasibility study for the State of Vermont, which investigated the possibility of building and fueling a 50-megawatt wood-fired generating plant in that state. Our answer was negative at the time, because of the economics. Everything else disclosed in the study was a "go." I believe this was the first such study in the United States.

Our next study was for the Department of Energy, under contract with Wheelabrator-Frye who were investigating the possibility of building a wood-fired generating facility in Maine.

Both these studies showed that wood was not only viable but desirable as a fuel choice for a small generating facility in those two states where there is an abundance of currently unusable forest material, whose removal would only improve the value of the remaining trees.

Vermont again led the way and we were asked by the Burlington Electric Department to investigate methods of fueling their converted coal/oil/gas boilers (2-10 megawatt units) with wood, and to prepare documents for presentation to the Public Service Board of Vermont showing both the feasibility and the non-detrimental nature of fueling a 50-megawatt generating facility in the planning stages. This project is particularly exciting to me, because Burlington is burning wood now and their new McNeil station is going to be built. I find it personally rewarding to see some of this stuff come off paper and into the boiler. It has even been suggested that if all the paper generated in various feasibility studies were burned, it might provide more energy than whatever alternative fuel has been studied. And that sounds like a subject for yet another study.

We got another chance for doing something that could be immediately hands-on useful when we were awarded a grant by the New England Regional Commission (the gathering of New England governors) to provide a Whole-tree Chippers' Handbook, which is a how-to book for would be entrepreneurs in the production of whole-tree chips, showing techniques, methods of analyzing costs, equipment alternatives, cutting patterns, and other aspects of whole-tree chipping that differ from conventional logging. The Evergreen Energy Corporation of Waltham, Massachusetts, has kindly funded the publication of the handbook.

We also worked with S. D. Warren Paper Company in Westbrook, Maine. This far-sighted company, under the piloting of their forestry department, has built a wood-fired 35-megawatt co-generator to power their plant.

In working with these studies, but particularly with Burlington Electric and S. D. Warren, we discovered the absolute necessity of ascertaining landowner attitude and of the work required to educate the landowners.

Out of this, we were called to Maine to work with yet another company to look at landowner profiles and attitudes in their particular procurement area, as they prepared to consider the wood-fuel alternative for their manufacturing facility.

We prepared a document for the Department of the Navy for one of their bases in Maine, which laid out the required steps and techniques for wood procurement for a 50,000 green tons/year facility proposed for that base.

Right now our largest wood-energy project is in investigating the resource and in developing procurement plans for the Evergreen Energy Corporation, based in Massachusetts, which is proceeding with the steps required to build a 1.2 million green tons/year methanol manufacturing plant.

In the early days of our interest in wood energy, we developed a "pet" project of our own to invent, manufacture, and distribute a wood-chip-fired gasifier for home heating, where the chips would be delivered and stored like oil or coal and the heat would be called on by a thermostat. This "pet" has proved to be something of a wild beast, but we still work at it, and have four working units ready for placement in the field for further research and development. This project is in a very real way a matter of "putting our money where our mouth is." It has been expensive and time consuming, and most of the dollars and all of the large number of days of donated time have come from our own families and friends.

84

I have outlined this lengthy resume of our activities, not to blow my own horn, but to give you some basis for listening to what I have to say and for judging its truth and viability.

Do I have a bias?

Of course. I want to see improved markets for forest weeds. This is particularly evident in my own home area in Lamoille County in Vermont. Our forests are a mess. That's my bias. I don't care what you do with these 40-foot dandelions as long as they are correctly removed and leave the lawn. Fuel, where I stand, is just about the only use for this stuff, and so that's where I've concentrated my efforts. If a better and more efficient use of this material comes along, I'm ready to move my alliances there.

Where did I get my information?

Most of our experience is in the Northeast and Scandinavia, though we stay in touch with what is happening internationally and in other areas of the United States.

The three main areas of expertise that we concentrate on are (1) Harvesting systems--how you get the wood out, (2) Landowner attitude and public relations, and (3) How you structure a procurement staff and how to handle that staff in order to purchase the raw material you need.

How it all used to be done, and how it presently is still being done in most places.

In general, up until now in the United States, wood-using plants have been located, built, and operated quite independently of any forestry advice. Foresters have been kept in the woods, if not in the closet, and mostly at lower level administrative positions. Mill managers, accountants, and non-forestry brass have dictated procurement policies and prices.

What this has meant is that there has been little regard for forest management and even less regard for providing steady employment for woods workers or a smooth flow of material out of the woods and into the mill. Wood supply has been treated like a pipeline to be turned off or on at will.

There were many good reasons for that, not the least of which was the profitability of the mill operation. And there was no reason not to treat wood procurement in that fashion, because (1) There was plenty of wood, (2) Public opinion directed toward "conservation" and preservation of forest areas was minimal and resulting public pressure was easily fielded, (3) Land was cheap and available, and (4) Loggers didn't need a large financial investment in equipment or in a trained crew. Thus, no greater attention to the problems of trees and people was necessary.

85

How it will be done.

Well, the worm is slowly turning, and he's moved out of the apple and into the trees. Existing wood-using plants, but especially new plants, are going to have to take a more responsible position on environmental and social questions. And, there are going to be solid financial reasons why this is necessary, such as: (1) Competition for the material is increasing, which will make it necessary for procurement to be more carefully designed and carried out; (2) New plants will ordinarily have no land ownership and will not be able to purchase the amount of land necessary at a cheap price. Therefore, they will have to deal with private landowners; (3) Loggers producing whole-tree chips require a large investment in equipmnet (as much as $500,000 is not extraordinary). The bankers loaning them money will want long-term, irrevocable contracts. Their operators, who take a long time to properly train, will require steady employment. This will mean that the facility using their product will have to plan for procurement on a steady basis; and (4) Public awareness of and concern for environmental matters have been steadily heightened and will continue to be a greater part of the data that any wood-using plant will have to carefully consider.

The net result of this future picture will mean that sound forest management with long-range vision will bring dollars into the pocket of those far-sighted enough to begin using it, before troubles appear. Sound forest management policy and implementation will certainly be a bottom line necessity for successful plant management as pressure on the resource and the way it is removed and used increases.

Why forest biomass?

Forest biomass has advantages over every kind of fossil fuel. Primary among these is the fact that it is renewable. In addition, its current state is one of liability to forest managers--cull and weeds. Forest biomass is a local fuel; it is ours. Air pollution is at a minimum when compared with coal.

How do you use it?

If you want to tap this source of energy, here's my advice to you.

(1) Involve knowledgeable forestry people right from the beginning on plant location. This may be a problem, because up-to-date knowledgeable people are scarce. Take the trouble to look them up and involve them. It could save untold trouble and money in very short order. One paper company I know went through three foresters before they found one who was trainable in these new concepts.

(2) Don't put the plant someplace that is a handicap to procurement unless you have some good, some very good, reasons and some sound economic explanations to back up your decision. Only knowledgeable forestry personnel can give you the necessary data on the forest resource.

(3) After you have decided on a location for a plant, a procurement

program with sufficient staff and necessary involvement with top-level management is necessary to insure the steady, responsible flow of wood out of the forest to your plant.

(4) Whole-tree chipping is currently the best and most economical method of removing forest biomass. In order to go into whole-tree chipping it is necessary to allow sufficient start-up time to bring the new whole-tree chip harvesters on line (one year at least--maybe two to four)!!

Why whole-tree chips?

When I talk about wood for energy, I talk about whole-tree chips, which is the process of severing the tree from its stump, probably with a machine called a feller-buncher; transporting the whole-above-ground tree to a landing area which is roadside; then sorting out the more valuable parts of the tree and turning the rest of the tree into energy wood by running it through a whole-tree chipper, which blows the chips into a trailer truck for transport to the mill.

Is anyone doing it successfully?

Burlington Electric Department

Burlington Electric Department is, for one. They don't own an acre of land, and the plant has Lake Champlain on one side, cutting its possible harvest area by fifty percent, a handicap for sure. And it is in a small city with traffic congestion and neighbors. They are at the mercy of the small private landowner and the general public.

Yet, the Moran Station has two, 10-megawatt boilers producing electricity with wood at this moment. They started by converting one of their existing coal-fired boilers, and have since converted another one. When they started, they were procuring wood the same way they had procured all the other fuels they had used (oil, gas, and coal), with the engineering approach--the pipeline mentality--turn it on-turn it off.

They didn't want to change this--obviously, it's easy, but . . . they needed the wood and they needed the people out there to get it, so:

(1) They started a chip certification program. Once a week a professional forester with the ability to shut down the harvesting job checks out the soundness of silviculture and ecology of each job.

(2) They hired foresters to procure stumpage for chip production in order to insure year-round work places for private operators.

(3) They began a Tree Farm Family, for which we designed a solicitation brochure for landowners. Eventually, the Tree Farm Family will provide their insured land base, not only for this current operation, but for their proposed McNeil Station.

The proposed Burlington Electric Department McNeil Station will produce

50 megawatts of power, and use half a million green tons of wood. Approval from the Vermont Public Service Board was received, largely because we had worked hard and long to address concerns in advance of their appearance. It is desirable to get your white hat fixed firmly on your head before the opposition starts looking for the bad guys.

One of the major factors in achieving white-hat status is public relations. Burlington Electric, at our suggestion, helped the State of Vermont Department of Forest and Parks finish up an experimental chipping operation with a real chunk of dollars, which not only exhibited their concern, but also provided an example of a successful chipping operation in the area. The state agencies were involved with harvesting guidelines right from the beginning of our work on this proposed facility.

S. D. Warren Company

This company is building a new 35-megawatt co-generation facility at a pulp mill, using 700,000 green tons of chips a year. This particular project resulted from the early work done in our Department of Energy research with Wheelabrator-Frye. S. D. Warren had some advantages Burlington Electric didn't have, since they have been in the wood procurement business since approximately 1880. The profile of their current successful procurement is based on the following:

(1) They have a 25-year-old Tree Farm Family that is considered the most successful in the Northeast. They meddle little and provide good service to their members. They have a yearly picnic that they host which underlines the concept of "family."

(2) Foresters were in on the beginning on the plant design, helping with scale placement and type, dumpers, and working with truckers.

(3) The foresters work with the business staff in procurement and pricing control.

(4) In order to have crews on the ground when the plant began operation, S. D. Warren subsidized 5-6 weeks of hands-on operation with advice from their trained staff and experienced chip operators.

(5) They subsidized and continue to underwrite experimental logging systems that might be useful to them, such as a small cable system that originated in Scotland.

(6) S. D. Warren aided local banks in setting up a lease arrangement for equipment procurement for loggers.

On the boards - Evergreen Energy Corporation

This project, in the advance planning stages, is going to use 1.2 million green tons of wood fiber annually. This means 38 chippers in the woods every day and availability of 24,000 acres of forest land for a single year.

Wood for energy--a growing thing

From the four cords a year I used to burn in my wood stove, to the 10,000 green tons per year in the Moran Station's first boiler, to the 1.2 million green tons planned by Evergreen, the magnitude of the increase in the use of wood for energy over the past eight years can be plainly seen.

I have to admit to being a "wood freak." I'm interested in what is happening, and I'm interested in trying to direct this new and increasing usage in the most efficient and conservative use of the forest resource. I am first a forester and only second a businessman.

Much of the work we have done is available in published form from our office for the price of printing and copying. If you are interested in following up on any of the matters I've touched on, please drop us a line, and we'll send you a list and description of materials we can make available to you, along with the cost.

A DIFFERENT PERSPECTIVE

Thomas F. O'Connell
Manager, Biomass Energy Program
International Harvester Company
16 West 260 83rd Street
Burr Ridge, IL 60521

I am in a very uncomfortable position standing here before you for
several reasons. First, I wasn't originally supposed to present this
paper. Secondly, the man I most respect in this field, who has con-
sulted as a specialist to International Harvester and who has 30 plus
years experience in biomass collection, is scheduled as the next
speaker, Mr. Tom Miles. Lastly, and perhaps most importantly, I am
not particularly qualified as an expert on the "technology"of agricultural waste supply and recovery. My academic training is in
business and finance and I have been with IH only for less than two
years. There are many people employed by IH who are much more qualified
than I to address you on the topic assigned.

Why am I here? Well, after undertaking my own investigation during the
past two years into the ag waste land, and in a moment of supreme ego,
which I may today severely regret, I decided I could possibly provide
a different outlook on this subject. My qualifications include the
creation and building of high technology companies. Perhaps I can
convey some feeling as to how a "venture capitalist" or "investor"
views this field as well as passing on some of my own analysis
methodology and thereby make a contribution to this august group. So
with apology to Tom Miles and International Harvester, here goes!

A venture analyst looks at technology situations differently than a
technologist, not better, not worse, just differently. Initially he
seeks to know whether the existing technology in a particular segment
qualifies economically for its role in the entire system. If the
answer is yes, he goes on to check the economic justification of the
balance of the system. At some later date, if all answers are positive,
he returns to the original system to look at possible cost reduction
options. If, as is usually the case, this cost reduction involves either
R&D dollars or capital expenditures, he attempts to weigh the risk
versus the reward. Hopefully this analysis is made quanatively, often
it is not. What does any of this have to do with agricultural waste
and recovery? When I first entered this field, I was given two
screening criteria to accept: a wide availability of biomass supplies
and a cost availability of less than $35 per ton using technology for

both wood and agricultural waste. I was quickly convinced in the wood case that significant supplies were available, however, I remain suspicious in many cases as to their true costs. For agricultural waste, I was not so sure. So, first step, the literature and second step, the IH pros. As you all know, and I found out, there is an established collective wisdom in this field. OTA and its sub-contractors at Purdue University catalogued agricultural waste crop availability in the United States quite thoroughly. Crop residue availability was estimated for every region in the United States. These studies indicated that on a gross basis over 400 million tons per year were available. OTA estimated that in the U.S. alone as much as 12 to 17 quadrillion BTU's could be produced from sources by the year 2000. That was equivalent to all projected oil imports during that period. But wait! That amount must be qualified as to true availability after consideration of recovery costs.

Fortunately this work had also been done. Usable residues in the two crops in which I had an interest (corn and small grains) was estimated to be 79 million tons per year, all at or below $35/ton. My next question was how reliable was the $35 per ton collection cost ceiling? That too had been documented. Purdue had actually directly measured the costs involved in each step of a corn stover collection system. These steps included: windrowing and flail pickup for collection, big roll baling and stackwagon stacking for packaging, initial on-field storage, subsequent roadside storage, transport to plant site and plant storage. They stated that while stack collection was the cheapest in the field, bales were cheaper if any haul distance was involved due to their greater density, which pointed out the sensitivity of total ag waste cost to transportation. They also noted, and I quote, "The greatest obstacle to efficient collection of stover is trampling of the stalks during the harvest operation." At the time, this comment did not disturb me because the collection costs quoted were within my guidelines: eighteen to $32 per dry ton or under $35 initial screen. I then went on to qualify other parts of my proposed system.

I have brought a few slides of these various collection methodologies which, if you don't ask penetrating questions, I would like to show you.

From these slides one can easily see that we are not dealing with high technology. The technology of collection is thousands of years old with the only real change being the addition of mechanization, using the internal combustion engine. Further, you can see from these slides that the machinery utilized was designed not for waste collection but for food production, in this case for animals.

By now the advantages and disadvantages of ag waste as a feedstock were well known to me. The advantages included low cost, if collected within a small area, large available supply, low alternative use value, low ash and low sulfur content and perhaps, most important, annual renewability. The disadvantages included low geographical concentration and low BTU's per unit of weight.

When I had concluded my qualification analysis on the balance of my system, I returned to ag waste area more informed as to what I wanted and with the definite thought of reducing recovery cost. I found that ag waste is not free. In addition to the costs of collection, there are the replacement costs. These include the replacement nutritional costs and the soil erosion prevention costs. After a detailed analysis, I concluded, based on both the literature and IH's ag engineers, that my leaving at least a 1/4 of the crop on the ground, soil erosion would not accelerate. This was confirmed to be conservative by other sources. Nutritional loss component was not so easy. The literature said that removing corn stover required artificial fertilization costing between $3 and $10/ton removed. The IH people, however, said the exact opposite or that leaving the stover on the field actually inhibited the nitrogen flow into the soil and acted as a penalty to the farmer. I settled on a total cost penalty to the farmer of $7.50/ton for removal.

The next question to be asked was who did the removal. Obvious answer, the farmer. Well, no! First, nothing, and I mean nothing, will get in the way of the farmer in harvesting his food crop. The reason. $110/ton for corn kernels versus $10-$15/ton for corn stover.

So, I had to create a new business separately capitalized with a 30% ROI, another cost increase. So far, I have looked to reduce costs and had only identified increased costs. At this point, I began to look at new technology as a possible solution to reducing costs. I considered the ideal. The ideal consists of the output product characteristics and the type of machine necessary to provide those characteristics at the lowest possible cost. Surely I could beat 2000 year old technology. Initially though, the ideal ag waste characteristics: first, uniform small size (a cutting process); second, low moisture content (a drying process); third, maximum retention of BTU value (a fungicide process); fourth, an easy handling method (a co
The ideal machine would perform at high speed, make a single pass through the field, possess low labor content and rates, use little energy, have the lowest possible capital cost and operate very reliably over sustained use. I knew this type of perfection was a pipe dream but asked myself why such a total machine didn't exist in some less perfect form.

Being a venture analyst, my first answer was because no real market existed for ag waste. In other words, a chicken and egg problem. Well, I wasn't totally wrong this time. No market for the machine existed because the value of the feedstock was low. But if a market was created then such a machine would be economically justifiable? Right? You got it -- wrong! The real issue was the economics of on-board mobile processing versus cutting, hauling and fixed site processing. During the past 75 years, we the agricultural equipment companies, have been able to increasingly add processing equipment to our mobile harvesting equipment. We have been able to do this because energy costs were low and, like the automotibe industry, we could built bigger and bigger pieces of equipment. Also, interest costs were low so we were able to continue to build bigger and more expensive pieces of equipment and pay them off with minimum increases in productivity. Also, like the

93

utilities, the farmer could pass through his increased cost in the form of subsidies. Initially, all of our equipment was built to conform (or maybe to create) relatively high crop values. At $35 per ton, I had little choice to be able to put any processing on my mobile equipment. This then is the point. If the value of the crop is high, mobile processing can pay off up to a point. I might add, serious questions are being raised today even about the economies of processing done on today's corn combines. If the crop value is low, as in my case, the cutter must be kept simple and processing done at fixed locations. If you doubt this concept look at alfafa pelletizing, which is always done at fixed locations but could easily be done mobilely.

There are gray areas and it is in these areas that some savings may come. For example, if the combine could cut the stover at a predetermined height using a simple attachment instead of mashing it into the soil, the collection process would be much easier and cheaper. If field drying could be accelerated chemically, less fixed site drying would be required. If decomposition could be slowed, yields could be improved.

The technology of harvesting corn stover and wheat straw is old. It originated 2000-3000 years ago. Yet the simple baler still remains, in my mind, the cheapest way of handling the problem. If there a new technology that can reduce ag waste recovery costs? Probably yes! Do I know what it is? No! What can I do, the financial man? Throw you, the technologists, the problem.

Thank you

THE PREPARATION OF BIOMASS FOR GASIFICATION

Thomas R. Miles
Consulting Design Engineer
Portland, Oregon

The preparation of biomass for gasification or any other process - combustion, chemical utilization, etc. - involves reducing a wide variety of naturally occurring fibrous biomass materials to as uniform a feedstock as practical. The chemical process industries characteristically are continuous flow processes that depend upon uniformity of particle size, bulk density, specific density, moisture content, materials handling characteristics and chemical composition.

Most chemical process feedstocks can be fairly readily and predictably tailored to a specific requirement by simple processes such as grinding coal or minerals to a given particle size or fractionating petroleum products into relatively dense flowable forms or consistencies. These forms, usually uniform powders, slurries or liquids, can be stored in bulk tanks and are readily pumped or metered through the process and do not include substantial percentages of air or voids.

In order to approximate these required properties biomass materials must be subjected to a series of quite different preparation processes. Nearly all biomass raw materials consist principally of hollow cellulosic cells, which encompass substantial percentages of air and contain relatively high percentages of moisture. They also contain sugars which necessitate drying in order to be stored.

Woody materials with their higher lignin and resin content can be stored in the green state outside without serious degradation, while straws, stalks and cobs have limited storage life unless dried. 15% moisture (wet basis) is generally recognized as an optimum for efficient gasification. Percent Moisture (Wet Basis) is that percentage of water contained in the weight of the green or wet product. Virtually all biomass materials contain from 40% to 60% moisture in their natural state with the exception of the straws which are 10-15% moisture at harvest.

Thus the necessity for drying is common to nearly all biomass materials including wood at 50% moisture (W.B.). Drying energy can be produced either by separately combusting a portion of the green feedstock and using the hot gases to dry the main product, or by utilizing waste heat streams from the process. Approximately 15% more green feedstock is required to dry the main product from 50% moisture to 15% moisture. Primary size reductions such as chipping or grinding customarily precede drying. For most biomass it is false economy to consider partial drying - viz. down to 30% moisture - as opposed to going on to 15% moisture. In practice, if one is to dry at all, you might as well dry to the optimum of 15%. Drying to 15% moisture is mandatory if densification methods such as pelleting or cubing are involved.

Comminution or size reduction of cellulosic biomass materials is best accomplished by cutting rather than crushing or attrition grinding. Clean cut fibres result in higher bulk densities with a minimum of fines. Hammermilling frays the fibres resulting in low bulk densities, substantial percentages of fines and very difficult bulk handling characteristics.

Wood chips as developed for the pulp industry are the most universally produced and consumed form of biomass raw material. The 38° cutting angle used in chipping wood requires a minimum amount of horsepower and also produces a relatively uniform thickness due to the "carding" or splitting off of the solid wood along the grain. Denser hardwoods (specific density of .6) produce thinner chips than softwoods (specific density of .3).

Chips are too large and with too smooth surfaces for densification. Hammermilling or disc refining produces a smaller fibrous particle that will permanently deform under pressure while the fibres mesh to help maintain the integrity of the densified product. Finer milling (through a 3/16 inch screen) is required for pelleting and for cubing. Although densification is an ideal method of reducing the character- istically bulky, fibrous biomass materials to a uniformly sized, dense feedstock that meets chemical process industry standards it is also expensive in energy, maintenance and capital cost. It often adds 50% to the cost of the prepared biomass feedstock.

Cubing as a densification method is not included in these preparation procedures since the large (1¼" x 1¼" x 2") cube with its low surface- to-volume ratio results in very slow gasification and the large cubes are virtually impossible to handle in automatic feeding equipment, unless pulverized. Further, the large particles (1" screen) usually cubed do not pulverize to a satisfactory form. Roll compacting has been neglected as a biomass and RDF (refuse derived fuel) densifica- tion method but our recent work indicates that its lower power and maintenance requirements and tolerance of tramp materials make it a very promising replacement for pelleting or cubing.

Obviously all of these preparation steps entail additional and sub- stantial amounts of energy, both thermal for drying and shaft horse- power for cutting, grinding and densifying. These energies are critical factors in the selection of a given gasification process to process a particular biomass feedstock, and greatly influence not only operating costs but capital requirements.

A common fallacy in planning biomass feedstock systems is to consider drying and/or densifying in the field to save transportation costs. Experience has shown that it is usually more practical to do the preparation with permanently installed equipment at the plant site on a 24-hour-a-day basis rather than depending upon a number of field units with their inherently lower utilization productivity resulting from the moving from site to site, higher maintenance, variable weather, 8-hour daylight operating limitation and personnel availability.

The following charts and figures are self-explanatory and illustrate:

1) Characteristics of various biomass particles relative to gasification,

2) Process and quantity flow sheets for various biomass feedstocks,

3) Approximate energy requirements,

4) Typical processing equipment.

PARTICLE vs. GASIFIER

CHIPS
PELLETS
LOOSE CUBES
($\frac{1}{4}$-$\frac{1}{2}$" Max. Thickness)

UP   DN

FIXED BED

5 Min.   LONG RESIDENCE TIME

CHIPS
SMALL PELLETS
POWDERS, GRANULES
DENSIFIED FLAKES
(1/8" Max. Thickness)

FLUID BED

1 Min.   MED. RESID. TIME

POWDERS, GRANULES
DENSIFIED FLAKES
($<$ 8 Mesh)

ENTRAINED FLOW
VERY SHORT
2 Sec.   RESIDENCE TIME

TRM BIO-METH CONF MAR '82

EFFECTS OF PARTICLE CHARACTERISTICS
ON BIOMASS GASIFICATION

AFFECTING GASIFICATION .

SIZE & UNIFORMITY - TO SUIT PROCESS

THICKNESS - OR LEAST DIMENSION - RATE

SHAPE - FLAKE, PIN, PELLET, GRANULAR

BULK DENSITY - BED POROSITY, GAS FLOW

SPECIFIC DENSITY - REACTION RATE

SURFACE TO VOLUME RATIO - OPTIMIZE FOR PROCESS

MOISTURE CONTENT - EFFICIENCY

ASH OR DIRT CONTENT - SLAGGING, BLINDING

AFFECTING HANDLING, FEEDING

SIZE & UNIFORMITY - TYPE & SIZE OF EQUIPMENT

SHAPE - BULK HANDLING CHARACTERISTICS

BULK DENSITY - FEEDING RATES, METHODS

SPECIFIC DENSITY - FEEDING RATES, CYCLES

TRM BIO-METH CONF MAR '82

PROPERTIES OF WOOD CHIPS
AND DENSIFIED WOOD

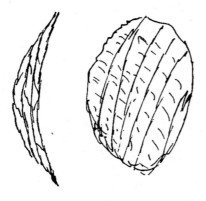

BEAVER CHIPS

WEE CHIPS

1/4"-3/8" Long x 1/32"-1/16" Thick
Dry Bulk Density 12 Lb/Cubic Foot

HARDWOOD CHIPS & PINS

5/8"-7/8" Long x 1/16"-1/8" Thick
Dry Bulk Density 14 Lb/CF
Spec. Dens. 30-38 Lb/CF (.48-.6)

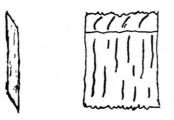

SOFTWOOD CHIPS & PINS

5/8"-7/8" Long x 1/8"-1/4" Thick
Dry Bulk Density 11-12 Lb/CF
Spec. Dens. 20-30 Lb/CF (.3-.48)

PELLETS

1/4:-3/4" Diam. x 1/4"-3/4" Long
Dry Bulk Density 38 Lb/CF (.6)
Spec. Density 62 Lb/CF (1.0)

**GROUND PELLETS OR
ROLL DENSIFIED FLAKES**

<8 Mesh)
Dry Bulk Density 32 Lb/CF (.5)
Spec. Dens. 60 Lb/CF (.9-1.0)

ACTUAL SIZE   TRM BIO-METH CONF MAR '82

TYPICAL WOOD STRUCTURE
Port Orford Cedar (Approx. 100X)
ANNUAL GROWTH 1-5 MM/Yr

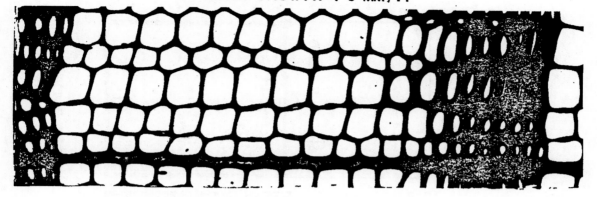

EARLY WOOD 60-70% VOID   10-15% Void LATE WOOD

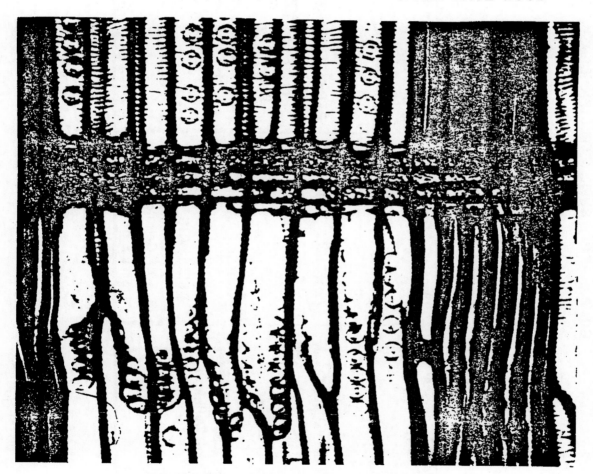

TRACHEID CELLS WITH BORDER PITS

COMPOSITION:	Hardwood	Softwood
Cellulose	50%	50%
Lignin	16-20%	23-33%
Hemicellulose C_5	20-30%	15-20%

TRM '82

COMPARATIVE BULK & SPECIFIC DENSITIES
WOOD & COAL

SOLID DRY WOOD
15% M – 30 lbcf

10 cf – 300 lb
.48 sp. gr.
CELL VOID
3.3 cf Cellulose
1.5 sp. gr.

CHIPS DRY WOOD
15% M – 12 lbcf

10 cf – 120 lb
PARTICLE VOID
4 cf Solid Wood
.48 sp. gr.
CELL VOID
1.3 cf Cellulose
1.5 sp. gr.

PELLETS DRY WOOD
10% M – 35 lbcf

10 cf – 350 lb
PARTICLE VOID
5.6 cf Solid Pellets
1.0 sp. gr.
CELL VOID
3.7 cf Cellulose
1.5 sp. gr.

COAL POWDERED
10% M – 50 lbcf

10 cf – 500 lb
PARTICLE VOID
5.5 cf Solid Coal
1.5 sp. gr.

TRM BIO-METH CONF MAR '82

BIOMASS FEEDSTOCK CANDIDATES
FOR GASIFICATION

WOODY MATERIALS

CHIPS FROM THINNINGS, CLEAR CUT, PLANTATIONS, WOODLOTS
  GREEN: 50% Moisture,   4500 Btu/Lb,   21 Lb/c.f.
  DRY: 15% Moisture,   7500 Btu/Lb,   12 Lb/c.f.
  C - 50%, H - 6%, O - 42%, N - 1%, Ash 1-2%
  12 Month Supply, Store Outside, $20-$25/Green Ton

HOG FUEL FROM SAWMILL RESIDUES

  Same Properties, Diminishing Supply, 3-10% Ash

NON-WOODY MATERIALS

STRAWS: CEREALS, GRASS SEED, FLAX, OIL SEEDS
  15% Moisture,   7000 Btu/Lb,   10 Lb/c.f. (Bales)
  C - 47%, H - 6%, O - 40%, N - 1%, Ash 5-7%
  Seasonal Supply, Covered Storage, $40/Ton

STALKS, COBS, HULLS: Corn, Sunflower, Almonds
BAGASSE: 70% Moisture, Stringy, Low Cost,   Outside Storage
KENAF; Stalks, 50% Moisture, Plantations,   "   "
COCONUT HUSK FIBRE: 20% Moisture, Fibrous Mat, "   "
PEAT: 90% Moisture, Granular/Fibrous, Site Specific, "   "

RDF [REFUSE DERIVED FUEL FROM MUNICIPAL SOLID WASTE]

Fluff Form, 5-7 Lb/c.f., Disposal Problem
4500 Btu/Lb @ 35% Moisture,
7000 Btu/Lb Dry
C - 51%, H - 7%, O - 32%, N - 1%, Ash 10-15%
Some Chlorides, Sulphates, Trace Metals Pb, Fe
Cannot Store, Stable Supply, Must Densify
$6 - $10/Ton
Gasification Would Eliminate Toxics

                              TRM BIO-METH CONF MAR '82

WOODY BIOMASS

SUPPLY & PREPARATION

OF 5 TPH (120 TPD)

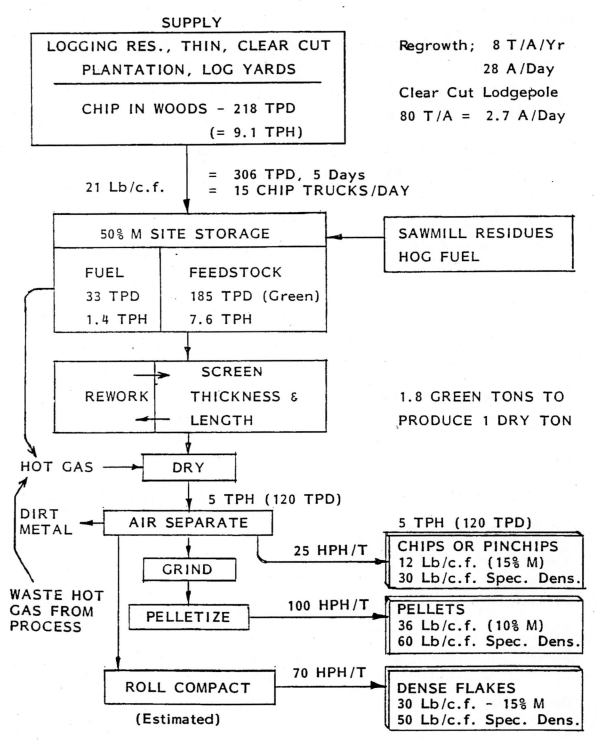

SUPPLY

LOGGING RES., THIN, CLEAR CUT
PLANTATION, LOG YARDS
_____
CHIP IN WOODS – 218 TPD
(= 9.1 TPH)

Regrowth; 8 T/A/Yr
28 A/Day
Clear Cut Lodgepole
80 T/A = 2.7 A/Day

21 Lb/c.f.   = 306 TPD, 5 Days
= 15 CHIP TRUCKS/DAY

50% M SITE STORAGE

FUEL	FEEDSTOCK
33 TPD	185 TPD (Green)
1.4 TPH	7.6 TPH

SAWMILL RESIDUES
HOG FUEL

REWORK | SCREEN THICKNESS & LENGTH

1.8 GREEN TONS TO
PRODUCE 1 DRY TON

HOT GAS → DRY

5 TPH (120 TPD)

DIRT METAL ← AIR SEPARATE

5 TPH (120 TPD)

WASTE HOT GAS FROM PROCESS

GRIND

25 HPH/T

CHIPS OR PINCHIPS
12 Lb/c.f. (15% M)
30 Lb/c.f. Spec. Dens.

PELLETIZE

100 HPH/T

PELLETS
36 Lb/c.f. (10% M)
60 Lb/c.f. Spec. Dens.

ROLL COMPACT

(Estimated)

70 HPH/T

DENSE FLAKES
30 Lb/c.f. - 15% M
50 Lb/c.f. Spec. Dens.

TRM BIO-METH CONF MAR '82

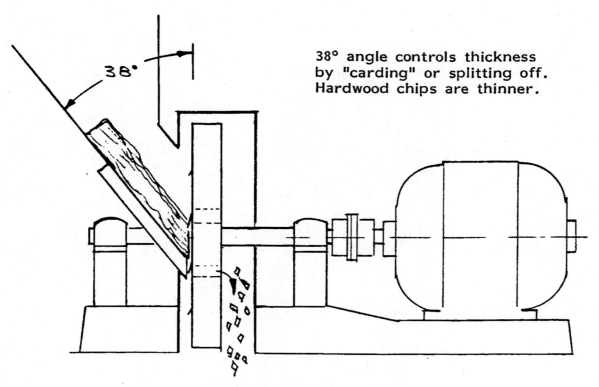

38° angle controls thickness
by "carding" or splitting off.
Hardwood chips are thinner.

DROP FEED WOOD CHIPPER
8-15 HPH/TON (Dry Equivalent)

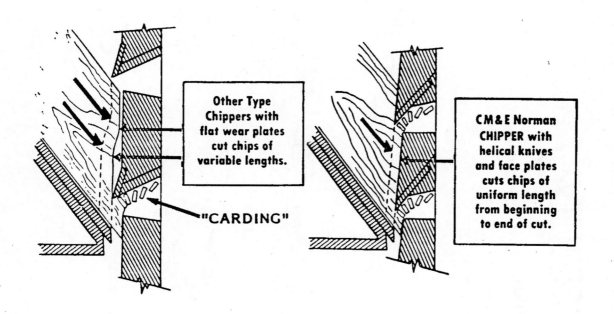

Other Type
Chippers with
flat wear plates
cut chips of
variable lengths.

"CARDING"

CM&E Norman
CHIPPER with
helical knives
and face plates
cuts chips of
uniform length
from beginning
to end of cut.

COMPARISON OF DISC TYPES

NICHOLSON

Wood Fuel Processor

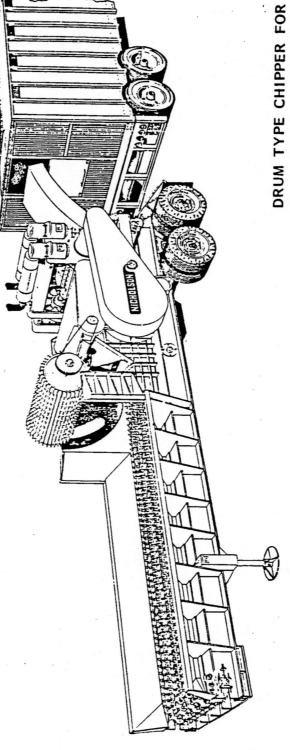

DRUM TYPE CHIPPER FOR
WHOLE HARVEST & ORCHARD
PRUNINGS. 63" x 39" OPENING
525 HP - 60 TONS/HR
PRODUCES CLEAN-CUT CHIPS

TRM BIO-METH CONF MAR '82

Morbark Total Chiparvestor

The focal point of the forest harvest and processing starts with the Total Chiparvestor. The Chiparvestor operator performs all chipping functions, off the ground in a weather protective cab. Whole trees with limbs intact, are chipped in a matter of seconds. The chips are blown directly into waiting vans or the in-woods screening system.

An important feature of the Morbark Chiparvestor, is the separator which eliminates up to 90 per cent of the dirt and grit during the chipping process.

While the illustration pictures the Model 22 Total Chiparvestor, the Morbark Model 550 and the Model 12 may also be used in conjunction with the woods operation for processing smaller diameter material.

The Chiparvestor is a one-man operated machine that will achieve high chip production in any woods operation.

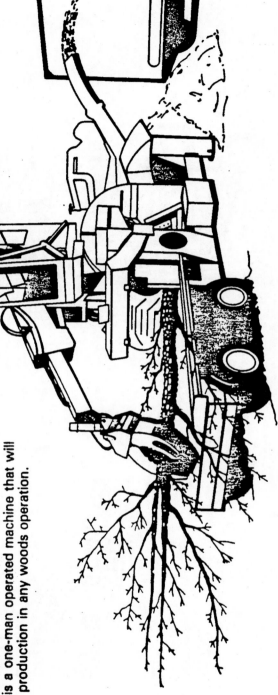

TRM BIO-METH CONF MAR '82

107

CHIPPER TYPES

DROP FEED

HORIZONTAL FEED   TRM '82

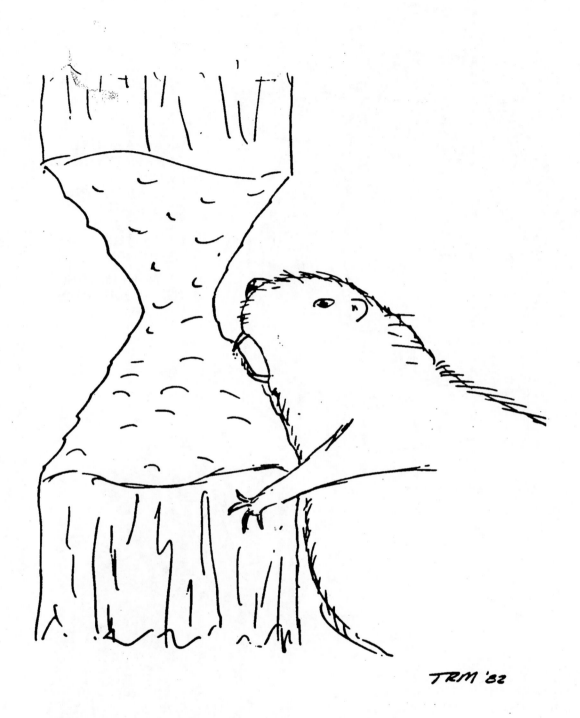

THE ORIGINAL CHIPPER -

38° CUTTING ANGLE, CARDING AND ALL

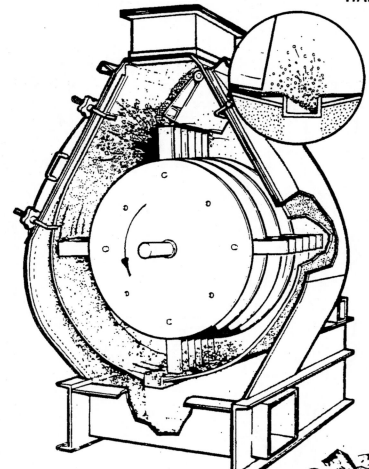

WRAP-AROUND
SCREEN-TYPE
HAMMERMILL
FOR REDUCING
CHIPS AND
AG RESIDUES.
BLOW-THRU
REQUIRED.

20-30 HPH/TON
(Dry equivalent)

Champion Hammermill

HEAVY DUTY BAR TYPE
HAMMERMILL FOR LARGE
CHUNKS, SAWMILL WASTES
PRODUCT SOMEWHAT STRINGY

20-30 HPH/TON
(Dry equivalent)

Cross-section of Jeffrey Hammer Hog

TRM '82

110

NON-WOODY BIOMASS

SUPPLY & PREPARATION

OF 5 TPH (120 TPD)

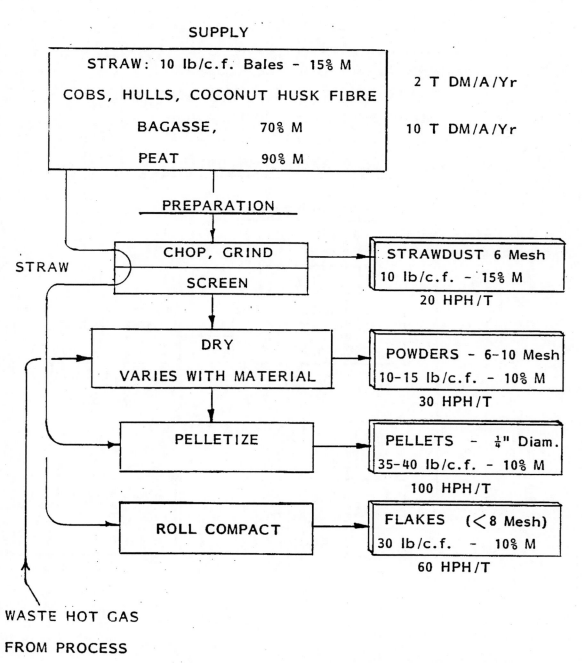

SUPPLY

STRAW: 10 lb/c.f. Bales - 15% M

COBS, HULLS, COCONUT HUSK FIBRE

BAGASSE,   70% M

PEAT   90% M

2 T DM/A/Yr

10 T DM/A/Yr

PREPARATION

STRAW

CHOP, GRIND

SCREEN

STRAWDUST 6 Mesh

10 lb/c.f. - 15% M

20 HPH/T

DRY

VARIES WITH MATERIAL

POWDERS - 6-10 Mesh

10-15 lb/c.f. - 10% M

30 HPH/T

PELLETIZE

PELLETS - ¼" Diam.

35-40 lb/c.f. - 10% M

100 HPH/T

ROLL COMPACT

FLAKES (<8 Mesh)

30 lb/c.f. - 10% M

60 HPH/T

WASTE HOT GAS

FROM PROCESS

TRM BIO-METH CONF MAR '82

RDF [REFUSE DERIVED FUEL]

SUPPLY & PREPARATION
OF
5 TPH (120 TPD)

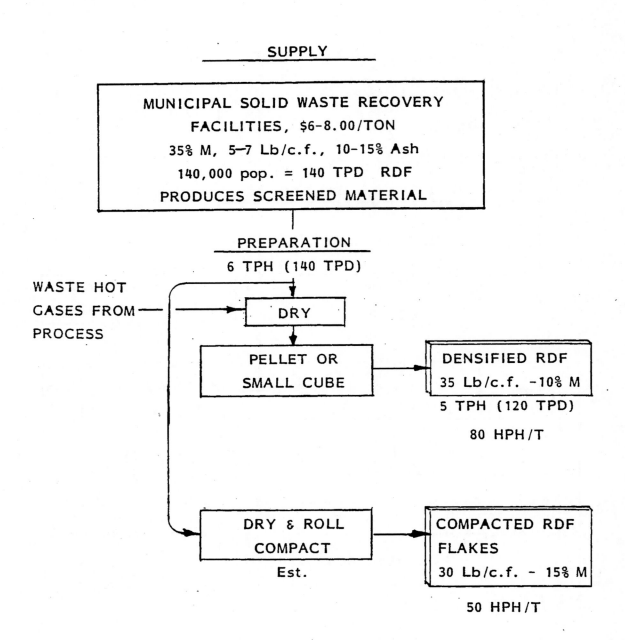

SUPPLY

MUNICIPAL SOLID WASTE RECOVERY
FACILITIES, $6-8.00/TON
35% M, 5-7 Lb/c.f., 10-15% Ash
140,000 pop. = 140 TPD RDF
PRODUCES SCREENED MATERIAL

PREPARATION
6 TPH (140 TPD)

WASTE HOT
GASES FROM
PROCESS

DRY

PELLET OR
SMALL CUBE

DENSIFIED RDF
35 Lb/c.f. -10% M

5 TPH (120 TPD)

80 HPH/T

DRY & ROLL
COMPACT

Est.

COMPACTED RDF
FLAKES
30 Lb/c.f. - 15% M

50 HPH/T

TRM BIO-METH CONF MAR '82

SCREEN TYPES

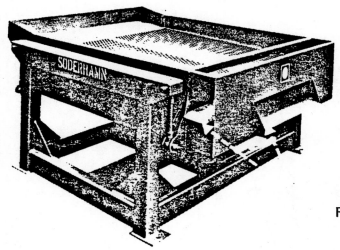

ROTARY SCREEN
FOR SIZE & LENGTH

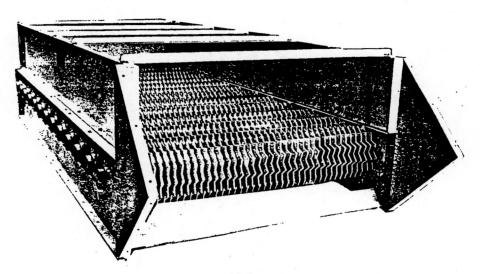

DISC SCREEN FOR
THICKNESS

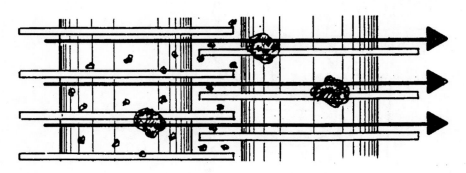

TRM BIO-METH CONF MAR '82

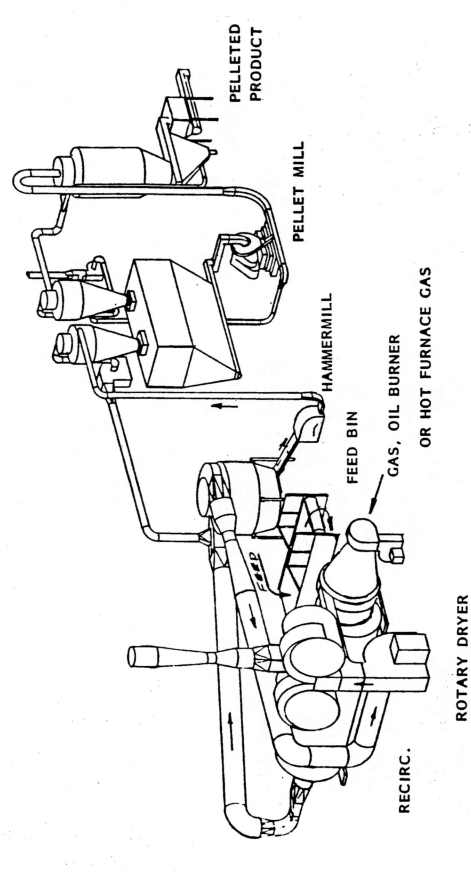

PELLETED PRODUCT

PELLET MILL

HAMMERMILL

GAS, OIL BURNER

OR HOT FURNACE GAS

FEED BIN

ROTARY DRYER

RECIRC.

TRM '82

TYPICAL DRYING, MILLING, PELLETING INSTALLATION

114

DENSIFICATION SYSTEMS

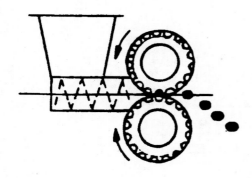

ROLL BRIQUETTER

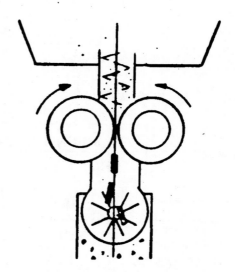

ROLL COMPACTOR

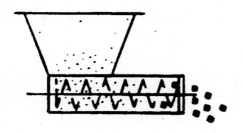

SCREW EXTRUDER

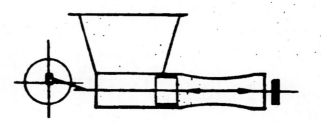

ECCENTRIC PISTON EXTRUDER

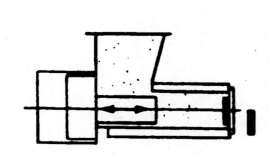

HYDRAULIC PISTON EXTRUDER

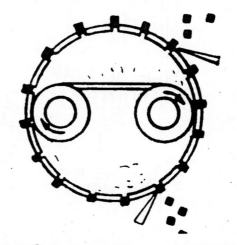

RING EXTRUDER - PELLETER

Courtesy FERROTECH

TRM '82

WOODCHIP FEEDSTOCK PREPARATION
TYPICAL FOR 5 TPH (120 TPD)

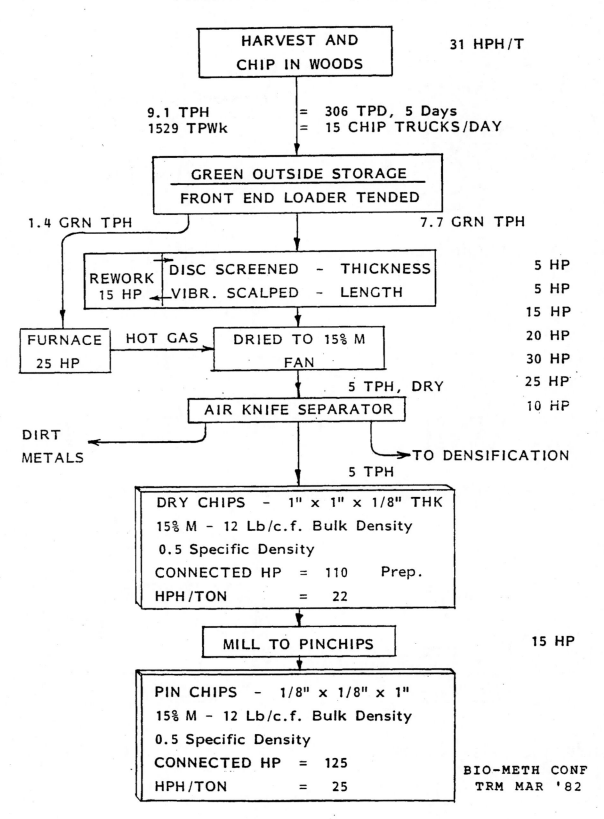

HARVEST AND CHIP IN WOODS

31 HPH/T

9.1 TPH   = 306 TPD, 5 Days
1529 TPWk   = 15 CHIP TRUCKS/DAY

GREEN OUTSIDE STORAGE
FRONT END LOADER TENDED

1.4 GRN TPH   7.7 GRN TPH

REWORK   DISC SCREENED - THICKNESS   5 HP
15 HP   VIBR. SCALPED - LENGTH   5 HP
                                             15 HP
FURNACE   HOT GAS   DRIED TO 15% M   20 HP
25 HP   FAN   30 HP
                                             25 HP
                      5 TPH, DRY
AIR KNIFE SEPARATOR   10 HP

DIRT
METALS   TO DENSIFICATION

                    5 TPH

DRY CHIPS - 1" x 1" x 1/8" THK

15% M - 12 Lb/c.f. Bulk Density

0.5 Specific Density

CONNECTED HP = 110   Prep.

HPH/TON   = 22

MILL TO PINCHIPS   15 HP

PIN CHIPS - 1/8" x 1/8" x 1"

15% M - 12 Lb/c.f. Bulk Density

0.5 Specific Density

CONNECTED HP = 125

HPH/TON   = 25

BIO-METH CONF
TRM MAR '82

DENSIFICATION

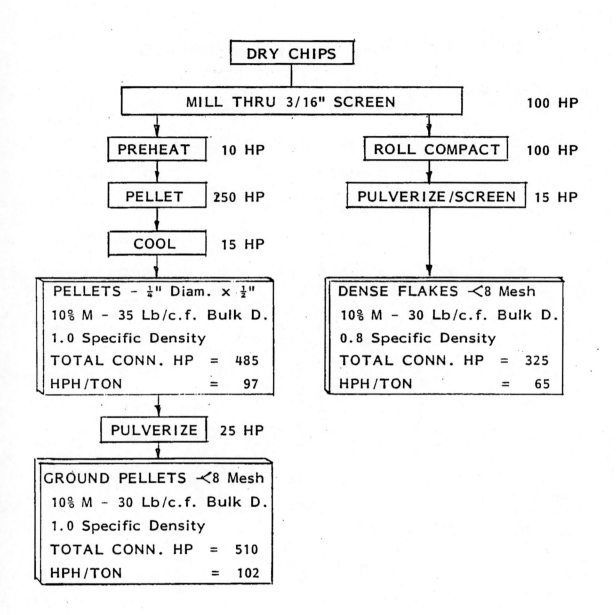

```
                        ┌─────────────┐
                        │  DRY CHIPS  │
                        └──────┬──────┘
          ┌────────────────────────────────────────────┐
          │         MILL THRU 3/16" SCREEN             │   100 HP
          └────────────────────────────────────────────┘
             │                              │
     ┌───────────┐                  ┌─────────────────┐
     │  PREHEAT  │  10 HP           │  ROLL COMPACT   │  100 HP
     └─────┬─────┘                  └────────┬────────┘
     ┌───────────┐                  ┌──────────────────────┐
     │  PELLET   │  250 HP          │  PULVERIZE/SCREEN    │  15 HP
     └─────┬─────┘                  └──────────┬───────────┘
     ┌───────────┐
     │   COOL    │  15 HP
     └─────┬─────┘
```

PELLETS - ¼" Diam. x ½"
10% M - 35 Lb/c.f. Bulk D.
1.0 Specific Density
TOTAL CONN. HP = 485
HPH/TON   =   97

DENSE FLAKES <8 Mesh
10% M - 30 Lb/c.f. Bulk D.
0.8 Specific Density
TOTAL CONN. HP = 325
HPH/TON   =   65

PULVERIZE   25 HP

GROUND PELLETS <8 Mesh
10% M - 30 Lb/c.f. Bulk D.
1.0 Specific Density
TOTAL CONN. HP = 510
HPH/TON   = 102

TRM BIO-METH CONF MAR '82

As Fired Heat Value Calculator

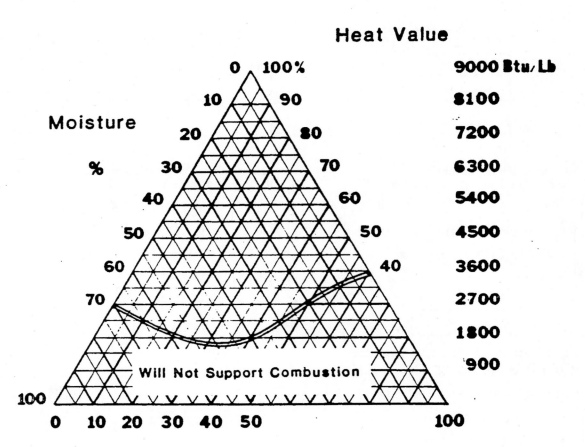

TRM BIO-METH CONF MAR '82

FEEDING COAL AND BIOMASS INTO HIGH PRESSURE REACTORS

A.R. Guzdar and A.C. Harvey

Foster-Miller Inc.
350 Second Ave.
Waltham, MA   02154

INTRODUCTION

Current state of technology of biomass gasification is primarily restricted to low pressure operation, atmospheric to 150 psi. However, as
with the technology of coal gasification, the state-of-the-art is being
pushed to the development of processes operating at higher pressures.
Such high pressure processes reduce the size and cost of equipment,
operate at higher temperatures which reduce tars and other volatile
products in the gas stream and can handle a greater variety of coal types.
Similar advantages can be projected for the gasification of biomass.

Higher pressure gasification is particularly suitable for the production
of methanol from biomass. Since methanol synthesis is performed at a
pressure of 750 to 1500 psi, gasification at high pressure avoids exces-
sive compression of the synthesis gas. Of course, this does require all
the reactant streams, including the solids feed, to be fed into the reactor at high pressure. Figure 1 shows the estimated variation of power
consumption with gasification pressure where solids feeding can easily
represent 25 percent of the total power consumption, particularly at the
high pressures.

Lock hoppers, rotary air locks, screw feeders and slurry pumps are the
most commonly used feed systems today, both for coal and for biomass.
Most of these systems become less economical at high pressures and large
sizes. This is probably more true with feeding biomass because of its
low bulk density and extremely bad flow properties. Typically, biomass
hoppers have to use a stirrer or other means, such as screws, for keeping
a smooth flow.

The low bulk density of biomass (10 to 15 lb/ft^3) means a correspondingly
large volume for all hoppers and consequently a high consumption of high
pressure inert gas for pressurization of the lock hopper type feed system.
The compression cost for this gas per ton of material is significant in
the design of high pressure coal feed systems; it would be three to four
times higher with biomass feed systems. Thus, the need for feed systems
which can conserve this high pressure gas is even greater.

119

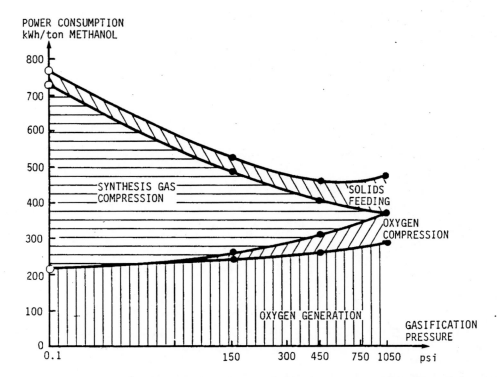

FIGURE 1.   POWER CONSUMPTION WITH CHANGE IN GASIFICATION PRESSURE

Recognizing these limitations with state-of-the-art, high pressure, feed systems, the United States Department of Energy (DOE) initiated a program to develop advanced feed technology for feeding dry coal into high pressure gasifiers.   The preliminary results of this effort as well as other state-of-the-art feed systems were reviewed at a Conference on Coal Feed Systems in 1977 [2].   This development has continued and its present state of technology is covered in this paper.

GENERAL REQUIREMENTS FOR FEED SYSTEM

Any feed system must be designed to satisfy the following requirements:

- Provide material at a controlled and metered feed rate

- Make the pressure seal between the high pressure reactor and the atmospheric pressure feed system

- Provide the desired material consistency and distribution that the reactor requires

- Operate economically with respect to power per ton of material feed

- Operate reliably and safely

- Control feed rate with a response time compatible with the gasifier operation.

120

Fixed bed gasifiers generally operate with large particle sizes (1 in. to 2 in.); medium pressure range, (atmospheric to 500 psi) have the slowest response time, and are the least sensitive to variation in feed rates. Entrained bed gasifiers generally operate with finely comminuted material at high pressures (>1000 psi), have very rapid response (less than 5 sec residence time) and are very sensitive to variation in feed rate. Fluidized bed gasifiers fall in between the two, operate with particle sizes in the range of 1/4 in. to 1/2 in. and at pressures less than 500 psi.

Thus, the feed to an entrained bed gasifier must be continuous, with very little variability in solids feed rate. Batch type systems though perfectly acceptable for fixed bed gasifiers, are likely to be unacceptable and would require an intermediate high pressure storage vessel with metering from which the material could be fed at a continuously metered rate into the gasifier.

Various feed system configurations can be developed using the feeder concepts described in this paper to satisfy the above general requirements for specific gasifiers. Rather than describe these we have chosen to concentrate on a discussion of the feeders only as they are the key to the overall feed system.

CLASSIFICATION OF FEEDERS

Feeders can be broken down generally into two classes depending on the way they make the pressure seal:

- Pressure seal is made mechanically, such as, lock hoppers, pocket feeders, piston feeders, rotary air locks, etc.

- Pressure seal is made by a plug of the material being fed such as, screw feeders, kinetic extruders, plug feeders, etc.

In general the former are least sensitive to material characteristics but require the most gas, while the latter depend very strongly on the type of material being fed. To achieve a gas tight seal, the material has to be compressed to a pressure high enough to form a plug of the right density and length so that the velocity of gas leakage through the plug is less than the velocity of the plug moving forward. For high reactor pressures, the high compression pressures required for sealing can lead to briquetting of the material resulting in a permanent change in the characteristics of the material being fed.

The state-of-the-art of high pressure coal feeding systems for coal conversion plants has been reviewed quite comprehensively in a paper presented by Mr. J.R. Hawrych at the 1981 International Gas Research Conference [3] and DOE Conference on Critical Components in Coal Conversion [4]. Some of the material presented here is abstracted from this review; greater details can be found in the paper itself.

121

Lock Hopper Systems

The lock hopper system has been in use for a number of years for the feeding of dry materials into high pressure reactors. Its most common use has been with the Lurgi gasifier where it has operated at pressures up to 450 psi commercially and up to 1200 psi at pilot sizes. A dual lock hopper system shown in Figure 2 was developed to reduce gas compression costs by blowing down the empty lock into the solids-filled one. Conceptually, a lock hopper system is simple, however, practical applications have experienced valve failures and solids holdup, decreasing system reliability and increasing maintenance costs. Recent advances in valve technology, sponsored by DOE are likely to mitigate the sealing problems, but hopper discharge with biomass is even more problematic than with coal. The lock hopper is a proven system for high pressure feed, however, its serious disadvantages may be intermittent operation, the requirement of pressurization gas and related supporting systems, pressure fluctuation of the process stream and high capital and operating costs.

As mentioned earlier, flow of biomass material through conventional conical bottom hoppers can be a problem. Tom Miles [5] has solved some of these flow problems with the Miles Biomass Gasifier Feeder shown in Figure 3. The system is divided into three separate functions:

- Pressure seal using a lock hopper with knife gate valves; the hopper is designed to have either a constant diameter or a slightly diverging taper to ensure material flow into the metering bin

- Metering using a "Live Bottom Hopper", consisting of a set of tapered screws capable of feed rates from 50 lb/hr to 2 tons/hr with a feed accuracy of ± 2 percent

- A separate injection screw which collects the material from the metering screens and transports it rapidly into the gasifier or into a possible pnuematic transport system.

A photograph of a typical unit is shown in Figure 4. Five such units have been built and have been operating since 1979; they range in pressure rating from 15, 150 and 300 psi and maximum capacity up to 1 ton/hr feeding various chip size and type.

A 1000 psi feeder for a biomass to methanol project is in the design stage. The maximum capacity of such units is estimated to be in the range of 2 tons/hr. However, larger capacities could be achieved with denser, pelletized material which can be more free flowing than the standard wood chips.

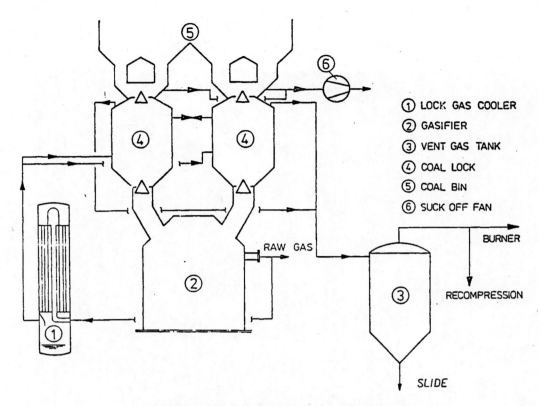

1 LOCK GAS COOLER
2 GASIFIER
3 VENT GAS TANK
4 COAL LOCK
5 COAL BIN
6 SUCK OFF FAN

RAW GAS

BURNER

RECOMPRESSION

SLIDE

FIGURE 2.   DOUBLE LOCK HOPPER SYSTEM

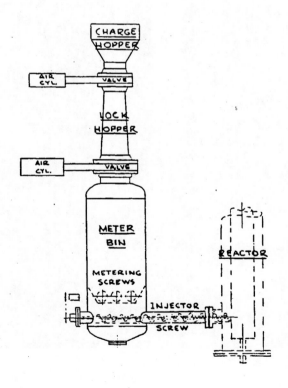

FIGURE 3.   MILES BIOMASS FEEDER

FIGURE 4. PHOTOGRAPH OF MILES UNIT

124

General Characteristics

Defining plug feeders as those in which the pressure seal is affected by
the packed solids, a wide range of concepts or devices are included. For
a better understanding of these devices a description of the characteristics of the plug is provided in this section. This is followed by a
description of the types of machines used to create such a plug and feed
it into a pressurized receiver. Although the concept of the plug feeder
is very attractive, the development of systems is made difficult by the
variability of feedstocks and the lack of specifically useful data and
analyses for gas-plug design. Development has been largely experimental
for certain material-plug-machine combinations, and so scale-up or extrapolation for other applications is problematic.

Figure 5 shows very generally the parameters affecting the operation of a plug being moved (fed) into a pressurized receiver. *Assuming*
that the plug is continuous, if perhaps anisotropic, to a fine scale,
the analysis of gas permeation is easily formulated, and the mechanics
of plug motion can be described in terms of friction and flow stresses.
The permeation and flow stress can be measured in static pressure stress,

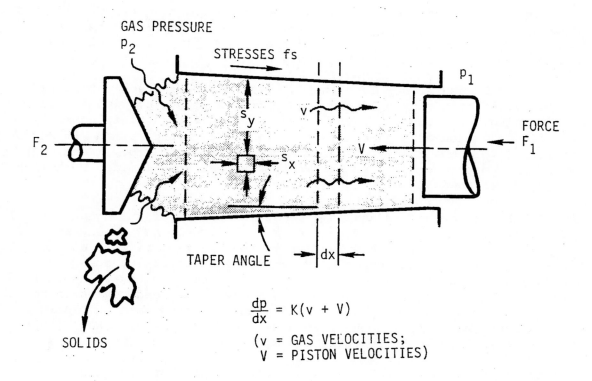

FIGURE 5. SCHEMATIC OF PARAMETERS INVOLVED
IN A SOLIDS GAS PLUG FOR FEEDERS

125

but the real plug properties depend on just how the plug is formed and moved, so that analysis has limited utility in design. Rather obvious qualitative factors are:

- The gas permeation velocity should be low compared to the plug velocity, at least so the back-leakage does not interrupt filling of the plug for further stuffing

- Ram pressure, solids size and shape, and moisture or binders have marked effect on gas permeation

- Plug taper or die angle has a very marked effect on the compaction, flow stress, and integrity of the plug

- Depending on feed material, moisture or binders, and the input specific work, the material properties can change slightly or greatly on the way through.

The various types of plug feeders that exist or are being developed may be discussed on the basis primarily of how the plug is compacted and moved, with secondary aspects relating to mechanical design, and method for delivering feed to the plug.

Screw Feeders

The simplest of plug feeders use an auger or screw to meter feed from a hopper, to compress the feed as it is moved down the barrel by the screw, and to pack the feed at the upstream end of the plug with sufficient pressure to move the plug continuously.

For low gas pressure, say less than 50 psi, a single, deeply-flighted "compression screw" having decreasing pitch is adequate, with a short sealing plug. The Fuller-Kinyon pump, shown in Figure 6, is commonly used for injection of dry cement into pneumatic transport, and it may be applicable for some finely granular biomass. Bonnot Corp., (Kent, OH) [6] has similar machines for granular pastes and has done limited work with wood chips or sawdust.

For much higher pressures and more positive control of throughput, twin-screw co-rotating extruders, shown in Figure 7, have been used for injecting materials from plastics to coal pastes, as well as some biomass feedstocks. Injection head pressures to several thousand psi are common, and a primary advantage of the co-rotating screws is that they wipe each other and the barrel and so keep the feed moving instead of caking on the flights. There is limited published data on biomass applications, but a firm such as Werner-Pfleiderer, Ramsey, NJ [7] has experience and equipment to carry out specific pilot demonstrations.

At extreme pressures, or with an added binder, the work input of screw-type machines usually transforms the biomass (lignin) so that the extrudate when cooled solidifies into a hard, dense material. Pellets or logs can be formed for subsequent feeding into a reactor. Although no such

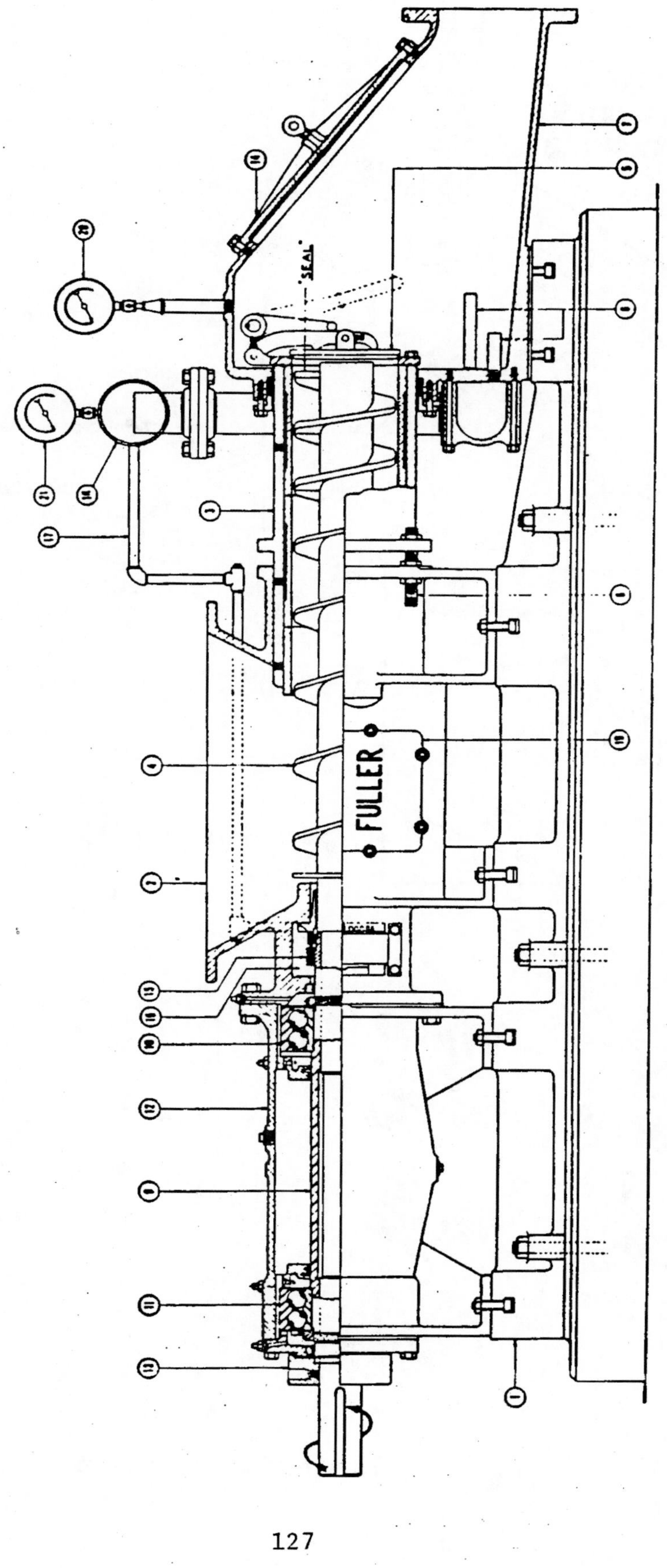

Figure 6. Fuller-Kinyon Pump

SEAL

FULLER

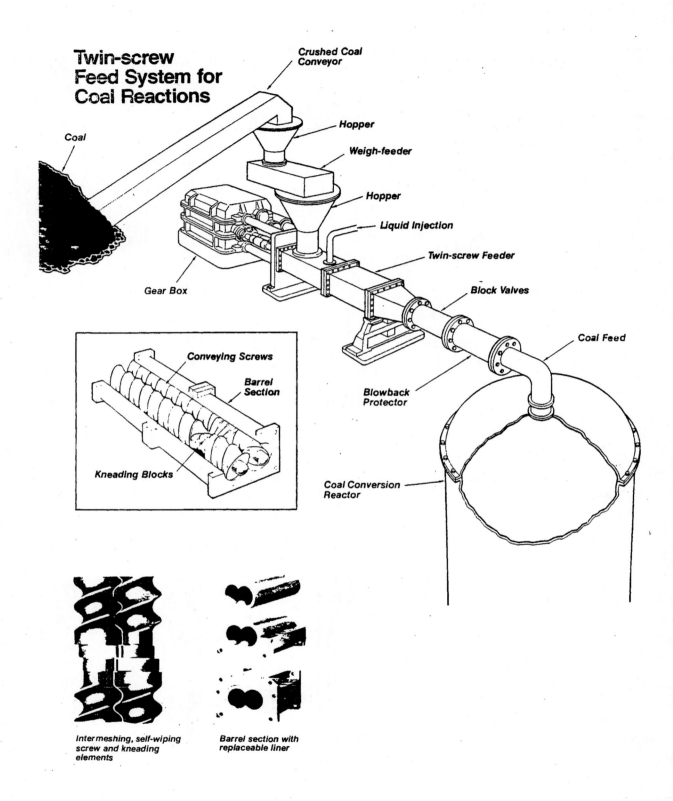

Twin-screw Feed System for Coal Reactions

Crushed Coal Conveyor

Coal

Hopper

Weigh-feeder

Hopper

Liquid Injection

Twin-screw Feeder

Block Valves

Gear Box

Coal Feed

Conveying Screws

Barrel Section

Kneading Blocks

Blowback Protector

Coal Conversion Reactor

Intermeshing, self-wiping screw and kneading elements

Barrel section with replaceable liner

FIGURE 7. TWIN-SCREW FEED SYSTEM

128

process is known, it is conceivable that pelletizing could be performed in a high pressure receiver for direct feeding of the reactor with uniformly sized stock.

Press logmaking is old art with machines such as made by the Potlatch Co. [8] using a compression screw wood chip feeder followed directly by a highly compressing spiral disk knife or slicer to transform and pack the stock. The Taiga International, Inc. [9], San Diego, CA has adapted this technology. In addition, Omni Fuels, Ontario, Canada is in a position to provide pelletized biomass equipment. Finally, the research work conducted by Professor Haygreen of the University of Minneapolis is interesting in connection with extrusion machines in that he has shown that pressing with ram stresses on the order of 10 kpsi will reduce wood chips from 50 to about 35 percent water.

The primary disadvantage of simple screw machines seems to be the high specific energy to push a plug with a screw because the compaction stresses "back up" into the screw and cause high friction torque. The power consumption of low pressure feed screw can be low, but that of high pressure extruders or pelletizers can be up to 50 kWhr/ton of wood chip feed.

Ram Type Plug Feeders

The next class of plug feeders avoids this by pushing with a piston or ram. This type of feeder is common in the pulp and paper industry as well as in plastic compounding and molding, and it has been tested on granular fuels such as coal. Perhaps the most directly applicable experience and machine is that of Stake Technology Inc., of Oakville, Ontario, Canada [10], who is largely involved with systems for digesting cellulosic biomass under pressure. Their feeder consists of a delivery screw constantly rotating coaxially within an annular piston that reciprocates to push the plug that is stuffed by the screw. One machine with a 5 in. screw, 8 in. piston, 4 in. stroke at 150 to 200 rpm feeds 4 to 5 tons/hr of typical tree chips, roughly 1 in. size and 50 percent moisture, into a steam digester at 300 psi, using less than 10 kWhr/ton of feed. Feed delivery pressure to 450 psi has been tested. Modified for a 10 in. piston and plug, the machine feeds up to 10 tons/hr of 10 percent moisture sawdust into an atmospheric pressure receiver; pressure capability is expected but has not been tested. Straw and bagasse feeds for digestion have also been demonstrated.

Another type of construction having effectively positive displacement of a feed plug is that of the injection molding machine commonly used for plastics. Ingersoll-Rand [11], sponsored by the DOE, developed such a machine for dry pulverized coal, and it undoubtedly would be useful for some types of comminuted wood or pasty biomass. The machine basically consists of a screw that first rotates and retracts as it stuffs feed against the upstream end of the seal plug, then stops rotating, and then translates forward to compress the feed and inject a portion of the plug into the receiver. A schematic of the machine and its all-hydraulic driven cycle is shown in Figure 8. The 5.5 in. screw machine, shown in Figure 9, is constructed with typical hard-hardness barrel and flights,

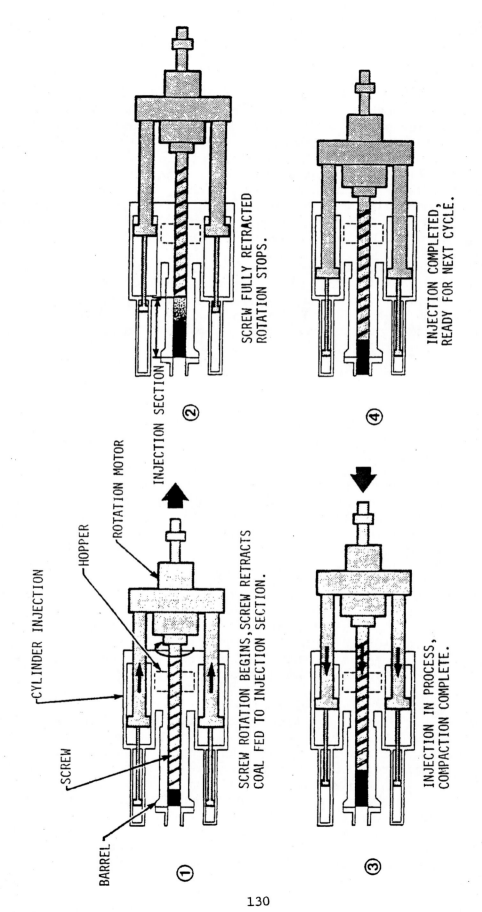

CYLINDER INJECTION

HOPPER

ROTATION MOTOR

SCREW

BARREL

INJECTION SECTION

① SCREW ROTATION BEGINS, SCREW RETRACTS COAL FED TO INJECTION SECTION.

② SCREW FULLY RETRACTED ROTATION STOPS.

③ INJECTION IN PROCESS, COMPACTION COMPLETE.

④ INJECTION COMPLETED, READY FOR NEXT CYCLE.

FIGURE 8. I-R SCREW EXTENDER HYDRAULIC CYCLE

FIGURE 9. I-R SCREW EXTENDER PHOTOGRAPH

131

and has forced cooling. With *coal* in steady state operation the maximum ram face stress of 9 kpsi produced a plug capable of sealing against 300 psig gas pressure with no binder, and 750 psig with some added binder such as pitch. Feed rate varied from 0.5 to 2 tons/hr while specific power varied from about 20 to 40 kWhr/ton. No clear dependence of power on receiver gas pressure is quoted, but it is interesting to note the plug dependence on binder and the fact that a *static* permeation test showed negligible gas leakage to 1500 psig, compared to 750 psig during plug feeding.

Comparison of the two positive displacement plug feeders just described shows that there is substantial difference in machine-feed characteristics and probably ample opportunity for optimization in a specific application.

Centrifugal Plug Feeder

Perhaps the simplest and yet most elegant method of compacted plug feeding is using a gravity or accelerational body force of the feed itself. Confined down-feed under gravity is ancient (silos) and has been used for solids feeding against gas pressure differentials in the oil and chemical process industries. Obviously the pressure differential is limited by the total height, perhaps in parallel stages. Decades ago a centrifugal pump for bulk dry cement was developed by Schmidt of Sweden but it lost out to the Fuller-Kinyon screw pump mentioned before for low pressures. Recently, Lockheed/Sunnyvale [12] and also Foster-Miller [13], both sponsored by the DOE, have demonstrated centrifugal machines for feeding pulverized coal against much higher pressures, and the basic similarity of the two independent designs and initial performance lends credence to the method.

Figure 10 is a schematic which helps explain the principles of this inertial plug feeding concept (also termed kinetic or centrifugal). Solids are fed into the center of the rotor, conveniently fluidized. There they sediment outward through the swirling transport gas and collect in one of several chambers disposed radially in the rotor. The solids are then compacted by centrifugal force in the sprue section and move outward at a rate determined at the hopper discharge tip. Gas back-leakage is limited by the impermeability and outward motion of the coal upstream of the hopper, while the solids rate is independently controlled by the size, "g" force, and pressure differential of the hopper only. Although we have not tested biomass materials, our data on coal indicates that the centrifugally formed and moved plug has very low permeability, lower than the statically compressed case indicates.

The pressure capability of the centrifugal feeder is primarily determined by the rotor tip speed; and the flow rate, by nozzle size and number. Power is required for slinging the solids and also for the rotor windage. These facts all make the machine more attractive as greater tonnage of feed is required, particularly if the nozzle must pass coarser material. Figure 11 presents performance estimated by Lockheed [12], who are continuing to develop the machine commercially. With nitrogen as the carrier gas, windage predominates until quite large size, 100 tons/hr;

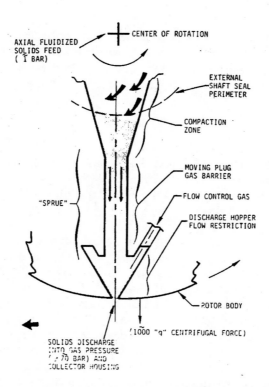

FIGURE 10. CENTRIFUGAL PLUG FEEDING CONCEPT

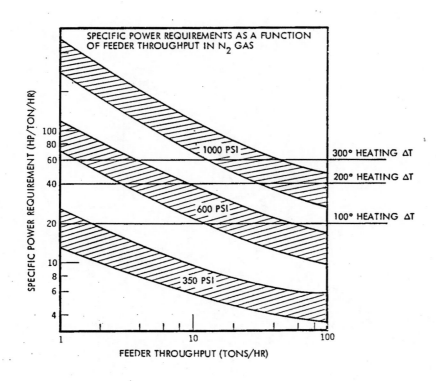

FIGURE 11. LOCKHEED POWER CURVES

with hydrogen (not shown) the low end of the specific power range is reached by about 10 tons/hr. For high mass flow or light gas, performance for biomass should approach that for coal. Figure 12 shows a sketch of the Lockheed Kinetic Extruder and Figure 13, a photograph of the rotor.

Piston Feeder

A piston feeder is conceptually the same as a mini-lock hopper with a displacer piston to conserve the high pressure gas. Many types of piston feeders have been developed only three of which are described here briefly.

A Schlepper type piston feeder [14] is being developed by Lurgi to provide semicontinuous feed to its gasifier and to minimize gas compression costs. Figure 14 shows a schematic of this feeder. The cylinder is filled with coal from a bunker with the piston on its upper end position and the bottom outlet closed. It appears that a limited charge must be metered in order to provide smooth piston passage past the fill port. The piston then moves down to seal the cylinder compartment and hold the coal drops into the reactor. The piston is forced down to the lower cylinder end displacing almost all coal and gas from the cylinder. Bottom valve closure and piston retraction complete the feed cycle. A demonstration feeder is currently being built by Lurgi and is expected to be tested shortly [14].

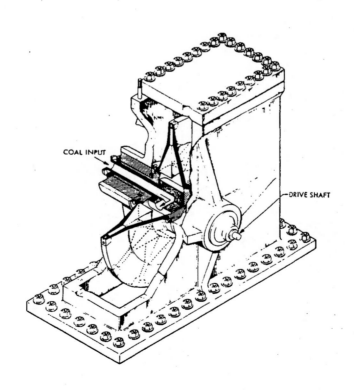

COAL INPUT

DRIVE SHAFT

FIGURE 12.   LOCKHEED KINETIC EXTRUDER

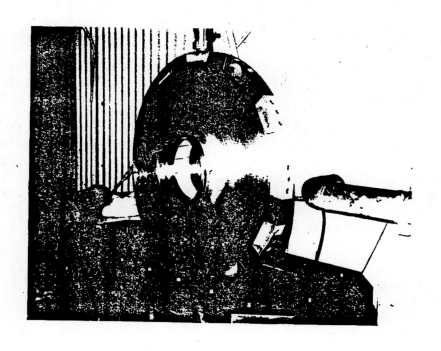

FIGURE 13.   ROTOR

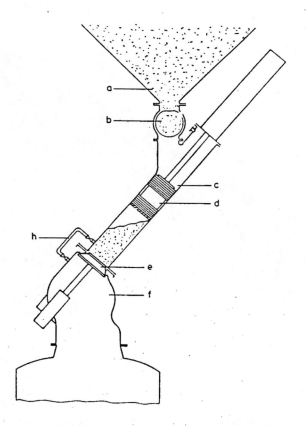

FIGURE 14.   SCHLEPPER PISTON FEEDER

135

Ingersoll-Rand (IR) has developed a single-acting two-opposed piston feeder under contract to DOE. The feeder and its operating cycle are shown schematically in Figures 15 and 16. The cycle is basically the same as any piston feeder - fill, trap, pressurize, dump, displace, shut off, re-expand, - but the functions are carried out by a "cat and mouse" action of the two pistons, hydraulically actuated. An interesting feature is that the pistons are so connected that one always is in the transfer cylinder blocking gas leakage even in the event of operational failure.

Data from the initial testing offers the following performance for the 125 mm (9 in.) bore prototype: 2 tons/hr feed, mixture of -200 mesh and -8 mesh eastern coal, 3.6 kWhr/ton at 35 bar (500 psig). Life testing and seal development is proceeding; it would seem much less difficult if it were with biomass rather than coal. The IR feeder appears competitive with the Schlepper piston feeder for biomass if positive stuffing and dumping means are provided, depending on the specific feedstock.

Another piston feeder being developed for coal under DOE sponsorship is that of Conspray Construction Systems, Inc., Santa Anna, CA [16]. The Conspray feeder is an adaptation of their commercial wet concrete pump, so the basic machine is well-proven. The fundamentals of cyclic piston feeding are the same as those just described, but the mechanics of the Conspray feeder have several clever features that should enhance its suitability for various forms of biomass, including wet or tack forms.

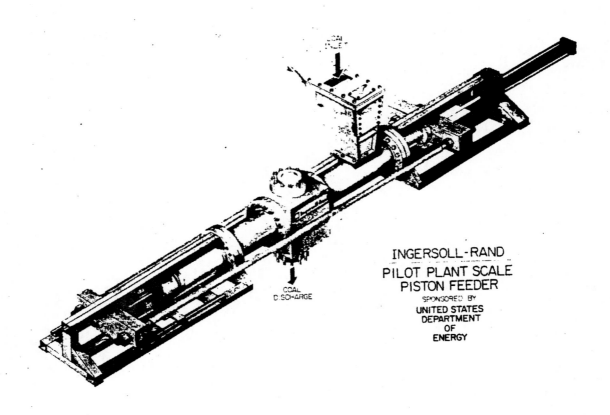

FIGURE 15. I-R PISTON FEEDER

136

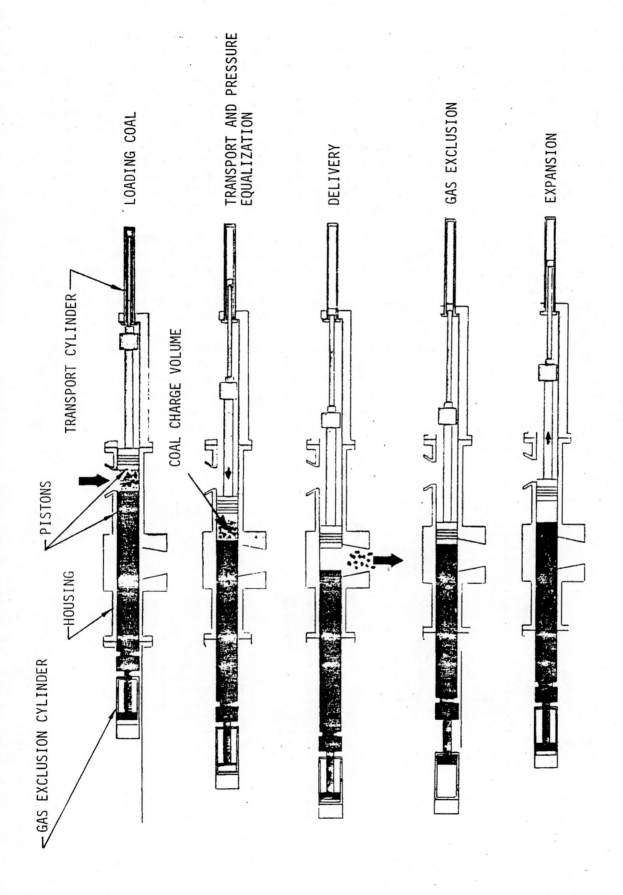

FIGURE 16. OPERATING CYCLE

137

Figure 17 is a schematic that helps explain the design and sequence of operations. Initially, say, the discharge slide valve is closed, the central rod is extruded along the hopper bottom to the slide valve, the coaxial annular sleeve and piston are retracted, and a stirrer in the hopper assures that feedstock fills the region around the central rod. First the sleeve extends to the discharge flange where it is sealed by pressure-loaded contact with a surrounding elastomeric sphincter ring. Then the central rod is retracted, which ensures that the feed trapped in the sleeve has sufficient voidage to be displaced easily by the piston. After rod retraction, the obvious sequence is to equalize gas pressures, sleeve chamber to receiver, open slide valve, extend rod and piston simultaneously, close slide valve, retract piston but not rod, and retract sleeve.

Actuation is all hydraulic, and control is with a microprocessor, check sequenced. The sleeve is capable of biting off chunks, even rocks, and still trapping a charge with an effective seal by the soft sphincter. The piston cup seal is water/oil film lubricated and cooled and has proven long life with concrete. Three cylinder versions that provide nearly continuous flow and utilize hydraulic power efficiently are typical.

The Conspray prototype dry solids feeder has been designed for operation up to 100 bar (1500 psi) and 4.5 tons/hr with coal. Development testing has proceeded to 2.5 tons/hr and 20 bar (300 psi) with pulverized coal (and problems extraneous to the feeder). Performance on material having the bulk density of coal is projected to be about 5 kWhr/ton and up to 40 tons/hr with two pistons of 9 in. diameter, current machine technology.

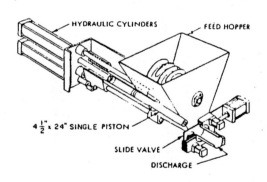

NOTE:
TEST UNIT BUILT. AWAITING
SELECTION OF TEST SITE.

PRESSURE (PSIG)	1500 (PROJECTED)
COAL SIZE	70%, 200M
FLOW (TPHR)	4
TIME W/COAL	0
HP	75

FIGURE 17.   CONSPRAY POSITIVE DISPLACEMENT PISTON COAL PUMP

138

The rotary air lock or star-feeder shown in Figure 18 is by far the most commonly used pocket feeder. The rotating vanes create pockets which are filled with the solid feed material. Rotation transports the material into the higher pressure reactor where it is discharged; the pocket is now filled with the high pressure gas which is transported and discharged to the atmosphere prior to receiving the solid material. This type of feeder is most commonly used in pneumatic transport systems and in one fixed bed type of gasifier. Its pressure rating is limited to less than 60 psi due to leakage past the blades and the rotor ends, which both interferes with feeding and is noneconomical.

Various designs have been developed over the years to increase its pressure handling capability to about 120 psi by making smaller pockets and adding multiple blade sealing. However, gas consumption, wear, and leakage still remain as problems.

Foster-Miller has developed a linearized version of this type of feeder which it calls the Linear Pocket Feeder shown conceptually in Figure 19. A cutaway view of a 5 tons/hr, 1000 psi operational prototype is shown in Figure 20. It is essentially a tubular conveyor in which a series of sealing pistons are connected together by a chain to form pockets. The pockets are filled with the feed material carried to the high pressure discharge area through a sealing tube, emptied of solids and then filled with water which displaces the pressurized gas that fills the pockets

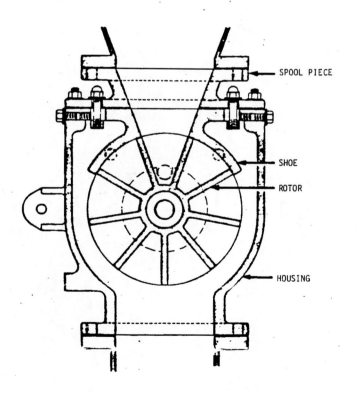

FIGURE 18. ROTARY AIR LOCK

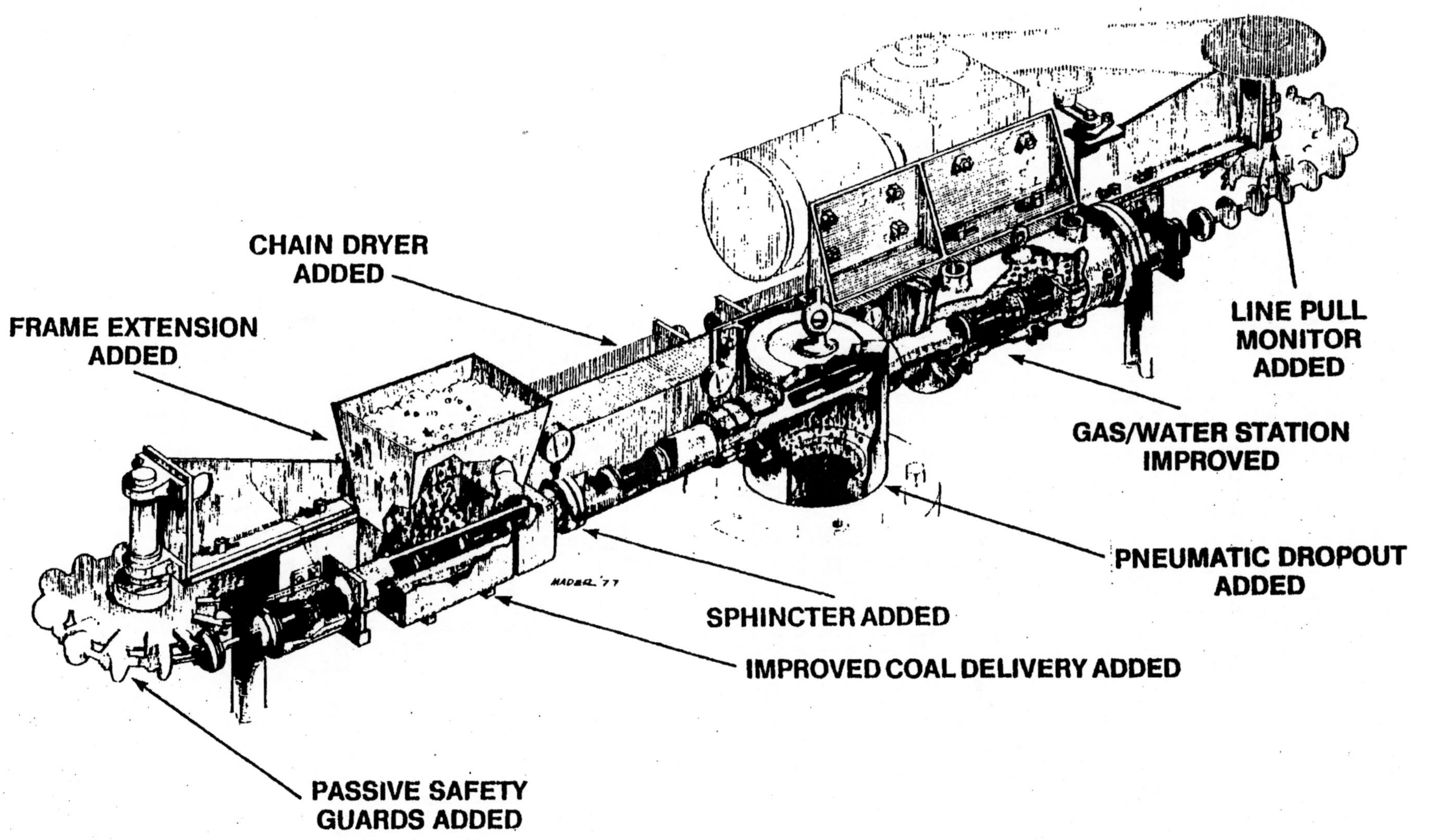

LINE PULL
MONITOR ADDED

GAS/WATER STATION
IMPROVED

PNEUMATIC DROPOUT
ADDED

IMPROVED COAL DELIVERY ADDED

SPHINCTER ADDED

CHAIN DRYER
ADDED

FRAME EXTENSION
ADDED

PASSIVE SAFETY
GUARDS ADDED

FIGURE 19. LPF CONFIGURATION

140

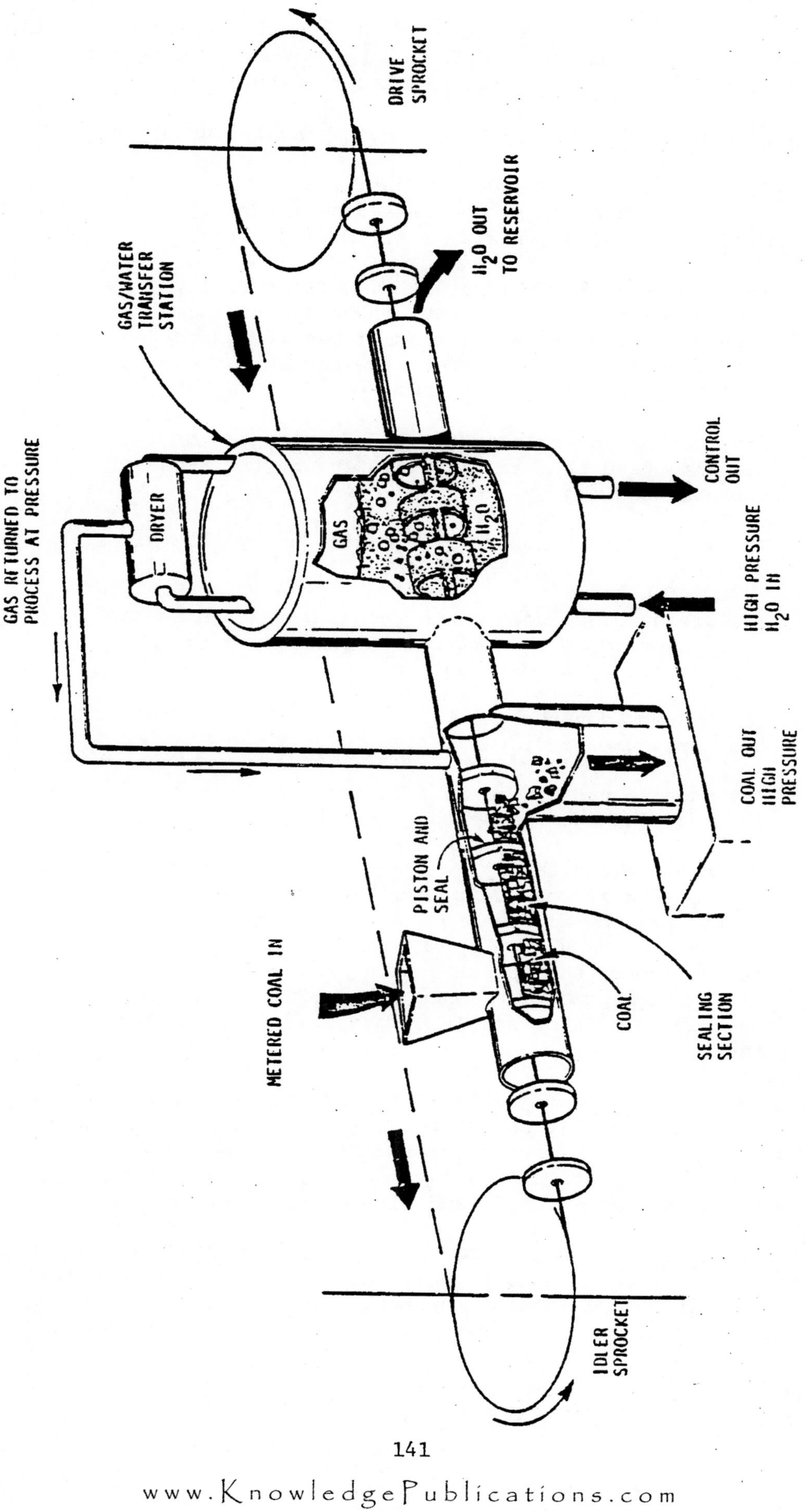

DRIVE SPROCKET

GAS/WATER TRANSFER STATION

H_2O OUT TO RESERVOIR

GAS RETURNED TO PROCESS AT PRESSURE

DRYER

GAS

H_2O

CONTROL OUT

HIGH PRESSURE H_2O IN

METERED COAL IN

PISTON AND SEAL

COAL

SEALING SECTION

COAL OUT HIGH PRESSURE

IDLER SPROCKET

FIGURE 20. CUTAWAY VIEW

141

back into the high pressure reactor. With respect to process functions it is similar to a number of mini-lock hoppers with displacer pistons - the water acting as the continuous displacer piston.

The system has the following desirable operating features:

- It is a universal feeder insensitive to feed stock characteristics, capable of feeding a variety of feed sizes and materials, coal, biomass, etc.

- Input to the LPF is metered using commercially proven components. The LPF discharges the same metered rate of material that it receives into the pressure reactor. The feed rate can be varied smoothly from zero to maximum.

- The machine can be started up independently of material feed rate and it will provide the necessary pressure sealing.

- It is a continuous feeder requiring no cyclic valves or controls for its operation.

- The pressure balanced chain requires a drive system only to overcome chain friction which is a small part of the total machine power.

- The PV work done by the LPF is supplied by a commercial high pressure water pump.

- The machine has a fail safe design. It operates with zero gas leakage when either running or stopped.

- The machine can easily be scaled up to large sizes - 250 tons/hr of coal unit possible with present day parts and tube fabrication.

- It has one of the lowest capital and operating costs of any high pressure feed system, rivaled only by positive displacement slurry pumps on a dry solids basis.

Figures 21 and 22 show photographs of a 3-1/2 in. diam machine, capable of feed rates exceeding 5 tons/hr of coal at 1000 psi. It is mounted on a special test facility built under contract to DOE. The system has demonstrated operation at 1000 psi with pulverized coal (minus 200 mesh), fluidized bed coal (1/4 in. x 0) and with coarse coal (minus 3/4 in.).

The system has the potential of being adapted to feed biomass, either wood chips or pulverized wood. Special designs have been conceived but not demonstrated for feeding the LPF to achieve high packing density, and for the dropout station to discharge these packed pockets.

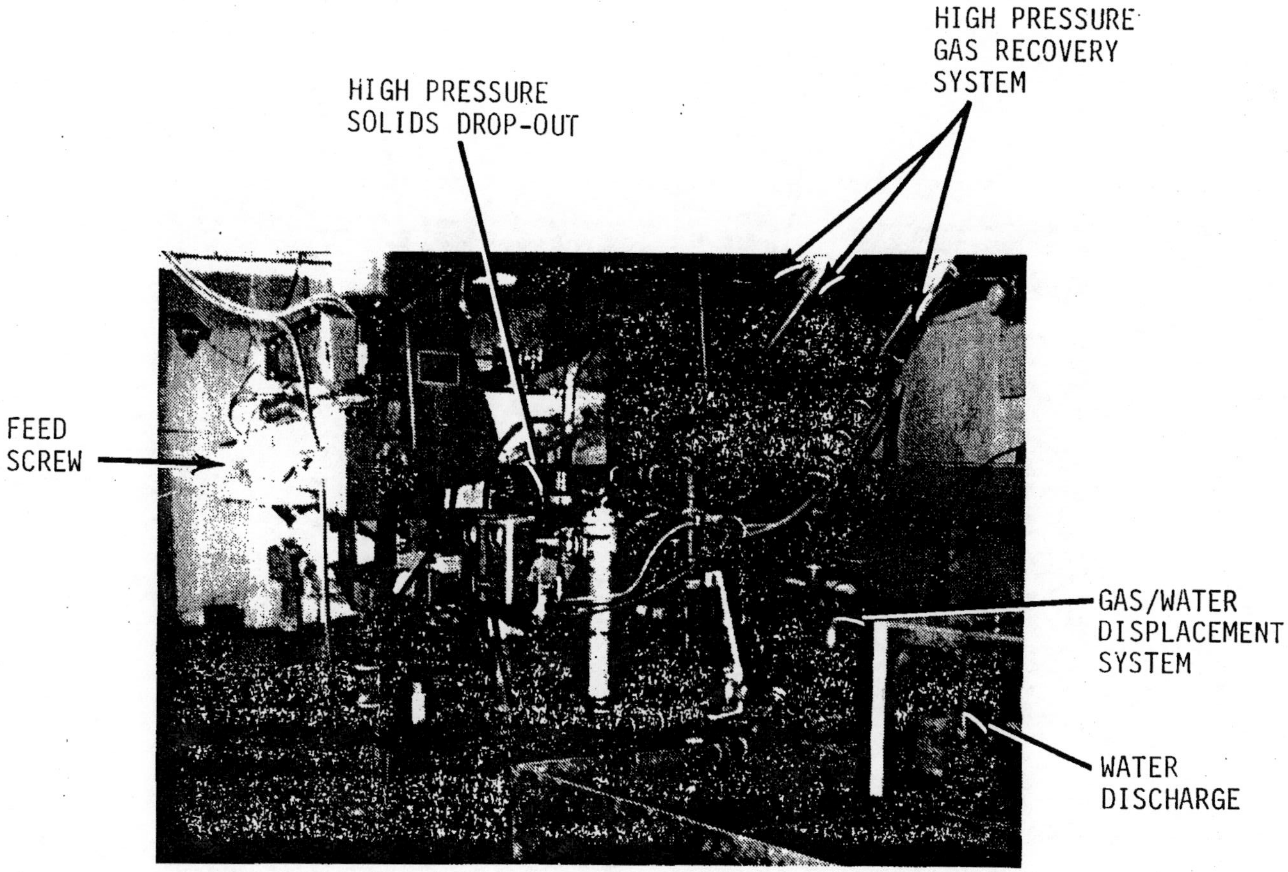

FIGURE 21. LINEAR POCKET FEEDER – FRONT VIEW

143

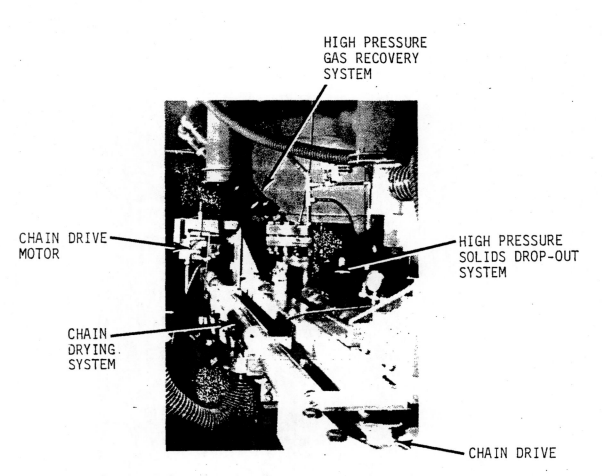

HIGH PRESSURE
GAS RECOVERY
SYSTEM

CHAIN DRIVE
MOTOR

HIGH PRESSURE
SOLIDS DROP-OUT
SYSTEM

CHAIN
DRYING
SYSTEM

CHAIN DRIVE

FIGURE 22.   VIEW OF THE BACK SIDE OF THE LPF FROM THE INLET END

144

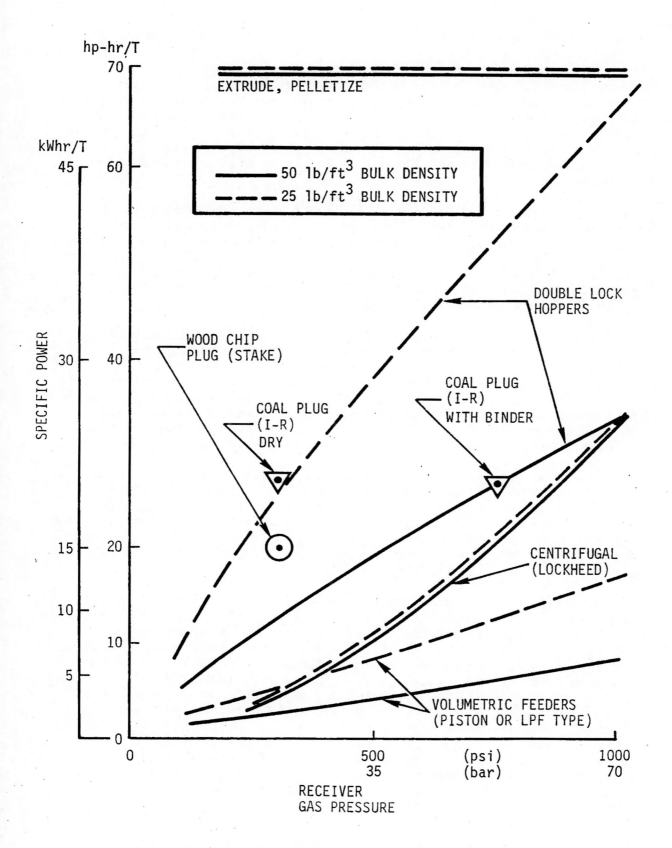

FIGURE 23.   ESTIMATED POWER REQUIREMENTS FOR
COMMERCIAL SIZED BIOMASS FEEDERS

145

GENERAL ASSESSMENT OF CURRENT STATE-OF-THE-ART OF BIOMASS FEEDERS FOR HIGH PRESSURE REACTORS

The Miles lock hopper system and the Stake Technology plug feeder are the only two systems being offered commercially for the feeding of dry biomass into high pressure reactors. The lock hopper system, in its present design, does seem to be limited in capacity, approximately 2 to 5 tons/hr, by the maximum diameter and cycle time of the valve. Operations at 150 psi has been demonstrated; 300 psi is in the startup stage, and 1000 psi is in design.

The Stake Technology plug feeder is offered commercially with the Omni gasifier where it operates only at pressures close to atmospheric less than 15 psi. However, these units are capable of operating up to 450 psi on wood chips (1 x 1/2 x 1/4 in.) at rates of 3 to 4 tons/hr. With very fine feed they predict they could feed up to 9 tons/hr of 90 percent dry matter. The power ratings being quoted are extremely low of the order of 20 hp-hr/ton of material at 300 psi.

The Werner-Pfleiderer twin screw feeder has fed cellulosic material up to 500 psi in pressure, and W-P offers system design capability.

The more advanced feeders being developed for coal have the potential for significant improvement in operating capacity, cost and power requirements over lock hopper systems and plug type of screw feeders. Figure 23 shows a comparison of specific power for the various feeders for two materials having bulk densities of 50 lb/ft^3 and 25 lb/ft^3.

Figure 24 compares the installed cost for various feeders of a commercial size (50 tons/hr) for feeding coal. Since feed capacity, in general, is volumetric and depends on the bulk density of the material, the cost for any given size could be scaled in proportions to bulk density. Though the absolute value of these cost estimates may be in question - depending on the basis used - the relative magnitude of the costs for various feed systems may be more acceptable.

The Conspray and I-R piston feeders as well as the LPF are all capable of dry feed of biomass at high pressures (up to 1000 psi). These systems should be capable of handling the full spectrum of biomass type of materials, from wood chips to pulverized wood and yield relative capital and operating cost advantages shown in Table 1. They save on gas compression costs by recirculating gas at pressure. The LPF is a continuous device and as such has the potential for scale up to very large capacities. The piston feeders are batch devices and would require multiple pistons to achieve steady flow.

The I-R screw extruder may have the potential for high-pressure wood feeding. It has been tested on coal up to pressures of 750 psi and 2 tons/hr. Its operation on biomass feed needs to be demonstrated.

147

GENERAL ASSESSMENT OF CURRENT STATE-OF-THE-ART OF BIOMASS FEEDERS FOR HIGH PRESSURE REACTORS

The Miles lock hopper system and the Stake Technology plug feeder are the only two systems being offered commercially for the feeding of dry biomass into high pressure reactors. The lock hopper system, in its present design, does seem to be limited in capacity, approximately 2 to 5 tons/hr, by the maximum diameter and cycle time of the valve. Operations at 150 psi has been demonstrated; 300 psi is in the startup stage, and 1000 psi is in design.

The Stake Technology plug feeder is offered commercially with the Omni gasifier where it operates only at pressures close to atmospheric less than 15 psi. However, these units are capable of operating up to 450 psi on wood chips (1 x 1/2 x 1/4 in.) at rates of 3 to 4 tons/hr. With very fine feed they predict they could feed up to 9 tons/hr of 90 percent dry matter. The power ratings being quoted are extremely low of the order of 20 hp-hr/ton of material at 300 psi.

The Werner-Pfleiderer twin screw feeder has fed cellulosic material up to 500 psi in pressure, and W-P offers system design capability.

The more advanced feeders being developed for coal have the potential for significant improvement in operating capacity, cost and power requirements over lock hopper systems and plug type of screw feeders. Figure 23 shows a comparison of specific power for the various feeders for two materials having bulk densities of 50 lb/ft^3 and 25 lb/ft^3.

Figure 24 compares the installed cost for various feeders of a commercial size (50 tons/hr) for feeding coal. Since feed capacity, in general, is volumetric and depends on the bulk density of the material, the cost for any given size could be scaled in proportions to bulk density. Though the absolute value of these cost estimates may be in question - depending on the basis used - the relative magnitude of the costs for various feed systems may be more acceptable.

The Conspray and I-R piston feeders as well as the LPF are all capable of dry feed of biomass at high pressures (up to 1000 psi). These systems should be capable of handling the full spectrum of biomass type of materials, from wood chips to pulverized wood and yield relative capital and operating cost advantages shown in Table 1. They save on gas compression costs by recirculating gas at pressure. The LPF is a continuous device and as such has the potential for scale up to very large capacities. The piston feeders are batch devices and would require multiple pistons to achieve steady flow.

The I-R screw extruder may have the potential for high-pressure wood feeding. It has been tested on coal up to pressures of 750 psi and 2 tons/hr. Its operation on biomass feed needs to be demonstrated.

The Lockheed Kinetic Extruder operation is restricted by orifice size to finely divided wood such as used in entrained bed gasifiers. Its capacity and pressure sealing capability are probably sensitive to the particle density, porosity and packing characteristics of the material. Whether it is too sensitive to the material behavior to ensure reliable continuous operation remains to be seen. In some range of parameters it is probably very competitive due to its simplicity and potential for high capacity and material stream distribution.

Considering the wide range of feeder and biomass types, it appears that the primary factors in matching the two are the pressure and importance of power, flowability and bulk density with or without compaction, feed rate tonnage and constancy desired.

The technology of high-pressure, biomass gasification appears to be in its infancy but growing. Advances made in feed system design for coal gasification have laid the foundation for the introduction of high-pressure feed systems for biomass. Systems can be designed, at the present time, for pilot-scale demonstrations. Scale-up to commercial size is within the capability of present-day technology.

REFERENCES

1. Lindman, N., "A New Synthesis Gas Process for Biomass and Peat" Symposium on Energy from Biomass and Wastes V, Lake Buena Vista, FL, Jan. 26-30, 1981

2. Proceedings of the Conference on Coal Feeding Systems, Pasadena, CA, June 1977, Jet Propulsion Laboratory Publication 77-55.

3. Hawrych, J.R., "High Pressure Coal Feeding Systems for Coal Conversion Plants", 1981 International Gas Research Conference, Los Angeles, CA, September 1981.

4. U.S. Department of Energy, "Workshop on Critical Coal Conversion Equipment", Huntington, WV, October 1980.

5. Miles, Thomas R., Portland, OR, personal communication.

6. Bonnot Co., Kent, OH, personal communication.

7. Mack, W., Werner-Pfleiderer Corp., Ramsey, NJ, personal communication.

8. Potlatch Co., personal communication.

9. Taiga International Inc., San Diego, CA, personal communication.

10. Wainless, B., Stake Technology, Oakville, Ontario, Canada, personal communication.

11. Mistry, D.K., Ingersoll-Rand Research Inc., Princeton, NJ, personal communication.

12. Bvruin, J., Lockheed/Sunnyvale, personal communication.

13. Reimert, R., "Feeding Systems for Pressure Vessels", Chem. Eng. Tech., Vol. 53, No. 5, 1981, pp. 335-344.

14. Peterson, D.D., Conspray Construction Systems, Inc., Santa Anna, CA, personal communication.

www.KnowledgePublications.com

Gasification of Peat and Biomass — U.S. Projects

THE SERI HIGH PRESSURE OXYGEN GASIFIER

T. B. Reed and M. Markson
Solar Energy Research Institute
Golden, CO 80401

M. Graboski
Colorado School of Mines
Golden, CO 80401

ABSTRACT

A 1 ton/day (900 kg/day), downdraft, oxygen biomass gasifier has been built and operated on wood chips and densified biomass for 18 months. The gasifier, which is a modification of the small gasifiers widely used in the past, has an extended char bed and staged oxygen injection designed to crack all the pyrolysis tars in order to eliminate downstream gas cleanup requirements. The gasifier is fed continuously, which allows high temperature combustion of the tars above the pyrolysis section. This in turn provides heat for the pyrolysis reaction.

Actual feed rates varied up to 62 lb/h (28 kg/h), or 314 lb/ft^2 h (1533 kg/m^2 h) with measured oxygen/fuel ratios varying between 0.35 and 0.44. A typical gas has a composition of 48% CO, 15% CO_2, 32% H_2, 3% N_2, and 2% CH_4. Organic content in the gas quench water is typically 0.02% to 0.1% of the feed and no tars are made. Heat losses through the insulation and grate are typically 6%-8% of the throughput energy in the 6-in.(150-mm)-diameter bed. The gasifier has been operated both at atmospheric pressure and at pressures up to 10 atmospheres. The gasifier has been operated at moisture levels from 0-40% (wet basis). The downdraft gasifier produces a gas close to that predicted by the equilibrium between C, H_2, CO, CO_2, and H_2O at temperatures between 700° and 900°C and is therefore particularly suited to producing synthesis gas for synthetic fuels. Two liters of methanol were synthesized from the gas by Chem Systems Inc. using the liquid-phase process. The gas was found to be similar to synthesis gas from coal and presented no difficulty in synthesis.

151

1.0 INTRODUCTION

There are a wide variety of commercial and experimental gasifiers for coal and biomass, differing in respect to the form and size of fuel required, end use of the gas, etc. The Solar Energy Research Institute (SERI) is presently developing a pressurized oxygen biomass gasifier to make a medium energy gas composed primarily of hydrogen and carbon monoxide (synthesis gas). This gas can be used for pipeline distribution, turbine operation, etc., but is especially suitable for chemical synthesis of methanol, ammonia, methane, gasoline, or other fuels and chemicals.

Gasifiers have been available since World War II for making synthesis gas and synthetic fuels from coal. Some gasifiers for biomass exist that could be used for making synthesis gas. The gasifier described here is, however, specifically designed for synthesis gas production, especially for methanol synthesis. This report describes the principles of downdraft gasification, initial testing of the gasifier, and the conversion of synthesis gas from biomass to methanol.

A wide variety of gasifiers exist for converting coal and biomass to gaseous fuels and these take many forms, depending on the feedstock used and the purposes for which the gases are produced [1]. We have completed an extensive survey of biomass gasification which describes most of the biomass gasifiers in detail [2].

2.0 DESCRIPTION OF GASIFIER

A major problem in almost all gasifiers is the production of significant quantities of tars and oils which must be removed at considerable cost unless the gas is burned in-situ.

Downdraft air gasifiers were widely used during World War II to operate cars, trucks, and small electric generators [3]. In conventional downdraft gasifiers (Fig. 2-1) air is injected between the incoming biomass and the charcoal produced by pyrolysis. The resulting combustion supplies heat for pyrolysis and burns much of the pyrolysis oils. The rest of the tars pass through the bed of hot charcoal where they are cracked to carbon and gases. This produces a relatively clean gas that can be used in engines with a minimum of filtering. Thus, low tar and oil production is one important characteristic of downdraft gasifiers, but because they lack insulation and have poor air distribution filtering is still required.

The SERI gasifier shown schematically in Fig. 2-2 is a modification of these earlier gasifiers (1) to provide clean gas, (2) to operate with oxygen below slagging temperatures, (3) to operate at a pressure greater than atmospheric pressure, and (4) to operate in a continuous rather than a batch process. A photograph of the gasifier installation is shown in Fig. 2-3.

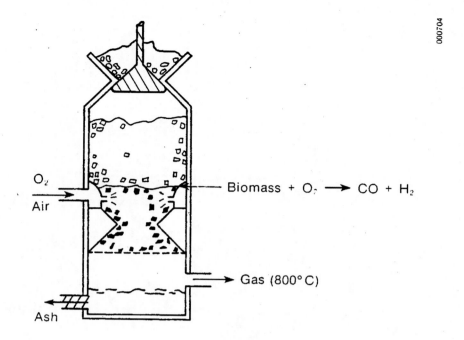

Figure 2-1.   Schematic Diagram of Downdraft Gasifier

The gasifier comprises four zones. In the topmost zone, tar vapor released by the pyrolyzing biomass is burned with oxygen to provide heat for pyrolysis:

$$Biomass + Heat \longrightarrow Tar + CO_2 + H_2O + CH_4 + Charcoal \qquad (1)$$

and

$$Tar + O_2 \longrightarrow CO + CO_2 + H_2 + H_2O + Heat. \qquad (2)$$

In the second zone (typically a few inches thick) pyrolysis is completed and pyrolysis products flow down to the char bed.

In the third zone, comprising the main body of the gasifier, these pyrolysis products are cracked and gasified:

$$Tar + CO_2 + H_2O + CH_4 + Charcoal \longrightarrow CO + H_2. \qquad (3)$$

Since these reactions are endothermic, oxygen is added to the bed in several stages to keep the temperature of the bed high enough to promote rapid gasification and cracking.

In the bottom zone char eventually is consumed, ash passes through the grate and the gas is quenched in a water spray venturi section. The overall reaction is then

$$Biomass + O_2 \longrightarrow CO + H_2 + (CO_2 + H_2O + CH_4). \qquad (4)$$

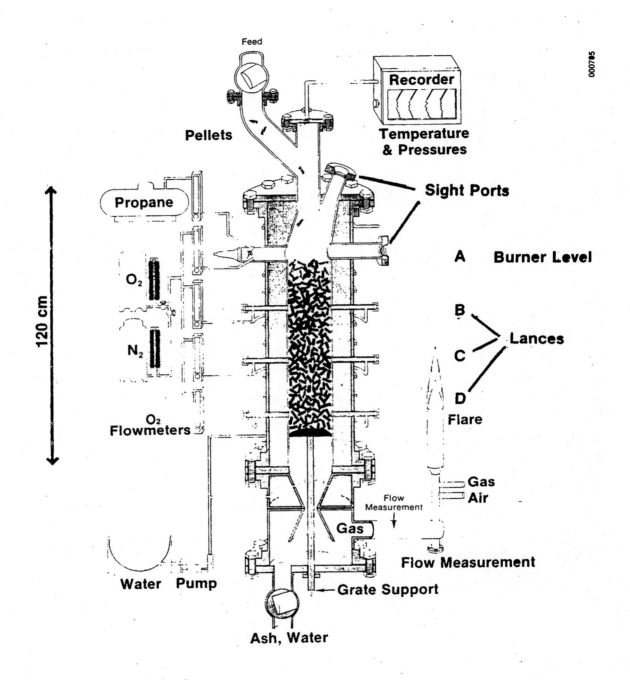

000705

Feed

Pellets

Propane

O₂

N₂

O₂
Flowmeters

120 cm

Water   Pump

Ash, Water

Recorder

Temperature
& Pressures

Sight Ports

A   Burner Level

B
            Lances
C

D

Flare

Gas
Air

Flow Measurement

Gas

Flow
Measurement

Grate Support

Figure 2-2. SERI Downdraft Gasifier

154

Figure 2-3. Photograph of SERI Downdraft Gasifier Installation

155

The gasifier is built of mild steel pipe, with a 12-in.(305-mm) outside diameter. It has a refractory insulation 3 in.(76 mm) thick and an inside diameter of 6 in.(152 mm). Provision is made at levels A-D (Fig. 2-2) for various services. In section A there is a burner for start-up that burns propane and oxygen. A second port contains a fire eye to insure ignition of the flame. Other ports contain sight glasses and thermocouples.

Sections B-D each contain four water-cooled oxygen lances for injecting oxygen into the bed to provide the energy for gasification of the char. In addition there is a thermocouple for monitoring bed temperature.

A rotary plug valve above the vessel supplies a continuous flow of pellets or wood chips to the vessel. Initially, a photocell at level B detects the level of the pyrolysis bed and increases or decreases the feeding rate to maintain a constant level at level B. More recently we have installed a gamma ray level detector which permits continuous control of bed level. In this way the required oxygen/fuel ratio is automatically maintained. The instrumentation and plumbing of the gasifier are shown in Fig. 2-4.

The gasifier is designed to operate at up to 1000°C and 150 psig (1000 kPa). The gas residence time is 1 to 2 seconds at 10 atm (1000 kPA) for 100 lb/h (45 kg/h) feed. Biomass residence time is 15 min. Under these conditions, any tars not immediately decomposed in the pyrolysis zone have sufficient time to crack in the char bed itself. (The reactor design pressure of 150 psig was selected to demonstrate pressurized gasification. There is no technical reason to limit operation to 150 psig in future demonstration and commercial facilities.) Steam may be fed to the gasifier if desired. Tests to date show that steam is not a necessary input to the reactor.

3.0 REACTOR OPERATION

For starting the reactor is filled to level B with wood charcoal. The reactor is brought to operating temperature using the oxygen-propane auxiliary burner which heats the refractory in the burner section and brings the charcoal to reaction temperature. Temperatures are recorded from thermocouples at each of the four stations. When the burner section reaches about 1000°C, biomass feeding is begun and oxygen is fed to the lances at predetermined levels to bring the char to temperature. Typically in 30 to 60 minutes the propane flame can be turned off and the gasifier then approaches steady state.

Pellets or wood chips are fed through the center feed pipe and oxygen is injected through a diffuser to the top of the bed. Typically more than two thirds of the total oxygen is fed through the diffuser into the freeboard zone of the reactor. Here, tars that are generated as the solids fall through the freeboard, plus tars issuing upward from the solid bed, combust to produce a yellow to white-hot flame which heats the refractory. The hot refractory and flame radiate to the top of the pellets and supply the heat for pyrolysis. The temperature

156

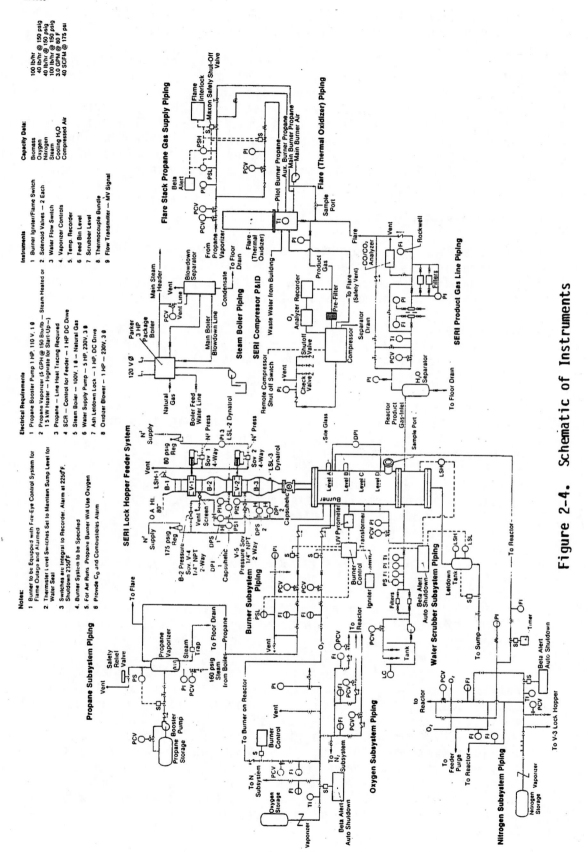

Figure 2-4. Schematic of Instruments

157

www.KnowledgePublications.com

above the pyrolysis zone is typically 900° to 1100°C. Steam may also be added to the freeboard.

As the solid particles completely gasify at the lowest section, ash and some residual carbon fall through the grate into a venturi scrubber where a water spray cools the gas and separates the gas from the solids. The solids are removed with the water through a solenoid valve while the gas passes to a knockout pot. The gas then is metered through an orifice and passed to a flare burner or to the compressor. Alternatively, the gases can be compressed into cylinders by a 100-lb/h (45-kg/h) three-stage compressor for future use. A manifold system holding 10 cylinders is attached to the compressor.

4.0 EXPERIMENTAL RESULTS

The gasifier was operated over a one-year period at atmospheric pressure in 15 runs generally lasting 6-12 hours. In early runs the data obtained were mainly qualitative, and improvements were made in the gasifier as the operators became more expert.

Although a variety of sizes of feedstock were tested, most of the work was done with the 3/16-in.(5-mm) wood pellets and small chips described in Table 4-1. Other feedstocks used are also described in this table.

Table 4-2 gives pertinent data on oxygen and fuel rates for several tests. Gasification tests using pure oxygen have been conducted at steady feed rates of 25 lb/h (11 kg/h) to 62 lb/h (28 kg/h) of biomass pellets. These feed rates translate to specific throughputs of 127 lb/ft^2 h (620 kg/m^2 h) to 314 lb/ft^2 h (1533 kg/m^2 h), respectively, at atmospheric pressure. The higher throughput does not appear to represent the maximum attainable throughput for the system since the highest feed rate was limited by the feeder and oxygen supply, not the gasifier.

By way of comparison, a typical throughput for the updraft pressurized Lurgi gasifier operating on coal is 140 lb/ft^2 h (680 kg/m^2 h), while for a pressurized slagging Lurgi, a throughput of 666 lb/ft^2 h (3252 kg/m^2 h) has been obtained. The latter unit operates at 1800°C (3300°F) in the oxygen injection region. Thus, the dry ash, downdraft oxygen gasifier described here operates at a feed rate similar to a much higher-temperature coal gasification system. The comparison should be somewhat tempered by the fact that the relative heating values of the feedstocks were 7950 Btu/lb (18.5 MJ/kg) and 12,200 Btu/lb (28.4 MJ/kg) for biomass and coal, respectively. The quality of the biomass-derived synthesis gas, however, is higher than that derived from the slagging Lurgi due to the absence of tars and the lower methane content. The oxygen-to-fuel ratio is 0.43 kg/kg for 3.8%-moisture fuel and to a first approximation appears to be insensitive to gasifier throughput over a 2.5/1 turndown ratio. There is a considerable potential for experimental error in determining this ratio; therefore, further quantitative analysis of Table 4-2 is not possible.

Table 4-1. Feedstock Analyses (Air-Dried Samples)[a]

| | Feedstock | | |
Component	3/16-in. Pellets[b]	1/4-in. Pellets[c]	1/4-in. Pine Chips[d]
Proximate (wt %)			
Moisture	3.58	8.36	7.02
Volatile matter	79.91	67.19	78.48
Fixed carbon	15.65	11.94	14.07
Ash	0.86	12.51	0.43
Ultimate (wt %)			
Moisture	3.58	8.36	7.02
Carbon	47.45	41.73	43.79
Hydrogen	5.83	5.03	5.31
Nitrogen	0.23	0.18	0.06
Sulphur	0.03	0.48	0.02
Oxygen	42.02	31.71	43.37
Ash	0.86	12.51	0.43
Gross heating value (Btu/lb)[e,h]	7944	7031	7938
Gross heating value (Btu/lb)[f,h]	8118	7260	7228
Gross heating value (Btu/lb)[g,h]	8419	7923	7773

[a] Analyses performed by fuel lab at Hazen Research, Inc.

[b] 3/16-in. (5-mm) sawdust pellets from Guarantee Fuels.

[c] 1/4-in. (6-mm) bark pellets from Tennessee Woodex, Inc.

[d] 1/4-in. (6-mm) average lodgepole pine wood chips from H. Schroeder, Colorado University.

[e] Measured as received by Hazen Research, Inc.

[f] Calculated from the IGT (Institute of Gas Technology) formula: HHV (Btu/lb) = 146.58 C + 568.78 H - 6.58 A - 51.53(O + N) + 29.45. C, H, A, O, N = dry wt % carbon, hydrogen, ash, oxygen, and, nitrogen.

[g] Calculated from IGT formula, dry basis.

[h] Multiply Btu/lb by 2324.444 to obtain J/kg.

Table 4-2. Oxygen and Fuel Rates for Atmospheric Runs

Run	Biomass Rate (lb/h)[a]	Oxygen Rate (lb/h)[a]	O_2/Fuel Ratio	Biomass Throughput (lb/ft^3 h)[b]
13A	33.6	14.9	0.443	171
13B	26.3	11.2	0.426	134
14A	37.8	16.3	0.432	193
14B	61.6	25.7	0.417	314
15A	36.3	15.4	0.425	185
15B	36.6	16.3	0.444	187
			Average 0.431	

[a]Multiply lb by 0.4536 to obtain kg.

[b]Multiply lb/ft^3 h by 16.01846 to obtain kg/m^3 h.

Dry product gas compositions for runs 10 through 15 are shown in Table 4-3. Runs 10B and 11A reflect operation with a considerable amount of nitrogen added to the system. The remaining runs reflect operation on pure oxygen. The small nitrogen concentrations in the product result from purges of the feeder and sight ports. From these results, it is evident that the H_2/CO ratio is almost constant at 0.66 ± 0.07 over a wide range of feed rates close to the H_2/CO ratio in the feedstock. In terms of the production of synthesis gas for chemicals, methane production is an important parameter since it acts as an inert diluent which must be purged from the synthesis loop for methanol or ammonia manufacture. On a nitrogen-free basis, the methane content of the dry product gas ranges from 2.3% to 4.4%. Run 15A shows a small amount of C_2+; in previous runs, concentrations of higher hydrocarbons were not determined because of analytical limitations.

Table 4-4 presents mass balances for runs 14 and 15. In all runs, only dry gas composition could be determined. In the material balance calculations, the product water condensed out of the system was calculated from the hydrogen and oxygen balance of the product. As Table 4-4(f) shows, this closes the balance and allows the wet product gas composition to be determined. The product gas contains nominally 10% water with the CO_2. Therefore, at the reactor outlet, there is not a shortage of reactant for char gasification. The equilibrium ratios presented show that (1) the outlet gas is in shift equilibrium, (2) methane can be cracked further, and (3) the steam-carbon reaction is far from equilibrium if the exit gas is at the experimentally observed temperature of 925°C (1700°F).

The cold gas efficiency and CO_2 content of the product gas are very sensitive to heat loss from the gasifier. Heat loss causes products to be burned to CO_2 and H_2O. Table 4-5 presents some information on

160

Table 4-3. Product Gas Compositions (vol %) for Atmospheric Runs

Component	Run				
	13A	14A	14B	15A	15B
CO	48.15	40.62	49.74	45.16	51.11
CO_2	14.72	18.76	14.61	18.18	14.51
H_2	31.58	31.56	32.87	25.09	26.84
N_2	3.32	5.15	2.76	7.27	3.61
CH_4	2.23	3.90	2.77	4.06	3.92
C_2+	NA	NA	NA	0.25	NA
Biomass feed rate (lb/h)[a]	33.6	37.8	61.6	36.3	36.6
H_2/CO	0.66	0.78	0.66	0.56	0.53

	11A	11B	10B
CO	22.92	49.2	28.59
CO_2	12.08	17.5	13.74
H_2	17.97	30.2	19.90
N_2	45.50	0.80	35.25
CH_4	1.53	2.30	2.52
C_2+	NA	NA	NA
Biomass feed rate (lb/h)[a]	25.0	25.0	33.8
H_2/CO	0.78	0.61	0.70

[a]Multiply lb by 0.4536 to obtain kg.

Table 4-4. Mass Balance Data for Runs 14 and 15

Component	14A	14B	15A	15B
Feed Data				
(a) Biomass feed rate (lb/h)[a]				
C	18.31	29.9	17.6	17.73
H	2.27	3.7	2.2	2.19
O	17.18	28.0	16.5	16.63
(b) Oxygen rate (lb/h)[a]	16.3	25.6	15.4	16.3
Product Data				
(c) Dry product (lb/mol h)[a]	2.41	3.78	2.16	2.13
(d) Dry product gas (vol %)				
H_2	31.56	31.99	25.09	26.82
N_2	5.15	2.70	7.27	3.61
CO	40.62	48.41	45.16	51.06
CO_2	18.76	14.21	18.18	14.50
CH_4	3.90	2.69	4.06	3.91
(e) Product rate (lb/h)[a]				
C	18.18	29.6	17.6	17.73
H	1.90	2.82	1.47	1.27
O	30.10	46.40	28.2	23.4
(f) Feed $H_2 \rightarrow H_2O$ (mol)				
H	0.185	0.44	0.232	0.353
O	0.211	0.45	0.365	0.355
Average	0.198	0.450	0.300	0.3549
(g) Wet product analyses[b] (vol %)				
H_2	29.2	28.7	22.0	23.0
N_2	4.8	2.4	6.4	3.1
CO	37.5	43.3	39.7	43.8
CO_2	17.3	12.7	16.0	12.4
CH_4	30.6	2.4	3.6	3.4
H_2O	7.6	10.5	12.2	14.3
(h) $K_{shift} = \dfrac{P_{CO_2} P_{H_2}}{P_{CO} P_{H_2O}}$ (0.69 @ 925°C)[c]	1.77	0.80	0.73	0.46
$K_{CH_4} = \dfrac{P_{H_2O} P_{CH_4}}{P_{CO} (P_{H_2})^3}$ (0.034 @ 925°C)[c]	0.293	0.14	0.58	0.51
$K_{CO} = \dfrac{P_{CO} P_{H_2}}{P_{H_2O}}$ (40 @ 925°C)[c]	1.44	1.18	0.72	0.70

[a]Multiply lb by 0.4536 to obtain kg.

[b]Calculated from (f).

[c]Equilibrium prediction.

the effect of overall heat loss on product gas quality. It can be seen that as the heat loss per pound of fuel increases, CO_2 production also increases. Heat loss arises from three sources. First, there is shell and oxygen lance loss to the cooling water. This loss was experimentally determined. Of equal magnitude is the radiation loss to the venturi scrubber. Assuming blackbody radiation and a grate temperature of 925°C (1700°F), this loss amounts to 7300 Btu/h(7.7 MJ/h). Finally, the nitrogen purges can be treated as a heat loss since cold nitrogen must be heated to 925°C to leave the reactor. For each mole of nitrogen processed per hour, this loss amounts to 12,000 Btu/h (13 MJ/h). For most runs, the nitrogen "loss" is on the order of 1000 to 2000 Btu/h (1 to 2 MJ/h). For high nitrogen runs, such as test 10, the loss is on the order of 14,000 Btu/h (15 MJ/h). In scaling up, the shell heat loss depends on the outer surface area while the throughput depends on cross-sectional area. The shell loss increases only by the square root of the throughput and becomes negligible for large enough units. Further, in larger units, the scrubber will be external so that the grate loss will be minimal. Therefore, a significant improvement in gas quality and reduced O_2/fuel ratio can be expected on scale-up.

The data in Table 4-5, plotted in Fig. 4-1, show the effect of shell and lance heat loss on methane production. This heat loss is important as related to the temperature gradient in the char bed close to the wall. Since hydrocarbon cracking is a strong function of temperature, cold zones will preserve hydrocarbons. The data in the table and the figure suggest that minimizing the shell losses will tend to minimize the methane content of the product gas.

Accurate temperature measurement in the gasifier is difficult because of a number of factors. It has been observed that the exit gas temperature is approximately constant for various solid feed rates. This is apparently the temperature below which the gasification kinetics "freeze." From runs 14 through 16, the temperature at the grate varied from 720°C to 888°C with a most common value of about

Table 4-5. Effect of Heat Loss on Gas Quality

Run	% CH_4 (N_2 free)	% CO_2 (N_2 free)	Total Loss	Btu[a] / lb Fuel	Shell & Lance Loss (Btu)
13	2.31	15.2	18,420	548	267
14A	4.11	19.79	20,846	552	314
14B	2.85	15.0	18,679	303	161
15A	4.38	19.61	19,508	537	280
15B	4.07	15.05	21,992	601	371
10B	3.88	21.13	23,565	697	296

[a]Multiply Btu/lb by 2324.444 to obtain J/kg.

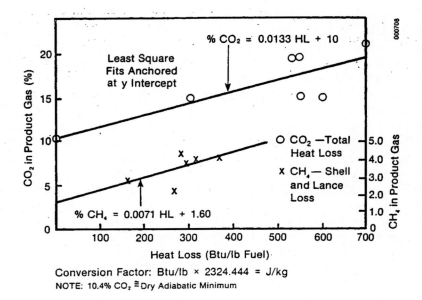

Figure 4-1.   Effect of Heat Loss on Gas Quality

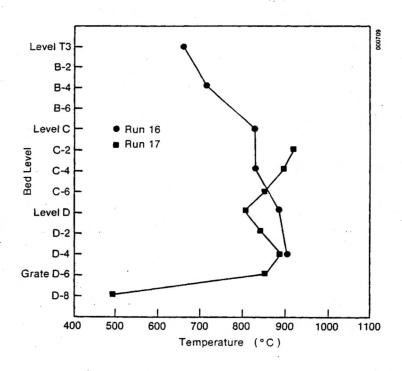

Figure 4-2.   Temperature Distribution in Bed

850°C (1560°F). This temperature is affected by radiation loss to the scrubber. Figure 4-2 shows a typical bed temperature profile from runs 16 and 17 [actually for 1/4-in.(16-mm) pellets]. The bed is nearly isothermal and the temperature of the solids at complete gasification is 890°C (1635°F). Under these test conditions, 60% of the oxygen was injected into the pyrolysis zone (A and B) and 40% into the char lances (C and D).

The gasifier was designed to eliminate tars and has been quite successful in this, since no visible tar is found in the scrub water. A measurement of chemical oxygen demand (COD) on run 15A gave 0.03 mg/L, which corresponds to a concentration of 30 ppm. The flow rate of scrub water was 1.0 gpm (3.8 L/min), so total collected COD was 0.014 lb/h (6 g/h), or 0.041% of the biomass feed.

The wood feedstock contains 0.03% sulfur. An analysis of dry product gas for run 15 showed 6.2 ppm H_2S, 130 ppm SO_2, and 20 ppm COS. The presence of SO_2 is not usually expected in gasification systems and probably is the result of sulfate decomposition in the ash. For test 15, the solids feed rate was 36 lb/h (16 kg/h). The sulfur in the gas was 0.0108 lb/h (5 g/h). Using the above concentrations for the product rate, the exit sulfur rate is determined to be 0.0108 lb/h. Thus, the sulfur is properly accounted for in the system.

The tests reported here were all performed at or close to atmospheric pressure. In most uses it is an advantage to operate at much higher pressures, and this gasifier was built to operate at 150 psig (1000 kPa). We have now (September 1981) operated successfully for five hours above 100 psig (700 kPa) and one hour above 150 psig with about the same performance. High pressure tests are continuing.

5.0 HIGH PRESSURE OPERATION

In Fall 1981, a lock hopper system shown in Fig. 2-3 was installed and tested on the gasifier. It consists of an upper atmospheric pressure hopper, a slide valve isolating this from the middle swing hopper, another slide valve, and a high pressure hopper. Below this is a star valve which delivers fuel steadily to the gasifier. Fuel is raised to the hopper by a bucket elevator from a storage bin at floor level.

In operation, level indicators determine when the pressurized hopper is low on feed. The lower slide valve opens, releasing a fresh charge to the pressure hopper, and then closes again. The pressure in the middle hopper is then released to atmosphere and the upper valve opens, releasing the charge in the fuel hopper. It then closes and the elevator delivers fresh fuel until the fuel hopper is full.

Operation at high pressure was surprisingly simple once the lock hopper system had been debugged. The oil vapors released into the freeboard above the bed are rather opaque and so the purge on the sight glass was increased. A gas analysis of a typical high pressure run is shown in Table 5-1. While high pressure operation could be expected to increase equilibrium methane concentration, it could also

Table 5-1. GC Data – Run Nos. 19 and 22
(High Pressure Operation)

	Run #19 9/15/81 3:27 p.m.	Run #22 12/28/81 12:17 p.m.	Run #22 12/28/82 2:02 p.m.
H_2	16.36	18.36	31.37
Propylene			0.25
CO_2	25.04	17.13	19.25
C_2H_4			2.0
O_2	--	--	--
N_2	--	--	--
CH_4	1.98	3.12	3.6
CO	53.56	56.44	43.0
CO/CO_2	2.13	3.29	2.23
H_2/CO	.30	.325	.729
Reaction Pressure	100 psi	60 psi	80 psi
Feed	1/4" wood chips	1/4" wood chips	1/4" wood chips

Remarks: $#N_2,O_2$ normalized out.

Gas samples taken at steady-state conditions.

166

give a closer approach to equilibrium. The gas analysis shows little change in methane.

6.0 EFFECT OF FUEL MOISTURE

We believe that drying of fuel should be done external to the gasifer since it is unwise to use oxygen and high pressure equipment to boil water when low-grade heat will probably be available in any commercial operation. Nevertheless, it is important to know the effects of moisture on gasifier operation. It is obvious from these results that high water contents can be accommodated kinetically by the gasification process (the PUROX process tolerates up to 50% moisture in municipal waste).

Water was added to the wood chips of Table 4-1 to produce nominal levels of 0, 10, 20, and 40% (wet basis), and the chips were equilibrated in a rolling drum. The gasifer was operated successfully at all four moisture levels and the gas analyses are shown in Table 6-1. Figures 6-1 and 6-2 indicate the relative effects of moisture content on oxygen consumption and gas quality, respectively.

7.0 METHANOL SYNTHESIS

The principal purpose of this gasifier is to create a synthesis gas, for the manufacture of methanol, for instance. Although the process is widely practiced with synthesis gas from methane and to a lesser extent from coal, it has not been used with wood gas before in the United States. Although no major differences are anticipated, it was felt that it would be valuable to convert a small amount of the gas to check its utility. A quantity of gas was compressed into 8 cylinders. These were then converted to about 2 L of methanol by Chem Systems Inc. in Fairfield, N.J., using their liquid-phase process on a once-through recycle basis. They reported that the gas was quite similar to a standard Koppers-Totzek gas derived from coal and no difficulties were encountered.

8.0 EQUILIBRIA IN DOWNDRAFT GASIFIERS

The temperatures and the quality of gases produced in gasifiers are dependent on the kinetics and equilibria of the various reactions occuring. In updraft gasifiers equilibrium conditions are initially attained a very short distance above the grate, where temperatures are typically 800°-1600°C. However, the pyrolysis occuring in the upper sections at temperatures of 200°-500°C produces a mixture of gases and oils having no relation to equilibria.

In the downdraft gasifier the gases pass through charcoal at temperatures of 700°-1000°C, so that there is an opportunity for the gases to approach equilibrium. The discussion below assumes that thermodynamic equilibrium occurs in the final product gas.

Fortunately only six major species exist at equilibrium above 750°C in the present context: C, CO, CO_2, H_2, H_2O, and CH_4 (we assume sulfur

Table 6-1. GC Data - Run No. 25 (1/28/82)
(Atmospheric Pressure)

	Standard (%)	Propane + P 9:47 (O₂ Free)	20% Oxygen at D + P 10:07	10% M-C 12:22	Baseline 10% M-C 12:37	23% M-C 13:35	39% M-C 14:56	39% M-C 16:00	39% M-C 16:47	Baseline Pellets 10:08 (O₂ Free)	Baseline Pellets 12:17 (O₂ Free)
H_2	22.9	27.8 (32)	18.8	27.0	31.5	28.8	32.9	21.3	27.0	24.8 (30.0)	21.0 (26)
Propylene	5.0	0.1 (0.2)	0.1	0.1	0.1	0.04	0.2	0.3	0.04	0.1 (0.1)	--- (--)
CO_2	6.8	14.2 (16.5)	24.7	19.5	23.1	22.6	30.3	>26.0	15.8	14.4 (17.4)	21.5 (26.5)
C_2H_4	11.2	1.3 (1.6)	1.3	1.0	1.5	1.2	1.7	1.6	1.0	1.2 (1.5)	1.0 (1.3)
O_2	0.4	2.8 (--)	1.6	0.3	0.4	0.9	0.5	1.1	0.1	3.5 (--)	3.8 (--)
N_2	1.3	14.3 (3.7)	17.0	9.4	12.3	8.8	1.9	18.8	2.5	14.1 (0.2)	23.4 (10)
CH_4	12.1	7.6 (8.9)	3.9	4.3	5.2	3.2	3.8	4.8	4.4	4.3 (5.3)	3.7 (4.6)
CO	40.3	31.7 (36.9)	32.7	38.6	26.0	34.5	28.7	26.1	49.1	37.6 (45.5)	25.5 (31.6)
CC	6	9.7	6.0	9.52	7.55	9.4	8.9	9.1	9.73	9.34	6.3
CO/CO_2 (Gas Quality)	5.9	2.24	1.33	1.98	1.13	<1.53	0.95	<1.0	3.1	2.6	1.19
H_2/CO	0.57	0.88	0.57	0.7	1.21	0.83	1.15	0.82	0.55	0.66	0.82

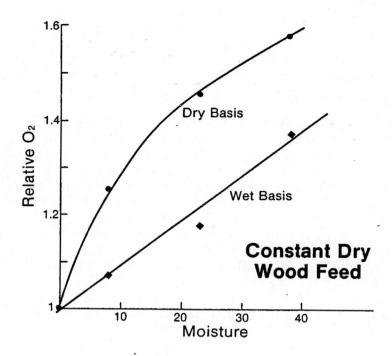

Figure 6-1. Relative Effects of Moisture Content on Oxygen Consumption

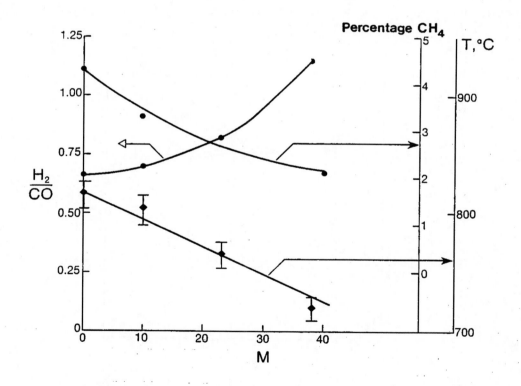

Figure 6-2. Relative Effects of Moisture Content on Gas Quality

169

compounds are negligible in biomass). These species are generated in the reactions shown in Fig. 8-1, which shows also the respective equilibrium constants calculated from data in the JANAF tables. The concentration of each of the gaseous species was determined at equilibrium at the point of complete carbon conversion.

Equilibrium temperature and composition for the 3/16-in. (5-mm) pellets used in most of the gasifier runs are shown in Figs. 8-2 and 8-3 as functions of the oxygen/fuel ratio R. These calculations were made for a carbon activity of unity, assuming no heat loss in the gasifier. Note that at low oxygen/fuel ratios the temperature is relatively constant and the methane concentration is rather high. The point where all of the carbon is consumed, R = R* and T = T*, corresponds to the operating point of the gasifier with fixed bed level. As R increases from 0 to R*, the methane concentration decreases and is replaced by CO and H_2 formed from the carbon, which decreases to zero (this is the pyrolysis range). If the gasifier operated at higher values of R (R > R*), the bed would be consumed; at lower values of R (R < R*), the bed would increase. Only at R* is it possible to have a steady state with no net carbon consumption or production.

For values of R > R*, note that the temperature increases very rapidly, at the rate of 55°C/0.01 R. This is due to the fact that all oxygen above R* burns CO and H_2 to CO_2 and H_2O with a very high heat release, obviously a very undesirable mode of gasifier operation.

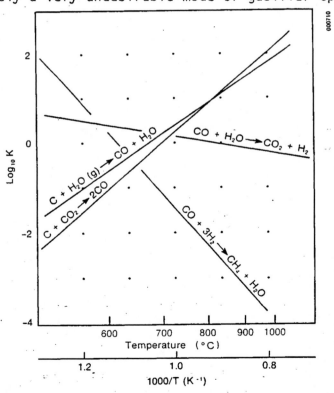

Figure 8-1. Equilibrium Constants for Biomass Gasification Reactions

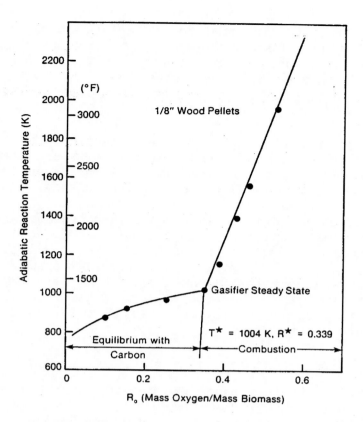

Figure 8-2. Calculated Adiabatic Reaction Temperature for 3/16-in. (5-mm) Wood Pellets

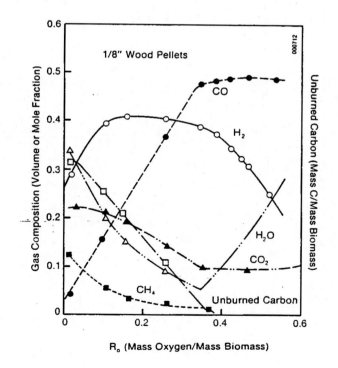

Figure 8-3. Gas Composition at Equilibrium

Values of R* and T* were calculated for a variety of cases covering different degrees of heat loss in the gasifier, moisture in the feed, steam addition, and pressure operation; the results are presented in Table 8-1. These values in turn were used to calculate the sensitivity of various output parameters to gasifier conditions (Table 8-2).

The total gas compositions of Table 8-1 were recalculated for a dry gas for the cases of 0% and 10% heat loss. These are compared in Table 8-3 to the gas composition from run 14A (adjusted to N_2-free concentraton). Agreement is excellent except for methane.

The value of R* represents a lower limit of oxygen consumption for the gasifier under normal operating conditions. Because of the sensitivity of oxygen consumption to heat loss it is obvious that a heat gain (in the form of recycled heat from the output gas, for instance) can reduce the oxygen consumption further and improve the gas. It is also clear that the wood heat of combustion is a prime factor in determining oxygen consumption, so that any method of increasing this should be investigated.

9.0 CONCLUSIONS

The gasifier discussed in this paper was designed for the production of synthesis gas with minimum tars and oils. The gasifier does produce clean synthesis gas and operates stably for long periods. Due to the low concentration of sulfur in the feedstock the gas is environmentally acceptable and is especially suited for chemical synthesis. High pressure tests are now underway, and the gasifier has been operated briefly at 150 psig (1000 kPa).

REFERENCES

1. Johnson, J. 1979. Kinetics of Coal Gasification. New York: Wiley Interscience.

2. Solar Energy Research Institute. 1979, 1980. A Survey of Biomass Gasification. Vols. 1-3. SERI/TR-33-239. Golden, CO: SERI. Reproduced as Biomass Gasification; T. B. Reed, ed.; Park Ridge, NJ: Noyes Data Corp; 1981.

3. Solar Energy Research Institute. 1979. Generator Gas. SERI/SP-33-140. Golden, CO: SERI. (Originally published in Swedish by the Swedish Academy of Engineering, 1950.)

Table 8-1. Calculated Equilibrium Gas Temperature and Composition for 3/16 in. (5-mm) Pellets

Case	P (atm)	Heat Loss ($\% H_c$)[a]	Steam Rate ($\frac{\text{mass steam}}{\text{mass biomass}}$)	Moisture (%)	O_2 Consumption ($\frac{\text{mass oxygen}}{\text{mass biomass}}$) wet	dry	Temperature °C	°F	Composition (vol %) CO	CO_2	H_2	H_2O	CH_4
1	1	0	0.0	3.6	0.339	0.352	731	1347	46.2	9.9	37.2	5.5	1.1
2	1	5	0.0	3.6	0.391	0.409	709	1307	42.7	13.3	35.5	7.1	1.3
3	1	0	0.0	20.0	0.285	0.356	660	1224	29.8	18.2	37.5	11.9	2.5
4	1	10	0.2	3.6	0.420	0.436	642	1187	25.9	22.3	34.8	14.1	2.5
5	1	0	0.2	3.6	0.315	0.327	672	1242	31.8	16.4	38.5	10.8	2.3
6	10	0	0.0	3.6	0.345	0.358	878	1613	46.2	10.0	32.5	8.3	2.9

[a]Percentage of heat of combustion.

Table 8-2. Gasifier Sensitivity to Changes in Input

	Decreases Temperature	Increases R	Decreases Methanol
Each 1% increase of:			
Heat loss	4.4°C (8.0°F)	1.0%	1.3%
Steam	2.9°C (5.2°F)	-0.1%	0.6%
Moisture	4.2°C (7.5°F)	0.02%	1.6%
Each 1-atm increase of pressure	-14.4°C (-26°F)	0.6%	0.9%

Table 8-3. Comparison of Calculated and Experimental Gas Compositions

	R^a	Temperature °C	Temperature °F	Composition (vol %) CO	CO_2	H_2	CH_4
Calculated							
0% heat loss	0.339	731	1347	48.9	10.5	39.4	1.2
10% heat loss	0.445	690	1273	42.8	18.4	36.9	1.6
Experimental Run 14A (N_2 free)	0.43	800	1470^b	42.8	19.2	33.3	4.1

[a] R = oxygen/fuel ratio.

[b] Off-gas temperature measured at grate. Probably high due to excess of methane over equilibrium value.

LARGE WOOD TO METHANOL PLANTS

W. A. Stevenson
Evergreen Energy Corporation
Waltham, MA 02254

Evergreen Energy Corporation was formed to continue the development of advanced technology for the conversion of low-grade wood feedstocks to high-grade liquid fuels. Upon completion of this development program in 1983 the company will license the technology worldwide, particularly to entities in developing countries which have large indigenous wood supplies, but depend on imported oil for liquid fuels.

Concurrently, Evergreen is planning the construction of the first commercial scale wood-based liquid fuels production facility at a site in New England.

Technology Development Program - Much of the process technology for the conversion of wood to high-grade liquid fuels already exists and is widely practiced on a commercial scale for feedstocks such as natural gas, coal, and heavy residual oil. The principal missing link is an efficient process for the conversion of the wood feedstock to a gaseous state known as "synthesis gas." All commercial synthetic fuel processes first convert the base feedstock to synthesis gas--a combination of carbon monoxide and hydrogen--which can be catalytically reacted by a number of proven processes to produce gasoline, methanol, ammonia, and other valuable liquid fuels and chemicals.

Evergreen's principals have been involved in the development of advanced wood-gasification technology since the early 1970's. Evergreen Energy Corporation is continuing this work and recently entered into a cooperative agreement with Texaco, Inc. and its subsidiary, Texaco Development Corporation to adapt the Texaco high-pressure coal gasification system to accept wood as a feedstock. Texaco's gasification system is generally recognized as the most advanced and efficient commercially available technology for the production of synthesis gas from coal or other hydrocarbon feedstocks. By gasifying at high pressure and high temperature the Texaco process yields highest conversion efficiencies while producing a minimum of undesirable byproducts. Although competing wood gasfication technologies are being pursued elsewhere, particularly in Brazil, Sweden, and Canada, Evergreen feels that the Texaco-Evergreen process will prove to be the preferred system.

<u>Production Facility</u> – Evergreen's proposed plant incorporating the Texaco-Evergreen gasification system will produce 330,000 gallons per day of methanol--a high grade liquid fuel and valuable chemical feed-stock--from 3500 tons per day of greed wood chips. The plant is being designed to satisfy all the environmental conditions. The process is closed-loop with only minimal waste discharges, principally wood ash and carbon dioxide. Process water requirements are less than 100 thousand gallons per day. Projected total cost including working capital for this facility is $250 million in constant 1981 dollars. Approximately 1500 permanent new jobs will be created--200 at the plant, nearly 1300 in wood harvesting, transportation and support activities. The facility will occupy approximately 300 acres and will require at least one satellite wood collection terminal to facilitate the shipment of wood feedstock by rail. Overall energy conversion efficiency is projected to be 55%.

Methanol has been selected as the end product because it represents the most economic and energy-efficient use of the wood feedstock. Primary market will be as a gasoline additive and octane booster. When used in this manner it represents wood's highest energy replacement value for imported oil--one cord of green wood can displace nearly 20 gallons of crude oil. This is almost twice as effective as any alternative use of wood for fuel. The plant's output can replace 3% of New England's total gasoline consumption. Methanol is also the principal chemical feedstock for the production of formaldehyde resins used by the growing chip, flake, and oriented-strand board industry. Projected selling price for the methanol is 80 cents per gallon in constant 1981 dollars. This is competitive with the current delivered cost of methanol made from natural gas in Texaco and Louisiana.

New England has been chosen as the site for the first production facility for the following reasons:

1. The region's forests contain an overabundance of low-grade, non-merchantable wood.

2. This technology now exists for the economic and environmentally compatible removal of this low-grade material without competing with the needs of existing forest products users.

3. New England is completely dependent on imported energy for its liquid fuels supplies. Through the Evergreen project, the region's forests can make a significant contribution to its gasoline needs.

4. Evergreen Energy Corporation is a New England based company with headquarters in Waltham, Massachusetts.

176

<u>Evergreen</u> <u>and</u> <u>the</u> <u>Forest</u> <u>Resource</u> – Evergreen feels that it will add a valuable new dimension to responsible forest management in the North- east by providing a large, stable market for low-grade material. Evergreen's process is flexible because it can readily utilize wood chips of all species produced from small diameter trees, rough and rotten, tops and limbs, etc. Evergreen has studied the economics of harvesting and transporting this type of material and is convinced that it will be able to pay a full and fair price. This will provide not only an immediate financial return to the landowner, but will enable him, through improved forest management, to increase the growth rate and value of the residual forest stand.

Evergreen will work closely with private landowners and forest manage- ment experts to make certain that its wood feedstock needs are properly and professionally met. When requested, Evergreen will provide forest management services to assist landowners in developing and implementing suitable management plans. Evergreen will contractually require that all its suppliers comply with qualitative harvesting guidelines to insure that all material is produced in accordance with the highest silvicultural and environmental standards.

<u>The</u> <u>Complete</u> <u>Evergreen</u> <u>Program</u> – Evergreen Energy Corporation will cooperate with other firms, governments and international corporations in developing forest mangement and biomass conversion technologies. Through an appropriate licensing arrangement with Evergreen, qualified parties in selected countries may gain access to all the key components required to build the most efficient wood-to-methanol commercial pro- duction facilities that can be established within the scope of technol- ogy availability in the world today.

This effort will, in the future, provide people elsewhere in the world--including those in a number of developing countries--with a prime energy source that can readily and abundantly be derived from our vast global forests. Evergreen Energy Corporation should be involved at an early date with all serious wood-to-methanol conversion programs.

177

CATALYTIC GENERATION OF METHANOL SYNTHESIS GAS FROM WOOD

L. K. Mudge, E. G. Baker, and D. H. Mitchell
Pacific Northwest Laboratory
Richland, Washington

INTRODUCTION

At the Pacific Northwest Laboratory (PNL) operted by Battelle, studies are in progress on steam gasification of biomass in the presence of catalysts. These studies are sponsored by the Biomass Energy Systems Division of the U.S. Department of Energy (DOE).

Gasification processes are commonly used to convert carbonaceous matter, including biomass, into gases and some condensable liquids [1,2]. The residues from such processes comprise principally the inert mineral constituents of the feed material and, in some cases, unconverted carbon (char).

The state-of-the-art procedure for conversion of a carbonaceous material to a synthesis gas involves several steps. These include: 1) gasification by partial combustion with pure oxygen and steam to form a mixture of gases, 2) shift conversion to yield the desired hydrogen-to-carbon monoxide ratio in the gas mixture, 3) acid gas removal, 4) reforming of hydrocarbons, 5) moisture removal, and 6) further gas cleanup to remove traces of sulfur compounds that would otherwise poison catalysts.

Partial combustion of the carbonaceous feed material with pure oxygen to provide heat for the endothermic steam-carbon reaction is currently used to produce the gas mixture. Such practice results in a relatively simple gasifier design but requires an expensive, energy consuming oxygen plant. Processes such as the CO_2 Acceptor [3], Ash Agglomeration [4], and electrothermal [5] offer schemes that avoid use of an oxygen plant.

The overall objectives of the studies at PNL are to determine the technical feasibility of catalytic processes for steam gasification of wood to generate specific products and to evaluate the economic viability of the technically attractive processes.

Use of catalysts for reaction of steam with wood to produce a synthesis gas mixture allows operation at temperatures under 750°C with good carbon conversion [6,7,8]. The required heat can be provided indirectly with heat exchanger bundles in a fluid bed system. No pure oxygen is used. In the case of methanol production from wood, yields are high relative to conventional processes. The technical and economic feasibility of producing methanol from wood by the catalytic gasification process is reported in this paper.

DESCRIPTION OF EXPERIMENTAL EQUIPMENT

Experimental investigations at PNL include laboratory scale and process development unit (PDU) scale studies. In the laboratory scale studies, wood chips of approximately 3 mm (1/8 in.) in size are continuously fed to a 5 cm (2 in.) inside diameter by 35 cm (14 in.) reactor. Steam contacts the wood chips in the reactor at a controlled temperature. Gasification products pass through a fixed catalyst bed, 25 mm (1 in.) inside diameter by 75 mm (3 in.), at the base of the reactor. The resulting gas mixture is cooled to remove condensables, passed through a wet test meter, sampled, and analyzed in a gas chromatograph.

In PDU operations wood was processed at a rate of about 25 kg (55 lb)/hr on a dry basis. Wood chips with about 5 wt% moisture were continuously fed submerged into a bed of catalyst and char which was fluidized with superheated steam. A schematic of the gasifier is shown in Figure 1; a PNL flow schematic is shown in Figure 2. The fluid bed section of the gasifier is about 20 cm (7.75 in.) inside diameter by 120 cm (4 ft) in depth. Overall gasifier height is 3 m (10 ft). Energy for the endothermic reactions is provided by electrical heaters surrounding and submerged in the fluid bed. Of course on a large scale, heat would be provided by other means, such as high temperature heat exchangers or circulating solids.

The PDU was designed for accurate control of all inputs and measurement of all outputs. All product streams are measured, sampled, and anlyzed before disposal. Operations to date have been at slightly above atmospheric pressure. Operations at 1000 kPa (10 atm) with the modified PDU illustrated schematically in Figure 3 have been initiated.

EXPERIMENTAL RESULTS

Laboratory studies were successful in developing operating conditions for generation of a methanol synthesis gas, a mixture of hydrogen, carbon monoxide and carbon dioxide. Some hydrocarbons remained in the gas mixture. Wood was reacted with steam at a steam-to-wood weight ratio of about 1 and a temperature of 750°C (1380°F) in the presence of several catalysts. Results are presented in Table 1 for a Ni-Co-Mo alloy catalyst at different exposures. No tars or condensable organics are produced with this alloy system after an exposure of 1100 g of dry wood per g of catalyst.

Standard heats of reaction (higher heating value of products minus the higher heating value of reactants) show that the system is endothermic. Potential methanol yields are shown for theoretical conversion of the hydrogen and carbon monoxide only with no further reforming of the hydrocarbons and with reforming of the hydrocarbons. These potential yields are significantly higher than obtainable from counterflow oxygen-steam, fixed-bed gasification of wood. The latter theoretical yields with reforming of the methane in the product gas were determined to range from 0.38 to 0.45 kg/kg dry wood (115 to 136 gal/ton) [9].

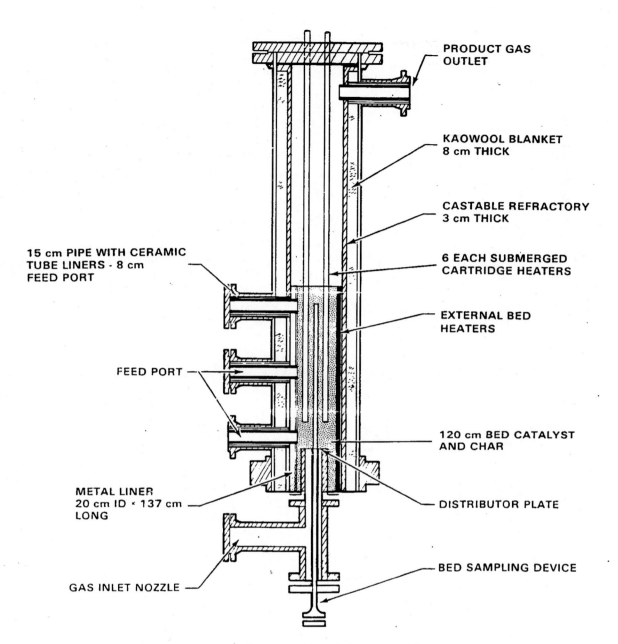

PRODUCT GAS OUTLET

KAOWOOL BLANKET 8 cm THICK

CASTABLE REFRACTORY 3 cm THICK

15 cm PIPE WITH CERAMIC TUBE LINERS - 8 cm FEED PORT

6 EACH SUBMERGED CARTRIDGE HEATERS

EXTERNAL BED HEATERS

FEED PORT

120 cm BED CATALYST AND CHAR

METAL LINER 20 cm ID × 137 cm LONG

DISTRIBUTOR PLATE

BED SAMPLING DEVICE

GAS INLET NOZZLE

FIGURE 1.   GASIFIER SCHEMATIC

Results obtained in the laboratory were confirmed in the PDU at throughput rates of 700 kg/m^{2}hr (140 lb/ft^{2}hr). Data from PDU tests at
atmospheric pressure with and without a hydrocracking catalyst are presented in Table 2. The catalyst was nickel on spheres (−12+20 mesh) of
a proprietary substrate prepared by Davison Chemical Division of W. R.
Grace & Co., Baltimore, Ohio. An inert material (−20+45 mesh alumina
spheres) was used for tests without catalyst. Tests with a Ni−Cu−Mo
alloy catalyst at a pressure of 1000 kPa (10 atm) are underway.

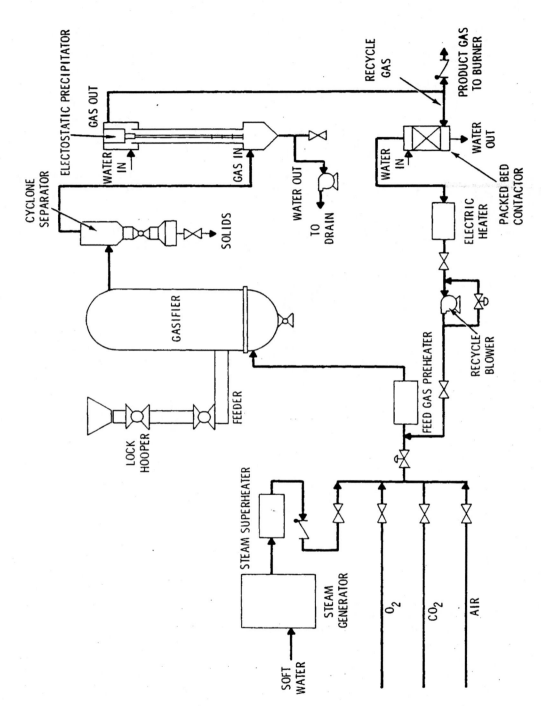

FIGURE 2.   PDU FLOW SCHEMATIC AS OF OCTOBER 1980

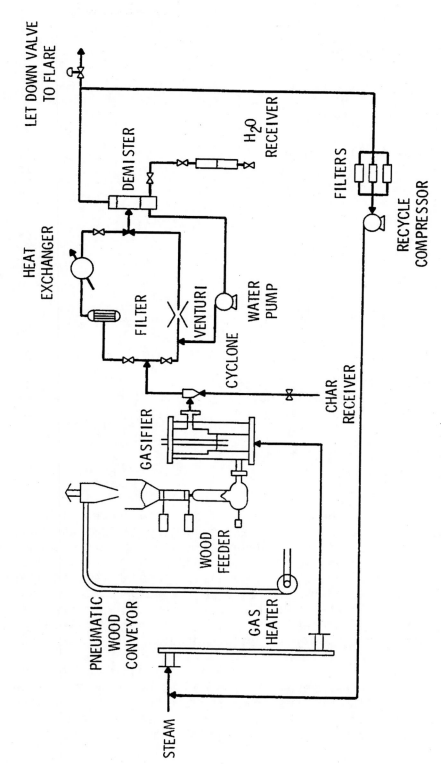

FIGURE 3. MODIFIED PDU FLOW SCHEMATIC

183

TABLE 1. ACTIVITY CHANGE WITH ALLOY CATALYST

Temperature, °C	750	750	750
Catalyst Lifetime, wt wood/wt catalyst	Fresh	300	1100
Carbon Conversion			
% to Gas	91	93	98
% to Solid	9	7	2
Gas Composition (Vol. %)			
H_2	51.5	48.8	44.1
CO_2	16.3	23.4	25.9
CH_4	4.0	7.0	7.9
CO	28.0	20.5	20.9
C_2H_4	0	0.1	0.7
C_2H_6	0	0.04	0.5
Standard Heat of Reaction			
Btu/lb wood	750	350	380
kJ/kg wood	1700	810	880
Potential Methanol Yield			
Wt. fraction (gal/dry ton)	0.64(190)[a] 0.74(220)[b]	0.54(160)[a] 0.70(210)[b]	0.48(140)[a] 0.68(205)[b]

(a) Theoretical yield from CO + H_2 in gas.
(b) Theoretical yield from CO + H_2 + CH_4 + C_2H_4 + C_2H_6 in gas.

Data in Table 2 illustrate the effectiveness of the hydrocracking catalyst for cracking condensable organics and reforming gaseous hydrocarbons. With the catalyst, yields of condensable organics and gaseous hydrocarbons are reduced significantly even though the temperature of the fluid bed was lower than without a catalyst. Endothermic reforming and cracking reactions caused the decrease in the temperature of the fluid bed. The standard heat of reaction with the catalyst is positive, which shows that the process is endothermic; whereas without a catalyst, the process is actually slightly exothermic.

The potential methanol yields in Tables 1 and 2 are based on the wood composition in Table 3. The methane is assumed to be reformed for the test with inert material but not reformed for the test with catalyst in Table 3. In both tests in Table 2, the potential methanol yield is greater than for counterflow fixed bed, oxygen-steam gasification as stated above [9].

Results of early PDU tests were used as the basis for economic evaluation of a wood-to-methanol plant. The economic evaluation was completed by Davy McKee, Inc., of Cleveland, Ohio, and is summarized in the following section.

TABLE 2. PDU RESULTS ON METHANOL SYNTHESIS GAS PRODUCTION

Catalyst	Inert	Ni Hydrocracking
Temperature, °C	750	700
Carbon Conversion (%) to		
Gas	80	80
Liquid	9	--
Char	11	20
Cold Gas Efficiency	80	90
Steam:Wood Wt. Ratio	.0.68	0.69
Gas Composition (Vol. %)		
H_2	31.6	55.7
CO	29.0	21.4
CH_4	13.6	2.0
CO_2	23.1	20.7
C_2H_4	1.7	0.09
C_2H_6	0.4	0.05
C_3H_n	0.6	0
Standard Heat of Reaction,		
kJ/kg Dry Wood	-190	1550
Btu/lb	-80	670
Potential Methanol Yield		
kg/kg Dry Wood	0.5	0.6
gal/ton Dry Wood	150	180

TABLE 3. WOOD COMPOSITION

Variety	Alder and Maple
Size	3 mm (1/8 in.)
Heating Value, kJ/kg (Btu/lb)	19,300 (8300)
Composition, Wt. %	
C	48
H	6
O	45
Ash	0.3

ECONOMIC PROJECTIONS

Data from operation of the PDU were used as the basis for design of a wood-to-methanol plant. Davy McKee, Inc., of Cleveland, Ohio, used the data from PNL to prepare the conceptual plant design for determination of the capital and operating cost estimates.

The wood-to-methanol plants are designed to process 1800 MT (2000 tons) per day of dry wood and 10% of this capacity. Production for the large plant is 900 MT (997 tons) per day of methanol with a HHV of 22,700 kJ/kg (9784 Btu/lb). For the small plant, methanol production is 90 MT (100 tons) per day. All process and support facilities necessary to convert wood to methanol are included in the estimates. A block flow diagram of the process area is presented in Figure 4.

Three gasifiers are provided for the 1800 MT (2000 tons) per day plant. Each gasifier is cylindrical with dimensions of 4.3 m (15 ft) inside diameter by 15 m (50 ft) total height. Each is provided with 360 m^2 (3900 ft^2) of 5 cm (2 in.) tubing (RA-533 or Incoloy 800 H) for heat addition to the fluid bed of wood char and catalyst. The operating depth of the fluid bed is 3 m (10 ft). A single, scaled-down version of the gasifier design is provided for the 200 ton per day plant.

Char and catalyst are collected in the overflow from the gasifier and in the cyclone solids. The char-to-catalyst weight ratio in the mixture is 50. Fines in the char-catalyst mixture are primarily char. Very little catalyst is in the fines which are removed by screening. The char and catalyst in the coarse fraction are then separated by a magnetic roll separator. Catalyst recovery is expected to be 90%. No regeneration of catalyst is considered.

Commercially available systems comprise the remainder of the operations. Acid gas removal is by the Benfield process. The ICI low pressure methanol process is used for the methanol synthesis. All liquid wastewater streams for the plant are treated in a neutralizing basin and a subsequent three stage biological treatment system before being allowed to overflow to drainage.

The thermal efficiency of the plants is defined as

$$\text{Efficiency, \%} = 100 \times \frac{\text{Methanol, HHV}}{\text{Wood, HHV} + \text{Electricity} + \text{Diesel Fuel}}$$

The thermal efficiency of the plants is 53%.

The capital cost estimates as determined by Davy McKee, Inc., are summarized in Table 4. The capital cost estimate (September 1980 basis) for the 1800 MT dry wood (2000 tons)/day plant is $120,830,000 and is $34,830,000 for the 180 MT dry wood (200 tons)/day plant. Estimate accuracy is reported to be ±25%. The major cost areas are wood storage and handling, gasification and wood drying. The gasification area includes the gasifiers, heat recovery equipment, char and catalyst recovery equipment, and wood and catalyst feed hoppers. The total capital requirements for the large and small plants are, respectively, $145,581,000 and $41,221,000.

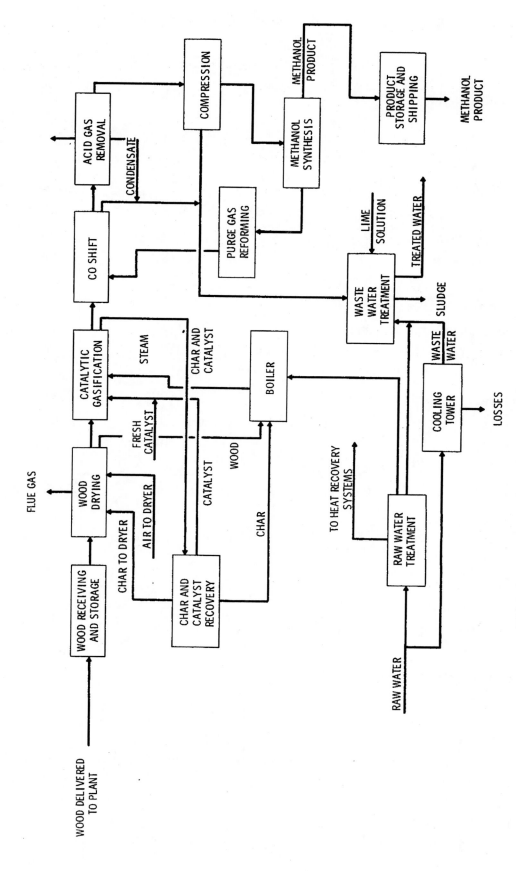

FIGURE 4. WOOD-TO-METHANOL PROCESS FLOW DIAGRAM

TABLE 4. CAPITAL COST ESTIMATES FOR WOOD-TO-METHANOL PLANTS

	Cost ($1,000)	
	2000 tons/day	200 tons/day
Wood Storage and Handling	$ 17,704	$ 6,263
Wood Drying	6,821	1,773
Gasification Area	17,889	2,508
Shift Conversion	850	202
Acid Gas Removal	4,539	1,150
Compression	5,412	1,084
Purge Gas Reforming	959	241
Waste Water Treatment	2,773	706
Raw Water and Cooling Water Treatment	2,316	711
Boilers and BFW Systems	4,828	1,217
Miscellaneous Utility Systems	1,405	318
Storage and Loading-Product and Utilities	1,554	398
Subtotal	$ 67,010	$16,571
Field Indirects	14,150	2,951
Pro-Services	15,920	4,860
Other	1,750	1,450
Methanol Plant (By Lakeland-T.I.C.)	22,000	9,000
9/12/80 Total Installed Cost (T.I.C.)	$120,930	$34,832

EXCLUSIONS:

- Property
- Startup Costs
- Plant Roadways
- Demolition of Underground Obstructions
- Premium Time
- Operating and Maintenance Costs
- Contingency

Capital cost estimates for the wood storage, wood drying, gasification and methanol synthesis areas for the 200 dry ton/day plant were determined by detailed analysis. The exponent scaling factors shown in Table 5 were used for the other process areas.

The production cost of fuel-grade methanol from wood is calculated based upon the capital costs and operating costs. The methods of

TABLE 5.   SCALE-DOWN FACTORS USED FOR PRICING EQUIPMENT
IN THE WOOD-TO-METHANOL PLANT

Process Area	Scale Down Exponent Factor		Multiplier
Shift Conversion	$(x)^{0.65}$	=	0.224
Acid Gas Removal	$(x)^{0.6}$	=	0.251
Compression	$(x)^{0.7}$	=	0.200
Purge Gas Reforming	$(x)^{0.6}$	=	0.251
Waste Water Treatment	$(x)^{0.6}$	=	0.251
Raw Water & Cooling Water	$(x)^{0.6}$	=	0.251
Boilers & BFW Systems	$(x)^{0.6}$	=	0.251
Misc. Utility Systems	$(x)^{0.65}$	=	0.224
Product Storage & Loading	$(x)^{0.6}$	=	0.251

Note: $x = \dfrac{200 \text{ ton/day}}{2{,}000 \text{ ton/day}} = 0.1$

calculating these costs are those presented in "Coal Gasification Commercial Concepts Gas Cost Guidelines," a paper prepared for the United
States Energy Research and Development Administration and the American
Gas Association by C. F. Braun & Co. (NTIS 8463). Production costs are
calculated using two potential methods of financing a plant of this
type: 1) utility financing and 2) private investor financing.

The annual direct operating costs for the plants include raw materials,
utilities, catalyst and chemicals, labor, administration and general
overhead, supplies, and taxes and insurance. Maintenance costs are
calculated as a percentage of capital investment, as suggested by the
cited guidelines. Contributions of operating and investment costs to
the price of methanol are shown in Table 6. The most significant
direct operating costs are wood, gasifier catalyst, labor, and taxes
and insurance. Labor costs are not very easy to reduce significantly,
while taxes will depend upon local conditions and incentives. The
major variable costs are wood and catalyst usage in the gasifier.
Studies on improvement of catalyst life are in progress.

For the 2000 ton per day plant, wood at $20 per dry ton comprises about
a third of the total direct operating costs and a fourth of the total
production costs. Either lowering the wood cost or improving yields
from the wood have more impact on costs than any other single variable. Investment and high labor costs make small scale operation economically unattractive.

The production costs were calculated for wood costs of $5, $10, $20,
and $40 per dry ton. For the 2000 dry ton per day plant, the methanol
production costs with utility financing are $0.45, $0.48, $0.55, and

TABLE 6.   CONTRIBUTION TO METHANOL COST

Plant Capacity, Tons/Day	Cost Contribution, ¢/gal	
	200	2000
Wood, $20/Ton	13.3	13.3
Utilities	7.7	5.7
Catalysts & Chemicals	4.0	3.5
Labor	21.8	5.3
Administration & General Overhead	13.0	3.3
Supplies	9.1	2.5
Taxes & Insurance	9.7	3.3
Total Operating Cost	78.6	36.9
Investment Costs (Util.)[a][PI][b]	(51.6)[91.4]	(18.3)[32.1]
Total (Util.)[a][PI][b]	(130.2)[170.0]	(55.2)[69.0]

(a) Utility financing.
(b) Private Investor financing.

$0.69 per gallon for wood prices of $5, $10, $20, and $40 per dry ton.
With private investor financing, the methanol production costs are
$0.59, $0.62, $0.69, and $0.83 per gallon for the corresponding wood
costs. The methanol costs as a function of wood cost for both plant
sizes are shown in Figure 5. A significant cost penalty results from
the reduced scale of operation.

Details of the economic analysis are presented in a report by Mudge
et al [10].

CONCLUSIONS

The following conclusions are based on current results from catalyzed
steam gasification of wood:

- Steam gasification of wood in the presence of catalysts to
  produce a methanol synthesis gas is technically feasible.

- Yields of methanol are greater from the catalytic process
  than from conventional processes that employ oxygen-steam
  gasification of wood in a fixed bed.

- Cost of methanol from wood by catalytic gasification is competitive with the current price of methanol for a plant
  capacity of 2000 tons dry wood (1800 MT) per day.

190

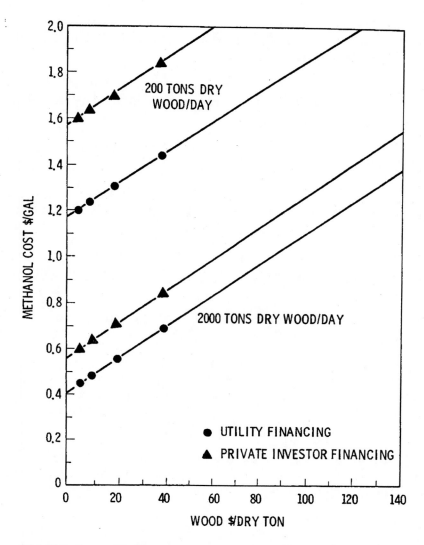

FIGURE 5. METHANOL COST FOR DIFFERENT WOOD PRICES

- Major operating costs are for wood, labor, gasifier catalyst, and taxes and insurance.

ACKNOWLEDGMENTS

The authors are especially grateful to T. J. Kendron, O. A. Kuby, M. McClintock, and J. H. Rooker of Davy McKee, Inc., who completed the economic evaluations. The efforts of J. E. Leonard, W. F. Riemath, G. L. Roberts, E. D. Smith, and W. A. Wilcox of Battelle-Northwest have been vital to the success of the experimental program.

REFERENCES

1. Von Fredersdorff, C. G. and M. A. Elliott, "Coal Gasification," in Chemistry of Coal Utilization, H. H. Lowry, Editor, Supplementary Vol., John Wiley and Sons, Inc., New York, NY, 1963, pp. 892-1022.

2. Fritz, J. J., J. J. Gordon, and V. T. Nguyen, "Status Review of Wood Biomass--Gasification, Pyrolysis, and Densification Technologies," MTR-79W00354, 1979.

3. Fink, C. E., "The CO_2 Acceptor Process," paper presented at the Symposium on Clean Fuels From Coal, sponsored by the Institute of Gas Technology, Chicago, IL, 1973, 11 p.

4. Goodridge, E., "Status Report: The AGA/OCR Coal Gasification Program," Coal Age 78:54-59, 1973.

5. Oliveira, E. S., "The Electrochemical Route to Wood Syngas," proceedings of the 4th International Symposium on Alcohol Fuels Technology, Guarujo, S. P., Brasil, October 6-11, 1980.

6. Mudge, L. K., L. J. Sealock, Jr., and S. L. Weber, "Catalyzed Steam Gasification of Biomass," Journal of Analytical and Applied Pyrolysis 1:165-175, 1979.

7. Mitchell, D. H. et al., "Methane/Methanol by Catalytic Gasification of Biomass," CEP 76(9):53-57, 1980.

8. Mudge, L. K., R. J. Robertus, D. H. Mitchell, L. J. Sealock, Jr., and S. L. Weber, "Economics of Methanol and SNG Production from Biomass Via Catalytic Gasification," proceedings of the Conference on Energy from Biomass and Wastes, Lake Buena Vista, Florida, pp. 687-722, 1981.

9. Mudge, L. K., D. G. Ham, S. L. Weber, and D. H. Mitchell, "Oxygen/ Steam Gasification of Wood," PNL-3353, Pacific Northwest Laboratory, Richland, Washington, 1980.

10. Mudge, L. K., S. L. Weber, D. H. Mitchell, L. J. Sealock, Jr., and R. J. Robertus, "Investigations on Catalyzed Steam Gasification of Biomass," PNL-3695, Pacific Northwest Laboratory, Richland, Washington, 1981.

DEVELOPMENT OF A PRESSURIZED FLUIDIZED-BED BIOMASS GASIFIER TO PRODUCE SUBSTITUTE FUELS

S. P. Babu
M. Onischak
G. Kosowski
Institute of Gas Technology
Chicago, Illinois

SUMMARY

The Institute of Gas Technology (IGT) is conducting a program to convert forest and crop residues to substitute fuel in a pressurized fluidized-bed biomass gasifier. The process is designed for operation at pressures up to 2.17 MPa (315 psia) and temperatures up to 1255 K (1800°F).

Various goals for synthesis or fuel gas processes are being pursued to develop an efficient process. Some of these goals are to maximize the throughput, the amount, and the quality of the gas, while minimizing both the amount of the feedstock preparation needed and the formation of condensible compounds that require by-product disposal and process wastewater treatment.

The process development results obtained from fluidization, biomass devolatilization, and char gasification studies were used to design a 30.5-cm (12-inch) ID adiabatic fluidized-bed gasification process development unit (PDU), capable of handling up to 455 kg (1000 lb) of biomass per hour. The fluidized-bed gasifier performance is to be determined as a function of the standard operating parameters to develop a basis for recommending processes to produce either an industrial fuel gas for energy generation or a synthesis gas for methanol and ammonia production.

This work is sponsored by Battelle Pacific Northwest Laboratories (BPNL) under a prime contract from the U.S. Department of Energy (DOE).

BACKGROUND

Because methanol is an intermediate product of wood combustion reactions, methanol production from biomass sources could be considered to be as old as wood fires. Wood alcohol was first identified by Boyle in 1661. For nearly a century and a half to follow, the differences between methanol and ethanol were not recognized because both produced

193

intoxication. The traditional method of methanol production from wood by pyrolysis continued until the mid-1920's. Then alternative carbonaceous feedstocks were gasified, and the synthesis gas (carbon monoxide and hydrogen) was processed to form methanol. The first methanol synthesis patent was issued in 1913.

Modern processes are based on reforming or gasifying natural gas, naphtha, low-grade oils, and coals, followed by synthesizing methanol from carbon monoxide, carbon dioxide, and hydrogen. In recent years, woody biomass resources have been recognized as a cost-competitive methanol-synthesis feedstock in some regions of the United States. The revival of interest in biomass-based methanol processes is based on wood gasification rather than wood pyrolysis. Gasification offers several advantages over pyrolysis. It almost totally converts the biomass to gases that can be quantitatively converted to methanol. It is estimated that methanol yields can be as high as 0.72 L/kg dry wood (172 gal/ton dry wood) or about 0.6 kg methanol/kg dry wood [2]. In comparison, wood pyrolysis produces about 0.02 kg methanol/kg dry wood; the rest of the wood is in the form of charcoal, fuel gases, and other dilute organic condensibles [5].

Even though emphasis has shifted since the mid-1920's from using wood to using other carbonaceous feedstocks for methanol production, developments are continuing in wood gasification, primarily to produce fuel gases. The commercially available wood gasifiers, producing either synthesis or medium-Btu gas, can be broadly divided into updraft moving bed gasifiers (e.g., Purox, Andco-Torrax), downdraft moving bed gasifiers (e.g., replacing air with oxygen in commercial downdraft gasifiers), fluidized-bed pyrolysis (e.g., ERCO), entrained gasifiers (e.g., Morbark), and rotary kiln pyrolyzers (e.g., Angelo Industries). These gasifiers and pyrolyzers have some limitations, and the present investigations are directed to develop efficient and economical alternatives.

The developing processes, several of which are presented at this conference, offer improvements, including the following:

- Minimize feedstock preparation

- Minimize the formation of condensible organic compounds

- Achieve nearly total carbon conversion

- Maximize the production of synthesis gas

- Produce a synthesis gas rich in hydrogen (preferably $\frac{H_2}{CO + CO_2} = 2.5$)

- Minimize raw gas cleanup and upgrading

- Improve gasifier throughputs

- Offer pressuried gasification to reduce the amount of energy needed to compress the gases prior to methanol synthesis

- Minimize process wastewater treatment.

It should be noted that the new processes are in various stages of development. It is desirable for these processes to demonstrate continuous steady-state operation at close to adiabatic process conditions; then a rational techno-economic assessment could be made to determine their readiness for commercialization.

PROCESS DESCRIPTION

Under DOE/BPNL sponsorship, IGT is developing a single-stage pressurized steam-oxygen fluidized-bed biomass gasification process for producing either a medium-Btu industrial fuel gas or a synthesis gas. A simplified process diagram for the IGT biomass gasification process is shown in Figure 1. The process will utilize a lockhopper and a pressurized live-bottom feeder to handle feed material up to the size of pulpwood chips. The biomass will be fed into the fluidized-bed gasifier with a screw feeder, which can be replaced by a nonmechanical "L-valve" if the L-valve can handle woody materials. A fluidized-bed gasifier with inert solids was selected for the present design because it is well suited for carrying out simultaneous exothermic and endothermic gasification reactions. Besides acting as an excellent heat-transfer and heat-capacity medium, the fluidized bed of inert solids provides the back-mixing required to ensure adequate residence time for the gasification of low-density biomass and its char. Inert solids containing alumina and silica can also contribute to the reforming of the hydrocarbons that result from the devolatilization reactions. The PDU test program will evaluate the role of inert solids.

The gasifier operating conditions can be chosen to maximize either the methane yields (for use as a pipeline fuel gas) or the synthesis gas yields (for methanol, ammonia, and chemicals production). For medium-Btu gas production, the 30.5-cm (12-inch) ID PDU, currently in the early stages of construction, is estimated to be able to handle biomass feed rates of up to 455 kg/h (1000 lb/h) at about 2.17 MPa (315 psia) and 1089 K (1500°F), producing a methane-rich fuel gas. For synthesis gas production, the gasifier would be operated at temperatures greater than 1089 K (1500°F), perhaps up to 1255 K (1800°F), to maximize the production of carbon monoxide and hydrogen while minimizing that of methane. At the higher operating temperature (1800°F compared to 1500°F), which can be achieved by a higher oxygen feed rate, the throughput rate can be greater than the estimated feed rate for fuel gas production.

The high-heat-capacity inert-solids fluidized bed would facilitate the use of a single-screened feedstock (including biomass fines, which may have to be removed in moving bed gasifiers). The back-mixed nature of fluidized beds, which ensures nearly uniform temperature and gas composition, should permit the use of feedstocks containing up to 50% moisture. It should also provide an opportunity for reforming both light and heavy hydrocarbons. The in-situ reforming of the condensibles in the gasifier should also contribute to a need for less process wastewater treatment.

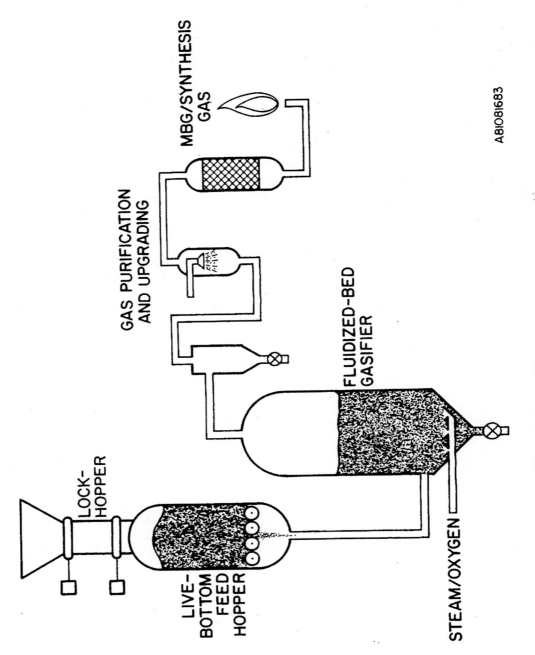

Figure 1. SIMPLIFIED PROCESS DIAGRAM

A81081683

LOCK-HOPPER

MBG/SYNTHESIS GAS

GAS PURIFICATION AND UPGRADING

LIVE-BOTTOM FEED HOPPER

FLUIDIZED-BED GASIFIER

STEAM/OXYGEN

196

Feeding biomass material into the fluidized bed close to the oxygen distributor should also aid in the rapid reforming of the biomass devolatilized products as they are formed. The use of pressurized oxygen gasification should promote nearly total carbon conversion coupled with high throughput rates. Pressurized gasification reduces the energy required to compress the clean raw gas for methanol synthesis. A proper design of the gasifier (including the gasifier feedboard space) and identification of appropriate operating conditions should selectively elutriate ash with the raw gas.

APPROACH

The program to develop the single-stage pressurized fluidized-bed gasification process is divided into three tasks of support research, one task of PDU design, construction, and operation, and one task of PDU data analysis and review. The support research tasks include biomass characterization and biomass handling, drying, size reduction, and fluidization studies. Also included are bench-scale process development studies of biomass devolatilization and char gasification reactions.

Under the biomass characterization task, physical and chemical properties have been determined for a hog fuel, jack pine softwood, maple hardwood, and corn stover. The tests have included standard proximate and ultimate analyses, analyses of biomass and char bulk and particle densities, analyses of ash fusion temperatures in reducing and oxidizing atmospheres, and a composition analysis of low- and high-temperature ash samples. The lignin, cellulose, and hemicellulose contents, as well as char surface areas and pore volumes, have been determined. Some of these results are given in Table 1, but more complete discussions of the results were presented in the reports done for DOE [1, 3].

To investigate the fluidization characteristics of dissimilar solids, mixtures of char with inert materials such as sand and alumina beads were studied in a transparent 20.3-cm-diameter (8-inch) fluidization column. At atmospheric pressure, char alone did not fluidize well. It exhibited slugging and particle segregation characteristics. But in the presence of inert bed material, fluidization improved dramatically. Figure 2 shows the fluidization behavior of various mixtures of char and inert solids. The difference between the complete fluidization velocity and the minimum fluidization velocity is plotted against char concentration. This difference remains constant for a wide range of char concentrations (from 20 to 50 volume percent char), indicating uniform bed behavior. Subsequent tests were made in a larger 30.5-cm-diameter (12-inch) column capable of pressurized operation. A pressure of 0.6 MPa (87 psia) was chosen at ambient temperature to simulate the gas density of the gasifier operating at 1089 K (1500°F) and 2.17 MPa (315 psia). As expected, the minimum fluidization velocity was about 30% lower than the atmospheric pressure minimum fluidization velocity for a similar solids concentration. The difference between complete and minimum fluidization velocities also exhibited the same constant behavior in the range of 20 to 50 volume percent char.

197

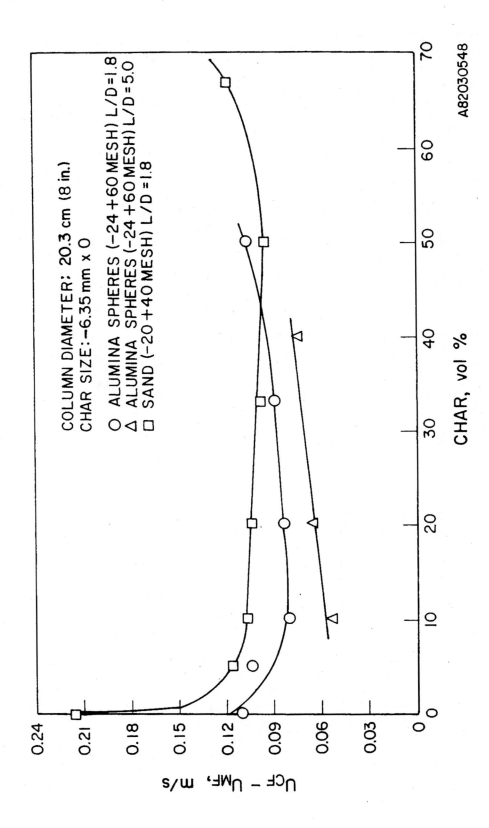

Figure 2. EFFECT OF CHAR CONCENTRATION ON COMPLETE MINUS
MINIMUM FLUIDIZATION VELOCITY

A82030548

198

Table 1.   CHEMICAL ANALYSIS, COMPOSITION, AND DENSITY OF MAPLE HARDWOOD (-4+8 USS Mesh)

Proximate Analysis, wt %
Moisture	8.7
Volatile Matter	77.2
Fixed Carbon	13.7
Ash	0.4
Total	100.0

Ultimate Analysis, wt % (dry)
Carbon	50.00
Hydrogen	6.05
Nitrogen	0.17
Sulfur	0.06
Oxygen (by Difference)	43.32
Ash	0.40
Total	100.00
Heating Value, MJ/kg (Btu/lb)	19.487 (8,378)

Composition of Maple Hardwood, wt % (dry)
Cellulose	38.1
Hemicellulose	24.3
Acid-Insoluble Lignin	27.3
Ash	0.2
Unaccounted-for Extractives	10.1
Total	100.0

Biomass	Particle Density, g/cm^3	Bulk Density, g/cm^3
Air-Dried		
-4+15 Mesh	0.61	0.16
-60+80 Mesh	0.83	0.18
Char		
-4+16 Mesh	0.62	0.13
-60+80 Mesh	0.67	0.15

The fluidization behavior was, overall, much smoother in the elevated pressure tests; even a bed of 100% char fluidized well. Bed density values ranged from 834.7 to 1107.6 kg/m^3 (52 to 69 lb/ft^3) for the pressurized fluidization tests with sand as inert solids.

The experimental and analytical research conducted as a part of the bench-scale studies was primarily designed to determine the effect of process variables (temperature, pressure, gas composition, etc.) on product yields during biomass devolatilization and char gasification reaction steps, and also to develop appropriate kinetic models useful for designing thermal gasification processes in general. The work included experiments in an isothermal laminar-flow devolatilization reactor to determine the effects of temperature, hydrogen partial pressure, and residence time on the devolatilization of maple hardwood under simulated process conditions of rapid heat-up rates [4] of about 5,000° to 10,000°C/s.

Figure 3 presents the devolatilization yields of maple hardwood as a function of temperature and residence time. The gas yield increases with temperature and residence time, while the char and liquids decrease correspondingly.

The char gasification studies include both nonisothermal and isothermal thermobalance experiments to determine the temperature-time history of biomass char under a wide range of operating conditions.

Figure 4 shows the thermobalance results of maple char gasified in a mixture of 5% hydrogen, 50% steam, and 45% inert gas at various temperatures. The char gasification reaction data was represented by a first-order reaction that was adequate for process design purposes.

PDU STATUS AND ESTIMATED PERFORMANCE

The mechanical and process design for the adiabatic, pressurized PDU gasifier and its supporting and auxiliary systems has been completed. The PDU procurement activities began in December 1981 and are on schedule; the PDU system is to be erected by mid-1982. The major PDU vessels are being fabricated and the auxiliary components of the PDU system are on order.

The bench-scale experimental results from the devolatilization and char gasification experiments (with 5% hydrogen, 50% steam, and 45% inert gas) were combined to estimate the raw material requirements and the medium-Btu fuel gas product yields for the adiabatic PDU gasifier. The raw biomass undergoes instantaneous devolatilization in a hydrogen-containing gaseous atmosphere. The high temperature of the bed of inert solids aids in reforming the heavy hydrocarbons that had formed during devolatilization into methane, hydrogen, carbon oxides, and steam. The devolatilized biomass char is then gasified by the usual steam-char reactions to produce carbon oxides and hydrogen. To supply the endothermic energy of devolatilization and char gasification, two methods of heat supply were considered. The first was the combustion of char to supply the process heat; in the second, a portion of the product gases was combusted to support the endothermic reactions.

The raw product gas is assumed to be in water-gas shift equilibrium at the exit gas temperatures. The relative extents of the competing endothermic and exothermic reactions were determined by establishing elemental and heat balances for adiabatic reactor operation. Estimated medium-Btu fuel-gas product yields are given in Table 2 for maple hardwood with 10% moisture at PDU operating conditions of 1089 K (1500°F) and 2.17 MPa (315 psia). The residence times given in the table were calculated using the bench-scale char gasification experimental data. These results suggest that 3 to 7 minutes of residence time may be sufficient to achieve 95% carbon conversion in the PDU.

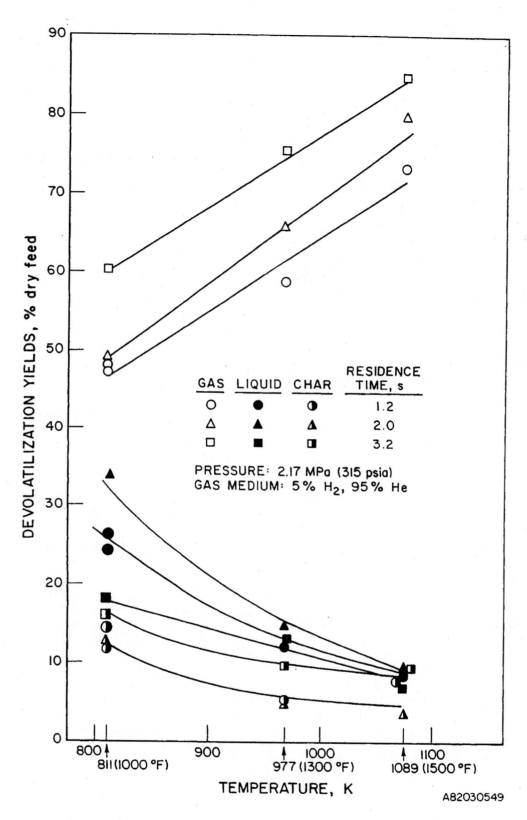

Figure 3.   DEVOLATILIZATION YIELDS FOR MAPLE HARDWOOD AS A
FUNCTION OF TEMPERATURE FOR VARIOUS RESIDENCE TIMES

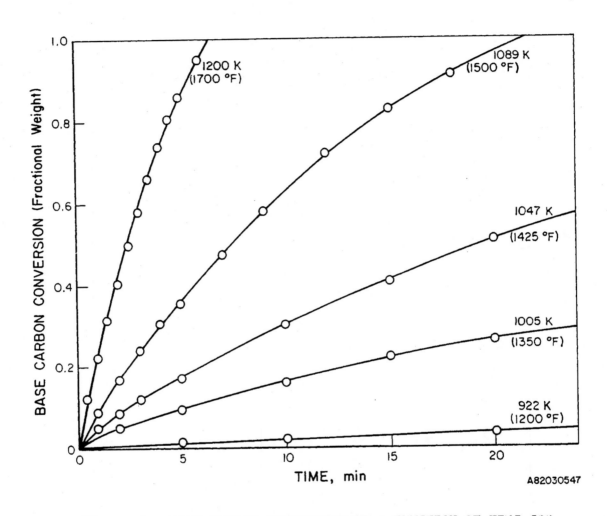

Figure 4. BASE CARBON CONVERSION AS A FUNCTION OF TIME FOR
MAPLE HARDWOOD CHARS IN 5% HYDROGEN, 50% STEAM,
AND 45% HELIUM AT 2.17 MPa (315 psia)

Table 2. ESTIMATED ADIABATIC PDU PERFORMANCE AT 1089 K (1500°F) AND 2.17 MPa (315 psia) BASED ON BENCH-SCALE DEVOLATILIZATION AND CHAR GASIFICATION OF MAPLE HARDWOOD

Product Gases	Process Heat Supplied by Char Combustion			Process Heat Supplied by CH_4, C_2H_6, CO, H_2 Combustion		
	kg-mol/h	(lb-mol/h)	mol %	kg-mol/h	(lb-mol/h)	mol %
CH_4	4.04	(8.9)	15.4	3.49	(7.7)	12.6
C_2H_6	0.86	(1.9)	3.2	0.73	(1.6)	2.6
CO	3.22	(7.1)	12.3	4.99	(11.0)	18.0
CO_2	7.12	(15.7)	27.1	6.12	(13.5)	22.1
H_2O	7.67	(16.9)	29.2	7.03	(15.5)	25.2
H_2	3.36	(7.4)	2.8	5.40	(11.9)	19.5
Total	26.27	(57.9)	100.0	27.76	(61.2)	100.0

Residence Time, min	3	7
Oxygen Input, kg-mol/h (lb-mol/h)	2.36 (5.2)	1.86 (4.1)
Steam Required for Fluidization, kg/h (lb/h)	122.5 (270)	122.5 (270)
H_2/CO Molar Ratio	1.04	1.08
Cold Gas Thermal Efficiency, %	85.2	89.7
Heating Value of Dry Raw Gas, MJ/m^3 (Btu/SCF)	15.4 (414)	14.8 (397)

Basis: 453.6 kg/h (1000 lb/h) material with 10% moisture
Conversion — 95% carbon conversion
Specific Throughput Rate — 5595 kg/m^2-h (1146 lb/ft^2-h)

So far in the program, the emphasis has been on process design for a thermally efficient, medium-Btu fuel-gas process. From this basis, process modifications could be made to favor synthesis gas production, which in general has more stringent gas composition requirements. Process operational tradeoffs — such as the effects that higher temperature, location and design of the oxygen distributor, or pressure operation will have on gas yield and composition — can then be evaluated.

The estimated performance for the PDU will be verified with actual operation tests. Several recognized problem areas will be addressed in the gasification process tests. The following areas especially will be evaluated:

- Lockhopper operation

- Uniform solids feeding

- Carbon loss

- Heat loss.

The PDU has been specifically designed to provide operational flexibility. The geometric relation between the feed position and the bed height relative to the steam-oxygen distributor can be varied. This permits feeding to different portions of the bed so that its effect on the product gas yield, as well as the effects of temperature and pressure, can be studied. Different types and sizes of feedstocks with varying amounts of moisture can be evaluated for optimum gasification performance to produce substitute fuels.

ACKNOWLEDGMENTS

This work is sponsored by Battelle Pacific Northwest Laboratories under a prime contract from the Office of Biomass Energy Systems, U.S. Department of Energy. The work described includes contributions from several IGT staff members, including Mr. I. Hirsan (fluidization studies), Dr. G. Rose (characterization and devolatilization studies), Dr. S. P. Nandi (char gasification studies), and Messrs. R. P. Bachta and J. Arnold (PDU mechanical design).

REFERENCES

1. Institute of Gas Technology, "Development of Hydroconversion of Biomass to Synthetic Fuels," Final Report. Chicago, December 1981.

2. Jones, J. L. et. al, "A Comparative Economic Analysis of Alcohol Fuels Production Options." Paper presented in the Proceedings of the 3rd International Symposium on Alcohol Fuels Technology. Calif.: Asilomar, May 1979.

3. Kosowski, G. M., Rose, G. R., Nandi, S. P., Singh, S. P., Onischak, M. and Babu, S. P. "Development of Hydroconversion of Biomass to Synthetic Fuels." Paper presented in the Proceedings of the 12th Biomass Thermochemical Contractors' Meeting. Washington, D.C.: U.S. DOE, Biomass Energy Systems, March 1981.

4. Rose, G. R., Singh, S. P., Onischak, M. and Babu, S. P., "Development of Biomass Hydroconversion to Synthetic Fuels — Effect of Operating Conditions on Devolatilization Product Yields." Paper presented in the Symposium Proceedings, Energy from Biomass and Wastes V, 612-621. Chicago: Institute of Gas Technology, 1981.

5. Wise, Louis E., Ed., Wood Chemistry. New York: Reinhold, 1944.

181(3)/PAP/dpfb

THE THAGARD HIGH-TEMPERATURE FLUID-WALL REACTOR
FOR SYNGAS GENERATION FROM BIOMASS

Dr. A. W. Hornig
Baird Corporation
125 Middlesex Turnpike
Bedford, Massachusetts 0173

J. D. Theis
Thagard Research Corporation
2712 Kelvin Avenue
Irvine, California 92714

INTRODUCTION

The use of methanol is expected to increase dramatically over the next few years due to its potential as a fuel additive, or as a feedstock for production of other energy-related materials. World War II Germany designed all vehicles to run on pure methanol, and both Ford and Volkswagen are now testing straight methanol fuel systems. Methanol can be added directly to gasoline in the range of 10 to 15 per cent as a version of "gasohol" with the same advantages as the ethanol variety, and Arco is marketing a 1:1 blend of methanol and tert-butyl alcohol under the trade name of "Oxinol" for blending with gasoline. Methanol is also used as one of the feedstocks in the manufacture of MTBE (methyl tert-butyl ether), increasingly used as an octane enhancer.

In the past, methanol plants relied heavily on methane or natural gas as a feedstock; however, many plants have been closed down because the rapid increase in feedstock prices has made methanol production prohibitive. The applications of patented technology utilizing the Thagard High-Temperature Fluid-Wall (HTFW) Reactor can bring some of these closed-down methanol plants back into production on a profitable basis, since the HTFW Reactor can produce a syngas suitable for methanol production from a variety of biomass feedstocks, most of which can be acquired on a cost effective basis.

The gasification of biomass (and coal) to produce fuel dates back to before 1850. After a rapid growth of the gas industry, the increasing availability of low-cost natural gas resulted in closing of most gasification plants. The dramatic increase in oil prices following creation of OPEC, plus growing awareness that oil stocks could be used up in the foreseeable future, resulted in renewed interest in gasification of biomass, which not only produces fuel, but gets rid of wastes which are in themselves environmental problems.

THAGARD HIGH-TEMPERATURE FLUID-WALL (HTFW) REACTOR

The HTFW Reactor is a novel device which operates in the $1000^\circ C$ to $2500^\circ C$ temperature range. In any process operating around $2200^\circ C$ (the normal operating temperature of the HTFW Reactor) energy transfer by radiative coupling will dominate over transfer by conduction. Thus, elimination of conduction transfer will result in little loss of energy transfer efficiency, but will allow protection of the reactor walls by a gas blanket, preventing deleterious slagging on the walls, which would be expected to be severe at this temperature, and early destruction of the walls. As a result of this design there is no physical contact between the reacting stream and the reactor's walls, and little net pressure on the radiating core. Since the reactor is configured as a blackbody cavity, all radiation not used directly in the chemical reaction, or in heating reactants, is returned to the radiator, resulting in an unusually efficient utilization of electrical energy.

The very high equilibrium temperature results in destruction of substantially all organic species, leaving simple atomic or molecular forms (e.g., CO, C, H_2, etc.). The very rapid rate of heating as the feedstock enters the hot zone and the rapid cooling rate as the product leaves the hot zone and enters the cooled heat exchanger (initially greater than $10^6 \ ^\circ C/sec$) prevents formation of complex reaction products (tars and distillates) which might be toxic or hazardous.

The HTFW Reactor is particularly suited to high temperature reactions such as pyrolysis and water-gas reactions. Because of the high temperature capability, high pressures are not necessary for completion of many of these reactions. Because the reactor is not dependent on catalysts for its operation, the purity of its feedstock with respect to water, sulfur, metal contaminants or inert filler is not important.

The reactor consists principally of a cylindrical core made of porous carbon. A protective blanket of gaseous nitrogen or hydrogen is passed through the porous tube wall. The core is heated to incandescence by means of an electrical heater constructed of graphite rods. The core and electrodes are enclosed by a heat shield made principally of graphite which forms the blackbody cavity alluded to earlier. These features can be seen in the cross-section of Figure 1 and the schematic of Figure 2.

PROCESS APPLICATIONS (OTHER THAN GASIFICATION)

The unique characteristics of the HTFW Reactor suggest application in an extremely wide variety of process applications. A sampling of these applications and processes is illustrated in Tables 1 and 2, and discussed below:

206

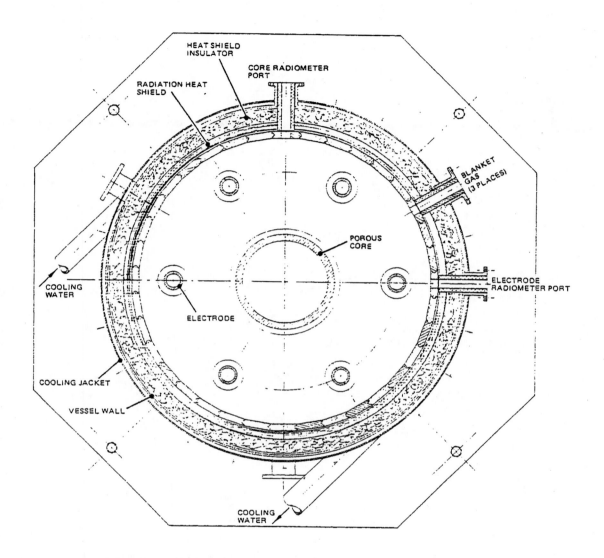

FIGURE 1: CROSS SECTION OF THAGARD HTFW TWELVE-INCH REACTOR

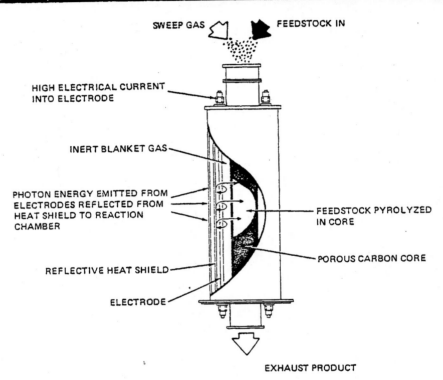

FIGURE 2:   SCHEMATIC OF THAGARD HTFW REACTOR

TABLE 1:

APPLICATIONS FOR
THAGARD HTFW REACTOR

ENERGY	DISPOSAL	CHEMICALS & MATERIALS
CARBONACEOUS MATERIALS	INDUSTRIAL RESIDUE	METHANE
BIOMASS	TOXIC & HAZARDOUS WASTE	METHANOL
PEAT	Propellants & Explosives	ACETYLENE
LIGNITE	Heavy Metals	OLEFINS
HIGH SULFUR COALS	PCB	HYDROGEN
HIGH SULFUR RESIDUAL OIL	Radioactive Materials	SYNTHESIS GAS
TOXIC & HAZARDOUS FUELS		CALCIUM CARBIDE
MUNICIPAL SOLID WASTE		SILICON CARBIDE
		TITANIUM DIBORIDE
		SILICON
		IRON
		NICKLE
		CALCINED LIME
		CEMENT
		GLASS
		LEAD
		ZINC

209

TABLE 2:

THAGARD HTFW PROCESS DESCRIPTION

FEEDSTOCK	EXAMPLE REACTION	PRODUCT
HYDROCARBON, OIL OR GAS	$CH_4 \rightarrow C + 2H_2$	CARBON BLACK
AGRICULTURAL WASTE MUNICIPAL SOLID WASTE BIOMASS PEAT MOSS WOOD CHIPS	$C_6H_{10}O_5 + H_2O \rightarrow 6CO + 6H_2$	SYNTHESIS GAS
METALLIC OXIDES	Fe_3O_4 + REDUCTANT (COAL, PEAT, BIOMASS) $\rightarrow$ $Fe^o + CO, CO_2, H_2, H_2O$	METAL
METALLIC HALIDES	$HSiCl_3 + H_2 \rightarrow Si^o + SHCl$	METAL
CHLORINATED HYDROCARBONS	$C_6Cl_6 + 3Ca(OH)_2 \rightarrow 3CaCl_2 + 6CO + 3H_2$	INERT MATERIAL
HYDROCARBON OIL EMULSIONS COAL/WATER SLURRIES	HYDROCARBON + $H_2O \rightarrow CO + H_2$	SYNTHESIS GAS
HIGH SULFUR OIL SYNTHESIS GAS	COAL + $Ca(OH)_2$ + AIR + $H_2O \rightarrow CO + H_2 + CaS$	SULFUR-FREE
HIGH SULFUR OIL	COAL + $Ca(OH)_2$ + AIR + $H_2O \rightarrow CO + H_2 + CaS$	SULFUR-FREE
CALCIUM CARBONATE AND SILICA	$CaCO_3 + SiO_2 \rightarrow$ CEMENT	CEMENT
SILICA AND FLUX	$SiO_2 + CaO + Na_2O \rightarrow$ GLASS	GLASS
COAL & CALCIUM HYDROXIDE	COAL + $Ca(OH)_2 \rightarrow CaC_2 + CO + H_2$	CALCIUM CARBIDE
NUCLEAR WASTE	WASTE + $Ca(OH)_2$ + CLAY $\rightarrow$ GLASS	INERT GLASS BEADS

Chemical Processes

Several general classes of chemical process industry operations have been conducted in the HTFW Reactor. For example, pure hydrocarbon feeds have been pyrolyzed to produce carbon and hydrogen.

A 12-inch Reactor has been installed for a major client to produce carbon black and hydrogen from carbon black oil. Hydrocarbons may also be pyrolyzed in the presence of other compounds to produce specialty chemicals. For example, a program is in the planning stage in which coal will be introduced with hydrated lime to produce synthesis gas and calcium carbide for acetylene production.

Synthetic coke may also be produced from any hydrocarbon feed (coal, resid, peat, waste, etc.). Pyrolysis of this feed yields hydrogen gas and finely-divided carbon solids which have been completely devolatilized. These solids may be mixed with a binder compound and briquetted or pelletized to yield a high-grade coke suitable for metallurgical applications.

In another application, the Reactor is being tested as a preferred method of pyrolyzing phosphogypsum for the production of SO_2 for subsequent production of H_2SO_4 and cementic materials from an otherwise hazardous waste stock generated in chemical fertilizer production.

Metallic Ores

The HTFW Reactor also has potential applications in ore processing and metal refining operations. Experimental data have shown that high-purity metals can be produced when a finely-divided metallic oxide feed is introduced into the Reactor with a reducing agent. Impurities in the ores are bound in an inert slag which can be separated from the product metal by screening, classifying, magnetic separation, or other conventional processes.

Metals may be produced from complex compounds as well as ores. For example, Thagard Research Corporation is now conducting a process development program on behalf of a licensed client for the production of polycrystalline silicon from trichlorosilane. The polycrystalline product can be used as Czochralski feed to produce crystalline silicon for semiconductor manufacture.

An attractive use for the Reactor is found in the recovery of zinc and other metals present as a fume emission from electric arc furnaces, or similar metal recovery from other finely divided waste streams.

The processing of non-metallic ores may also be enhanced by the use of the HTFW gasifier to produce hydrogen or carbon monoxide as an ore reductant. The hydrogen-rich syngas stream from the gasifier can be passed through a pressure-swing absorber or similar separator to produce high-purity (99+%) hydrogen.

Refractories, Glass and Cement

The manufacture of refractory materials is another area of application for the HTFW Reactor now under license with a European client.

The high temperatures attainable in the Reactor core along with the free space reaction facilitate the production of ultrafine, highly reactive powders of silicon carbide, titanium diboride, silicon nitride, and other refractory materials. These powders are the starting ingredients for the fabrication of advanced ceramic turbine blades, vanes, shrouds, pistons, and heat exchangers for high performance heat engines.

Lower-melting glasses may also be produced for the manufacture of glass mat and glass fiber. An extensive experimental program by TRC has resulted in production of glasses from a variety of silicic feed materials. Experimental data have demonstrated a total energy consumption significantly below that of conventional processing.

The HTFW Reactor has also been used successfully to produce finely-divided Portland cement clinker. In this process, the Reactor replaces a conventional kiln resulting in reduced capital and operating costs, as well as significantly lower energy consumption.

Cogeneration

An attractive feature of several chemical processes based on the HTFW Reactor is the potential for cogeneration. Since most organic feeds will produce medium-BTU synthesis gas in addition to the chemical product, these operations may be designed to generate their own process power requirements. Depending on feed composition, sufficient syngas may be produced for export to other units or users.

Waste Treatment

Municipal, Agricultural and Industrial Wastes.
TRC is currently involved in the development of several waste treatment processes for municipal, industrial and industrial refuse. These projects involve substantial volumetric reductions in conventional landfill waste, the production of inert, nonleachable slag, the destruction of certain wastes no longer permitted in landfills, and in some cases the production of refused-derived fuels as alternate energy sources.

Toxic and Hazardous Waste.
Under the sponsorship of a U.S. Government Agency and independent industrial clients, the Thagard Reactor has been

212

utilized on a test basis to destroy several classes of chlorinated hydrocarbons and similar substances with an efficiency greater than 99.9999% and further work is programmed and ongoing.

The company has a well developed plan to provide Reactors for these applications in a number of areas throughout the United States as soon as environmental and permitting authorizations are obtained. The characterisitic rapid dissociation to elemental or terminal oxide states that occurs to substantially all compounds in the Thagard Reactor appears to make it particularly attractive in disposing of such toxic materials without hazard to the environment. The high reaction temperatures of the HTFW Reactor are ideal for decomposing toxic chemical wastes without the formation of other potentially toxic intermediate compounds. Lime and/or clay are the only additives required to process most toxic chemicals, including chlorinated hydrocarbons, fluorocarbons and cyanides. The reaction products are synthesis gas and calcium salts.

Nuclear Waste.
Disposal of low-level and high-level nuclear waste materials is a promising application for the HTFW Reactor. The former, which includes clothing and cleaning materials, is a large-volume problem. The shredded waste is combined with clay and limestone and reacted to produce a clean gas, which may be flared, and a reduced volume of high-melting point vitreous, virtually non-leachable solid in which the radioactive material is dissolved. High-level wastes, such as spent cores, are treated in the same way as the low-level wastes except that additional pre-treatment chemistry is performed to assure the formation of a single-phase glass from the many diverse materials of the spent core. Since the high-level waste consists of inorganic material, synthesis gas is not produced. The radioactive material is dissolved in the non-leachable vitreous granules which are the reaction products.

Experimental work for a public utility with a simulated (non-radioactive) nuclear Reactor core has produced a slag with an extremely small high-temperature water leach rate of all components.

GASIFICATION OF BIOMASS
Waste materials such as agricultural wastes, biomass, peat and other cellulose-based materials are excellent feeds for the HTFW Reactor. They may be gasified to produce a clean, medium-BTU synthesis gas and an inert granular ash. The process minimizes or eliminates environmentally unacceptable end-products and produces only benign slags.

213

Gasification Chemistry in the HTFW Reactor

There are three distinct reactions in the gasification of solid hydrocarbon fuels. First is the pyrolysis, or thermal decomposition, which drives volatile components (such as H_2) from the feed materials, combines the oxygen present stoichiometrically with a fraction of the carbon to produce CO, and liberates the remainder of the carbon as elemental fines. Secondly, in the presence of oxygen, combustion oxidizes the carbon to CO or CO_2. The third reaction, which occurs in the presence of water, is gasification, whereby carbon and water combine to produce CO and H_2.

The Reactor operating temperature has the greatest impact on chemical kinetics of any process condition. As temperature increases, the transfer of energy to the feed shifts from the convective mode to a predominantly radiative mode. This effect, which becomes dominant above $1800^{\circ}C$, changes the reaction time as well as the nature of the reactions. Above this temperature, incomplete combustion (producing CO) and gasification (producing CO and H_2), proceed very rapidly to completion. In addition, the production of hydrocarbons falls off, so that a syngas composed almost entirely of CO and H_2 is produced. The quality of this gas makes it ideal for various chemical synthesis processes, e.g., methanol production.

In most conventional entrained-flow gasifiers, it is necessary to operate at higher pressure (above 300 psi) to increase the collision rate among molecules (thereby increasing conversion) in order to raise throughput. In the HTFW Reactor, where carbon conversion is not a collision-dependent process, gasification may be accomplished at low pressures (atmospheric) with high throughputs. Equilibrium trends for the carbon-hydrogen oxygen-water system are shown in Figure 3.

Performance of the HTFW Reactor

Gasification of solid fuel has been accomplished in Thagard Research Corporation's (TRC) 6" pilot Reactor with various forms and classes of feedstock, including sawdust, wood-slash, bog peat, dried peat, Canadian spagnum, bark, municipal solid waste and sewage sludge (Milorganite).

Theoretical Considerations.

The operating conditions in the HTFW Reactor (energy flux, short residence time, optical transparency of some species) make the gasification process different in kind from conventional equilibrium systems. However, the published data and theoretial analyses of such systems do indicate general reaction kinetic trends that are supported by empirical evidence from HTFW Reactor experiments. For example, the dominance of incomplete over complete combustion, the increase in H_2 concentration and the decrease in the formation of CH_4, all predicted as temperature increases, have empirical

$CH_{1.01}O_{0.21} \rightarrow 0.79C + 0.505H_2 + 0.21CO$

$C + H_2O \rightarrow H_2 + CO$

$C + CO_2 \rightarrow 2\,CO$

$C + \frac{1}{2}O_2 \rightarrow CO$

$C + O_2 \rightarrow CO_2$

$CO + H_2O \rightarrow CO_2 + H_2$

% C TO EACH REACTION IS A FUNCTION OF:
- COAL COMPOSITION
- TEMPERATURE
- MOLE PERCENT WATER IN REACTOR
- MOLE PERCENT OXYGEN IN REACTOR
- REACTOR PRESSURE

IN A SIMPLE SYSTEM OF CARBON, CARBON MONOXIDE AND CARBON DIOXIDE RELATIVE PRODUCTION OF GASEOUS COMPONENTS CAN BE REPRESENTED BY THE FOLLOWING CURVES:

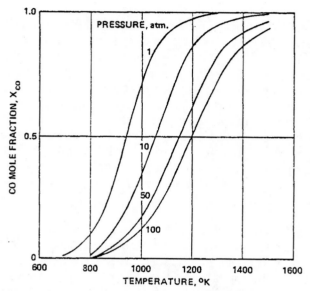

EQUILIBRIUM CHARACTERISTICS FOR C (GRAPHITE)—CO—CO_2 SYSTEM.

FIGURE 3:
REACTION KINETICS - COAL GASIFICATION

215

support as well. Specie concentrations approach their basic stoichiomentric limits as the temperature rises above $1900^\circ C$, with no formation of toxic intermediates.

The fluid dynamic behavior of the HTFW Reactor has also been analyzed and modeled. The fluid wall presents a protective barrier against reactive diffusive species, thus shielding the core from chemical attack. Mechanical erosion by spray impingement of liquid feeds can be minimized by proper Reactor configuration and appropriate spray technology. As diameter increases, impingement effect diminishes.

Heat transfer in the HTFW Reactor is a heterogeneous process. Optically opaque feeds (most solids and some liquids) absorb the radiative energy which exists at flux levels above 200 watts/cm^2. Many species (e.g., gases and water) are optically transparent to the infrared radiation, and absorb energy only by conductive and convective processes. Since these processes are slow compared to radiative transfer, and since transit time through the Reactor is very short, these materials show comparatively little change in temperature. Opaque materials, on the other hand, heat at rates of several million degrees per second and react very rapidly.

Empirical Work.
Several grades of coal have been characterized in the Reactor to determine the optimum mesh size for feed. Generally -100 mesh feed size will assure complete reaction of the coal.

Coal has been gasified in the HTFW Reactor in the form of coal slurry, coal fines (slurried), and dry coal. Higher throughputs and a more efficient process may be obtained with dry coal feeds. However, each application should be examined to develop an optimized process. Peat gasification has also been accomplished using the peat as a primary gasification feedstock and as an additive in other processes. Work at the HTFW Reactor pilot facilities has included basic pyrolysis, gasification, combustion and combinations of all three reactions. A major effort has been directed toward reducing the electrical power input by combustion. By this method, the endothermic and heating loads can be supplied by an exothermic reaction. Gasification of coal-lime mixtures has indicated that the addition of 1-2 times the stoichiometric requirement of lime to the feed will bind the sulfur present as CaS, which is dissolved in the vitreous non-leachable slag.

With proper feedstock preparation, the syngas produced from gasification of coal or peat consists primarily of CO and H_2 with only trace quantities of CO_2 and hydrocarbons. Low-grade coals or peat are actually preferable to higher-grade coals as HTFW Reactor feedstocks for a variety of reasons.

216

First, their higher oxygen-to-carbon ratio results in higher CO yields during pyrolysis, so that complete gasification requires less oxygen and water. Secondly, there are larger deposits of the low-grade materials, especially peat. Third, the low-grade feedstocks are less costly. As predicted, at 2000°C, gas yields correspond to the theoretical stoichiometric volumes. Carbon conversion efficiencies approach 100%, as expected for an entrained flow process.

Process Scaling

To prepare for the design of larger units, empirical data and simulation techniques have been developed to scale the gasification process.

Assessment of Technology

Research and development programs by Thagard Research Corporation have resulted in improved materials and construction techniques for the HTFW Reactor. Reactors of up to 24-inch core diameter are presently feasible. Scaling calculations suggest that size Reactor has a maximum capacity of 200 tons per day (TPD) of dry coal. It is projected that larger-diameter Reactors (up to 48-inch for a possible 950 TPD dry biomass) will be available within the next three years. Scaling studies and empiric testing thereof are continuing. In addition to the pilot Reactor, a large-diameter cold test simulator will be on-line by late 1982 for the development of feed injection and fluid-wall techniques, and investigation of fluid-wall stability at very high throughputs.

Scaling Relationships

Experimental data indicate that almost 100% conversion can be achieved with transit times of less than 50 milliseconds. Using this as a basis, throughputs have been found for a variety of operating conditions and biomass compositions, using computer simulation techniques. Throughput appears to increase with radius to the 2nd power, but less than linearly with length. As a result, best coal gasification efficiencies should be obtained with larger diameter devices of some nominal length (~6 ft.). Such a geometry will also result in lower gas exhaust temperatures, due to the lower surface-area-to-volume ratio.

Heat leakage from the Reactor increases linearly with diameter, and so will be a relatively insignificant fraction of total input power for larger diameter Reactors.

Economic Considerations

The Thagard process does not require many of the auxiliary units associated with conventional gasifiers, and offers greater flexibility in handling a variety of feedstocks. In addition, it consists of a more compact and less complex Reactor. Consequently, large cost savings can be realized in the construction of the gasifier system. For example, downstream gas processing is limited to particulate removal and dry ash handling. Small HTFW Reactors, or larger ones designed for power generation/fuel gas production, can be operated as air blown systems, eliminating the requirement for an oxygen plant. It is currently estimated that a 24" Reactor, capable of gasifying in excess of 200 TPD of biomass, with power supply, control and coolant systems, can be installed for $4MM. The existence of the patented fluid wall, a non-slagging feature, permits operational lifetime in components equivalent to normal 50-week cycles found in the high temperature industry.

METHANOL PLANT RETROFIT

Thagard Research Corporation is presently involved in a joint venture to combine the HTFW Reactor with an existing, permitted and licensed methanol plant in Hercules, California. The product will be 28,000 gal/day of chemical grade methanol (95% CH_3OH, 5% H_2O). Biomass feedstocks considered include peat, wood, cotton stubble, bark and rice hulls. The utilization of the HTFW Reactor for syngas production will result in the following advantages over other methods:

1. The syngas will be clean, with no tars or distallates, eliminating the need for gas-stream cleaning.

2. Carbon fines produced will be utilized to form metallurgical coke, a valuable by-product.

3. The process will not require an external oxygen plant.

4. The temperature may be adjusted to yield partial gasification (exothermic) with resultant decrease in electrical input energy demand.

5. The system will work efficiently on moderate feedrates (e.g., 200 TPD) which matches physical distribution of biomass feedstocks.

6. The HTFW Reactor will provide a simpler retrofit to the existing plant than any other competitive process.

The relatively small size and simplicity of the HTFW Reactor suggest that, in addition to retrofitting existing plants, the Reactor may be a good candidate for small packaged biomass to methanol plants in the agricultural community.

ACKNOWLEDGEMENT
The authors wish to thank Mr. E. Matovich for sharing ideas and data used in the preparation of this paper.

Production of Methanol from Biomass and Peat — Non-U.S. Projects

THE OUTLOOK FOR METHANOL IN BRAZIL*

Victor Yang
CTP - Centro de Tecnologia Promon
Rio de Janeiro, Brasil

ABSTRACT

The potential of methanol in Brazil is examined critically considering the country's ongoing alternative energy programs, with particular emphasis on PROALCOOL.

The outlook for methanol in Brazil is unique in many ways. A key issue to consider is the role, if any, for methanol is fuel in an ethanol-rich country such as Brazil. This paper addresses this issue by reviewing the background, status and problems confronting PROALCOOL, Brazil's national alcohol program — the world's largest ongoing biomass based synfuel program. I will try to focus on some of the major effects of a very rapid and successful large-scale penetration of ethanol into the Brazilian gasoline pool. This analysis leads me to discuss an overview of Brazilian alternative energy programs and the potential incentives/barriers for methanol from biomass in the Brazilian context.

1. Background and Status of PROALCOOL

Availability of historical production and use experience with fuel ethanol at a time of sudden changes in the relative prices of petroleum and sugar contributed much toward the implementation of PROALCOOL in 1975. Figure 1 shows the widening gap between world petroleum and sugar prices since 1973, enhancing the potential of sugar as raw material for energy and chemicals.

In Brazil, sugar from sugarcane became, in a relatively short time-span, a major source of fermentation ethanol. The bulk of this ethanol is used as fuel in Otto-engine vehicles, either in "alcohol" engines, burning neat (azeotrope) ethanol or in "gasoline" engines, burning a mixture of gasoline and ethanol with varying composition.

The anticipated ethanol production level of 4.3 billion liters during the 1981/82 season seems to support initial government plans. This amount of ethanol would in fact be sufficient to enable a 20/80 (vol %) ethanol/gasoline mixture (initial target of PROALCOOL), on a national basis, in addition to allowing for the requirements of the chemical industry and exports. Because of the sizable fleet of neat (azeotrope) ethanol vehicles (approx. 450,000 as of Dec/81).

219

actual average ethanol content in the Brazilian gasohol in 1981 was only approx. 9% (vol.). Recently, there are signs of a slowdown in the initial PROALCOOL momentum and a change in some early targets. Primary factors appear to be a country-wide economic recession, high inflation, capital availability and cost constraints and marketing problems with alcohol vehicles.

The social and economic costs of PROALCOOL - a highly subsidized alternative energy program, have become of increasing concern, especially in the face of escalating capital costs and investment requirements due to inflation. A much-publicized criticism to PROALCOOL, on purely economic grounds, is that the net savings achieved in imported petroleum as a result of accelerated gasoline-by-ethanol substitution fall short of early projections based on the energy contents of the two fuels. Moreover, the historical flexibility of the Brazilian sugar and ethanol industry enabling Brazil to benefit from favorable prices of the world sugar market cycle, may become jeopardized with an increasing commitment to the production of ethanol for fuel.

This possible situation is due to the swift change of the status of fermentation ethanol in the Brazilian economy: from a major byproduct of sugar mills obtained by fermentation of molasses to the role of primary and initially only product of so-called independent distilleries, where ethanol is obtained from direct fermentation of cane juice, without co-production of sugar. Ethanol byproduct from molasses meant in essence a diversion of sugar to the production of ethanol, an attractive scheme when world sugar prices were low and discouraged Brazilian exports. Since PROALCOOL, the number of independent distilleries have proliferated and the ethanol share due to molasses distilleries decreased. The implication of this trend is that Brazil may no longer promptly avail itself of temporary upswings in the world sugar prices in the future, such as the experience of 1980 (when sugar prices reached over 40 cents/lb.).

A common criticism to PROALCOOL's social aspects is the heavy concentration of sugar and ethanol production base in a single state: São Paulo. One of the effects of this concentration of activities, accelerated with PROALCOOL's attractive scheme of subsidized capital financing and guaranteed market, is the growing concern over the food vs. fuel vs. export issue. In São Paulo, there are news of food and export crops being displaced by large-scale sugarcane plantations grown for the production of fuel ethanol. In some regions of the state, land prices have escalated faster than inflation rates due to competition for prime agricultural land and beyond the reach of small and medium size farmers. Another effect of this concentration trend is the increasing competition for molasses, an abundant sugar mill byproduct prior to PROALCOOL. Molasses is used by the feed and sucrochemical industries, which have to compete with a large and growing fermentation ethanol industry, especially in the Southeastern states such as São Paulo.

220

2. Impact of Energy Substitution Projects on the Brazilian Refineries

One of the sectors most affected by the impact of PROALCOOL is the Brazilian refinery industry. Ironically, abundant supply of fermentation ethanol has led to temporary imbalance of the liquid fuels' market.

Around 1.4 billion liters of a low octane gasoline had to be exported by Brazil in 1981 as a result of blending ethanol into the gasoline pool (estimated at 1.2 billion liters) and a consumption of approx. 1.4 billion liters of azeotrope ethanol used for fueling neat-ethanol vehicles.

There has also been news about temporary surplus of fuel oil in 1981 as a result of ongoing energy substitution projects. Solid fuels such as wood, coal, charcoal and bagasse are penetrating the retrofit market in a few major industries, as substitutes for fuel oil. This trend was spurred primarily by a new fuel oil pricing policy combined with a restrictive allocation system started in 1979. Figure 2 shows that fuel oil prices in Brazil have escalated faster than alternatives such as wood and hydroelectricity, inducing investments in energy substitution.

Massive substitution of the gasoline and fuel oil fractions by alternative energy sources over a short time span underlie the Brazilian liquid fuels' market imbalance. Current oil refining capability is being strained to increase considerably the share of diesel oil--the fastest growing oil derivative consumed in Brazil. In fact, diesel oil requirements are commanding Brazilian imports of petroleum. Finding proper substitute for diesel oil , therefore, has become a major near and mid-term target of the Brazilian alternative energy programs.

Table 1 shows the rapidly changing Brazilian oil refining profile. Over a 15- year time period, Brazil has moved from a "US-like" barrel, dominated by the gasoline fraction, to a barrel increasingly led by the diesel oil fraction.

Petrobrás, the state oil prospection, refining and distribution company has announced investments to alter the Brazilian oil refining profile, to "squeeze out" more diesel. The strategy adopted include measures such as alteration of the spec. of fuel oil, to a heavier more viscous product, and plans to install coking units to process vacuum resid, generating more diesel and byproduct coke.

3. Overview of Brazilian Alternative Energy Programs

Blessed with abundant supply of alternative energy sources, Brazil has opted in the near-term for a major energy substitution effort. Figure 3 shows the range of synfuels being considered as substitutes for the three major oil fractions. The foremost example is PROALCOOL.

The continental dimension of Brazil (area of 8.5 million square kilometers) and increasing concern over the food vs. fuel vs. export conflict may foster the diversification of energy feedstocks and products. For example, high-ash coal reserves concentrated in the Southernmost states of Santa Catarina and Rio Grande do Sul are being considered by local industries, initially concerned with fuel oil substitution. Surplus hydroelectricity in a few Southern states may lead to increased use of electricity as a source of heat. Regional availability of wood, bagasse and other lignocellulosic materials may provide incentives for energy product diversification, to include products such as low-BTU gas, charcoal and methanol. Surplus vegetable oil processing capacity together with promising test results in diesel engines have encouraged Brazil to consider a PROÓLEO (a national program to produce vegetable oils for fuel).

Brazil's experience with synfuels suggests that a substitution strategy to decrease the country's reliance on foreign oil may only solve part of the energy problems. The social and economic costs of the transition period, in fact, appear to be high, especially considering the necessary contribution of government funds, in the early phases.

A balanced long-term strategy shall most likely exploit a proper combination of energy conservation and substitution efforts, maximizing efficiency of energy conversion and utilization at acceptable social and economic costs.

4. Potential of Methanol as Fuel in an Ethanol-rich Country: Brazil

The future of methanol as fuel in Brazil will be largely affected by the developments in the country's liquid fuels market. PROALCOOL's experience was invaluable to demonstrate the feasibility of a rapid penetration of a liquid synfuel in the refinery pools. An equally important lesson is that there is urgent need to diversify the base of energy feedstocks and products, in order to lessen the social and economic costs associated with a rapid move toward synfuels.

Judging from the worldwide energy distribution and use experience, economic incentives and user convenience, it is anticipated that liquid fuels shall continue to be major energy forms in the Brazilian context. This speculation is based on the following pieces of evidence:

● the bulk of gasoline and diesel oil are consumed by the transportation sector. Gasoline is primarily used to fuel passenger vehicles and light trucks. Diesel oil is mainly used by trucks, buses and agricultural vehicles. Due to underinvestment in railway transportation, over 70% of Brazil's commercial cargoes are transported in highways through diesel engine-powered trucks.

• fuel oil is mainly used by the industrial sector. Utility consumption of fuel oil is relatively small due to widespread availability of hydroelectricity. Many of the large industrial consumers are located near or within urban areas. Legislation controlling air and water pollution have become increasingly more stringent in the recent years, especially in heavily industrialized states like São Paulo.

Substitution of diesel and fuel oil fractions by fermentation ethanol have encountered technical and/or economic barriers, without clearcut solutions in the near-term notwithstanding likely ethanol utilization and production technology breakthroughs. This viewpoint seems to underlie the current Brazilian interest for vegetable oil, low-BTU gas, solid fuels and hydroelectricity.

In the long-run, a clean-burning relatively cheap liquid fuel, methanol, may penetrate the Brazilian energy market due to economic considerations and growing concern and awareness of the need to improve the quality of environment, especially in urban centers. In Brazil, this methanol for fuel will likely be produced either from newly found natural gas reserves (e.g. Jupiã, in the Amazon) or from abundant, low opportunity cost biomass sources such as wood, bagasse and agricultural residues.

By tapping a larger domestic resource base and, therefore, lessening problems associated with the food vs. fuel vs. export conflict, methanol may supplement the supply of ethanol in an integrated synfuel strategy designed to minimize the net requirements for imported petroleum, incurring in the process acceptable social and economic costs. If extensive methanol vehicle use is approved, it is conceivable a large-scale substitution of diesel oil by methanol. On the other hand, restrictive emission standards may encourage substitution of fuel oil by methanol in boilers and furnaces near urban centers.

Two major considerations bearing on the potential of methanol as widespread and large volume liquid fuel relate to the issues of safety-in-use and cost. Both issues will only be resolved with additional results of ongoing R, D & D programs.

CESP, an energy-utility company in the state of São Paulo is engaged in a 5-year US $130 million R & D program to demonstrate the feasibility of producing methanol syngas from wood. The original schedule of 1983 start-up of the first of three pilot-gasifiers (capacity = 100 ton/d methanol equivalent basis) may be delayed due to recent financing difficulties.

Tables 2 and 3 show the calculated costs for methanol from wood via gasification and ethanol from sugarcane via fermentation of cane juice, considering economic ranges of capacity. At current feedstock prices in Brazil and considering realistic unit investment range for cane ethanol and conservative unit investment range for

223

methanol from wood (due to non-demonstrated large-scale wood to syngas gasification), the calculated costs of the two synfuels, on a unit thermal content basis, appear comparable. Both are, in fact, considerably more expensive than gasoline from petroleum at US \$34/-barrel. The gaps between the cost of gasoline (approx. US \$9/10^6 BTU) and ethanol from cane (US \$16 - 24/10^6 BTU) or methanol from wood (US \$14 - 23/10^6 BTU) are wider than possible corrections accounting for higher user efficiency, even considering properly designed alcohol engines. It is not surprising, therefore, the existence of highly subsidized capital financing for ethanol distilleries in Brazil.

Comparing the cost breakdowns in Tables 2 and 3, it is readily apparent that fermentation ethanol is highly sensitive to agricultural yield improvements leading to lower feedstock cost whereas methanol from wood via gasification is dominated by the capital-related charges. It follows, therefore, that breakthroughs in gasification, gas purification and/or methanol synthesis shall have a strong impact on the economics and potential of methanol from wood.

5. **Conclusions**

The outlook for methanol in Brazil is mixed. PROALCOOL's experience and further development is bound to have a profound impact on the potential penetration of methanol, especially in the near-term. Assuming Brazil persists on a strategy of primary emphasis on substitution of all oil fractions, methanol from domestic sources such as wood may play an important complementary role to fermentation ethanol. For example, methanol may be preferentially directed toward substitution of the diesel and fuel oil fractions. Methanol may also substitute gasoline fraction in regions far away from ethanol producing units.

Major incentives to consider methanol as synfuel in an ethanol-rich country such as Brazil are related to the need to broaden the base of energy feedstocks and products. Economic exploitation of low opportunity cost lignocellulosic materials, abundant but widely distributed in a country of continental dimensions, hinges on the conversion of these biomass materials to a low cost, clean-burning liquid fuel.

Methanol from biomass is a prime candidate, assuming that the high conversion and utilization efficiencies are proven in commercial scales and the safey and environmental concerns with large-scale methanol use are properly resolved.

In the long-term, the potential of methanol will be largely affected by the economic/strategic/social values of a wider domestic feedstock base, a potentially more efficient liquid fuel in manufacture and utilization, and a cleaner environment, to the Brazilian society.

Table 1. Brazil's Oil Refining Profile History and Projections

Fraction	1970	1979	1980	1985
Gasoline	35	20	17	14
Diesel Oil	23	28	30	36
Fuel Oil	29	33	27	16
Others	13	19	26	34

Sources: MME
            PETROBRÃS

Table 2 Cost of Methanol from Wood through Gasification

Basis: Brazil, 2nd Sem., 1981
        Costs per ton of Methanol
        Wood as feedstock and only fuel

Item	Case A	%	Case B	%
Wood	US $ 46/t	15.1	US $ 92/t	19.4
Water & Chemicals	US $ 17/t	5.6	US $ 17/t	3.6
Labor	US $ 35/t	11.5	US $ 35/t	7.4
Capital-Charges (25%/yr.)	US $207/t	67.8	US $330/t	69.6
Total	US $305/t	100.0	US $474/t	100.0
	or		or	
	US $ 0.92/gal.		US $1.44/gal.	
	or		or	
HHV basis	US $ 14.4/10^6 BTU		US $ 22.5/10^6 BTU	

Case A: Wood at US $20/t (dry) and unit investment of US $2.50/gal.-yr.

Case B: Wood at US $40/t (dry) and unit investment of US $4.00/gal.-yr.

Capacity range: 400--1000 t/d methanol.

Note: Gasification technology assuming fixed-bed, atmospheric, oxygen-blown wood gasifiers.

Table 3 Cost of Ethanol from Sugarcane through Sugar Juice Fermentation

Basis: Brazil, 2nd Sem., 1981
        Costs per ton of Ethanol
        Bagasse only fuel/No byproduct credit

Item	Case A	%	Case B	%
Sugarcane	US $369/t	62.4	US $385/t	61.1
Water & Chemicals	US $ 24/t	5.6	US $ 24/t	3.8
Labor	US $ 14/t	3.3	US $ 14/t	2.2
Capital-Charges (25%/yr.)	US $124/t	28.7	US $207/t	32.9
Total	US $431/t	100.0	US $630/t	100.0
	or		or	
	US $1.31/gal.		US $1.91/gal.	
	or		or	
HHV basis	US $ 16.2/10^6 BTU		US $ 23.7/10^6 BTU	

Case A: Cane at US $14/t and unit investment of US $1.50/gal.-yr.

Case B: Cane at US $20/t and unit investment of US $2.50/gal.-yr.

Capacity range: 120 - 1000 x 10^3 liters/d distilleries.

FIGURE 1

HISTORIC WORLD PRICES FOR PETROLEUM, SUGAR AND CORN

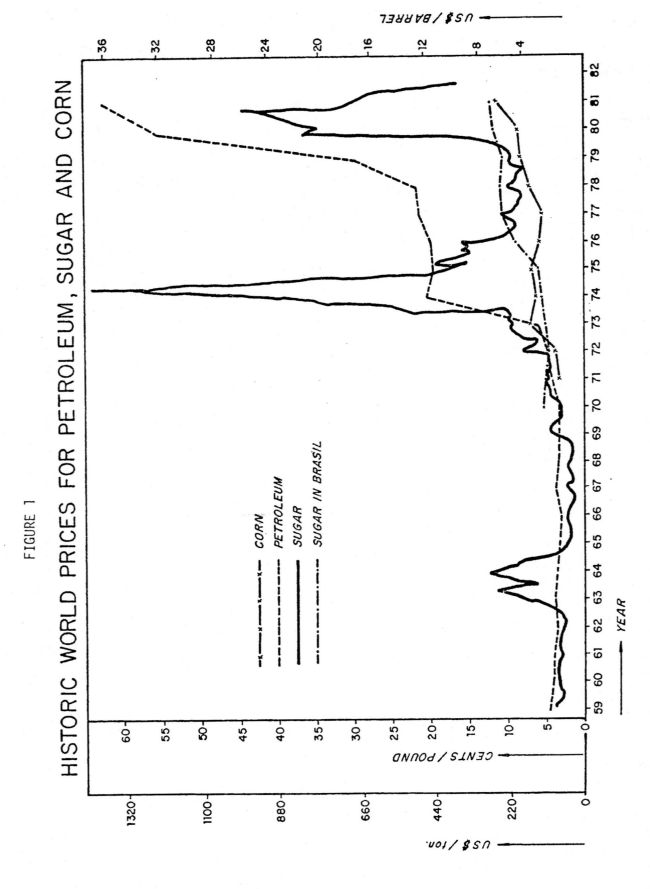

CORN
PETROLEUM
SUGAR
SUGAR IN BRASIL

US$/BARREL

YEAR

CENTS/POUND

US$/ton.

228

FIGURE 2
HISTORIC PRICES FOR FUEL OIL, ELECTRICITY AND WOOD IN BRAZIL

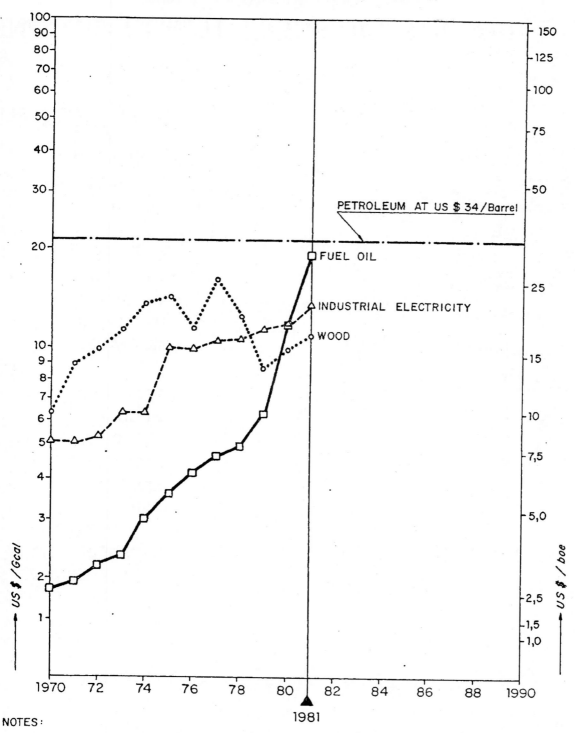

NOTES:

1 kWh ≡ 2580 kcal (Actual Thermal Equivalence of Electricity Adopted)

Basis : State of São Paulo

boe ≡ Barrel of Oil Equivalent

229

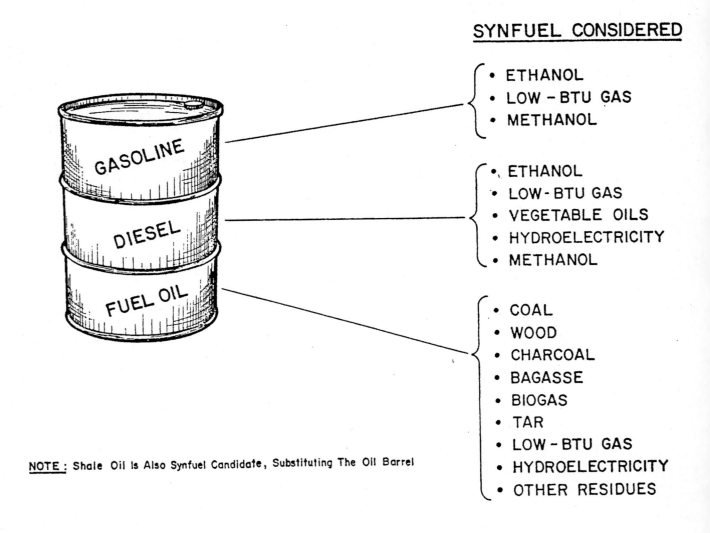

FIGURE 3

BRAZIL'S OIL SUBSTITUTION OPTIONS

SYNFUEL CONSIDERED

- ETHANOL
- LOW – BTU GAS
- METHANOL

- ETHANOL
- LOW-BTU GAS
- VEGETABLE OILS
- HYDROELECTRICITY
- METHANOL

- COAL
- WOOD
- CHARCOAL
- BAGASSE
- BIOGAS
- TAR
- LOW – BTU GAS
- HYDROELECTRICITY
- OTHER RESIDUES

NOTE : Shale Oil Is Also Synfuel Candidate, Substituting The Oil Barrel

THE PRESSURIZED FLUIDIZED BED GASIFIER
IN THE SYNTHESIS OF METHANOL FROM WOOD

J.W. Black
Omnifuel Gasification Systems
Toronto, Ontario

INTRODUCTION

Methanol is readily manufactured from a synthesis gas containing CO, CO_2 and H_2 by one of the established low pressure (50 to 100 atm) methanol technologies. For many years the principal source of the synthesis gas was the reformation of methane. To a lesser extent, naphtha was also used. In recent years, with the increased cost and reduced availability of these feedstocks, other sources of synthesis gas have been reviewed.

Coal is the most obvious choice because of its widespread availability and low cost. Although the technology for producing a clean synthesis gas from coal is more complex, and also requires a much larger capital investment, it is anticipated that increasing amounts of methanol will be manufactured from this feedstock in the future.

An alternate fuel for methanol synthesis, both renewable and readily available, is biomass which, like coal, is a raw material with a range of chemical compositions and physical properties. However, it also shares with coal, the feature that any single defined source is relatively consistent. Biomass has one significant handicap; it is extensively dispersed in comparison to fossil fuels. As a result the collection and transportation costs form a significant portion of the final fuel price.

To obtain a synthesis gas from biomass, the material is thermally decomposed via pyrolysis and/or partial oxidation to produce a gas containing CO, CO_2 H_2 H_2O and hydrocarbons. The particulates and tars are removed from the gas stream and the gas composition adjusted by a catalytic shift reactor and, if necessary, a reforming stage. Methanol can then be synthesized directly from the gas by conventional means.

GASIFICATION

The critical step in preparing the synthesis gas is the thermal conversion of biomass. There are a variety of techniques for accomplishing this, ranging from indirectly heated rotary kilns (pyrolysis) through two stage fluidized bed systems (combustion/pyrolysis) to autogenously heated moving beds (gasification).

As yet none of these systems is being used to commercially produce synthesis gas. However, there are efforts underway to rectify this situation and one such project involves a pressurized oxygen fluidized bed gasifier.

Fluidized Bed Gasification

A fluidized bed is comprised of a cylindrical reactor partially filled with small solid particles agitated by an evenly distributed upwardly flowing gas stream. Functionally the gas flow is sufficient to suspend the solid particles but not large enough to blow the particles out of the vessel. For a given particle size distribution, the range of gas velocities over which stable fluidization can be sustained is about 10:1 or higher. The solid particles in the fluidized state move rapidly throughout the vessel in a random fashion. The fluidizing gas however, has a tendency to pass through the bed in the form of bubbles. At the bottom of the bed the bubbles are small but as they pass through the bed, they grow by accretion to a size of about 20-30" in diameter. Solids mixing under these conditions is very intensive. The result of this is that fluidized beds have very good heat transfer rates and even temperature distribution throughout the bed.

When used as a gasifier for biomass, the fluidized bed, with its very high heat transfer rates, tends to promote rapid pyrolysis of the material. This results in a significant production of short chain hydrocarbons (methane, ethylene etc.). In addition, both the biomass, ash and the gas residence times are short. Therefore, equilibrium gas concentrations are not obtained without the use of a catalyst.

As with other types of autogenously heated gasifiers, the fluidized bed system requires oxygen or air to oxidize the residual char from the pyrolysis reaction. Fluidized beds are readily pressurized and if the oxygen or air is fed under pressure, both the energy and capital requirements for pressurizing the syn-gas can be significantly reduced.

Performance Data from an Air Fired Gasifier

Levesque Plywood Limited has installed a large air fired fluidized bed gasifier at their mill in Hearst, Ontario. The unit was purchased for two purposes; the disposal of 130 B.D. tons/day of mill residues and the displacement of over $1 million/annum of natural gas. The unit was started up in March 1981 and has been in full operation since June 1981. The complete system is shown in figure 1.

Because of the nature of the mill operations, fuel wood size ranges from chips to sanderdust with moisture contents (wet basis) varying from 7 to 50%. Typical data from the operation are featured in Table 1. The high hydrocarbon production rates are readily confirmed by these data.

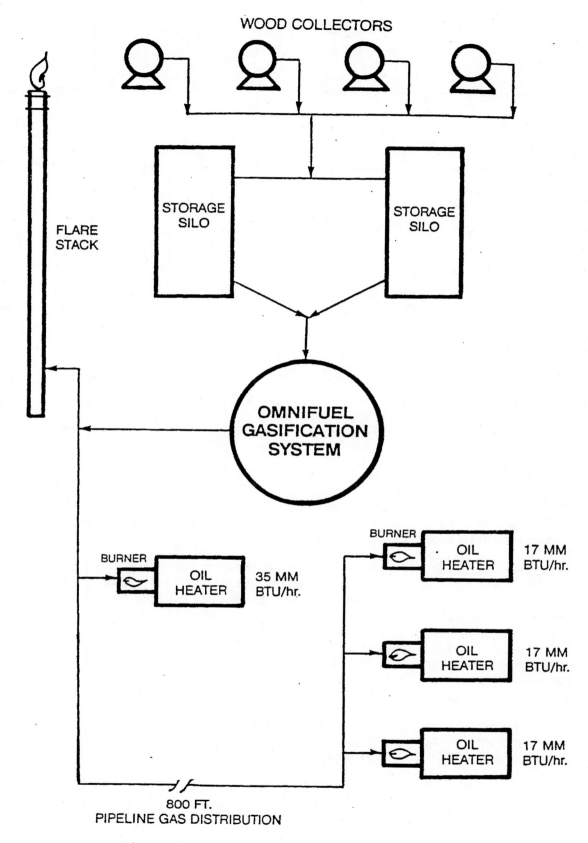

WOOD COLLECTORS

Figure 1. Energy Recovery by Gasification

233

Table 1

Typical Gas Analyses

Wood Moisture Content (Wt. %)	20%	44%
Component	Mole %	Mole %
H_2	5.3	5.6
CO	15.9	7.7
CH_4	7.0	3.3
C_2H_x	2.3	1.55
CO_2, N_2, H_2O	69.2	81.3
Heating Value (BTU/s.c.f.)	175	99

Predicted Oxygen Gasifier Performance

Although there are no data from commercially operated oxygen fluidized beds using biomass, sufficient information is available to provide a reasonable prediction of the performance of such a unit.

As compared to an air fed gasifier, oxygen systems have approximately twice the energy release and half the gas volume. As a result, the product gas distribution can be expected to remain similar to that of an air fired gasifier operating under the same conditions of temperature and pressure. Pressure increase might be expected to have some influence on the methane content of the gas but as has been shown earlier, the methane content of the product gas is well in excess of the equilibrium concentration. Thus increasing pressure, up to 20 atmospheres or more, should not markedly affect gas composition.

From this preliminary analysis and from data measured using oxygen, a typical gas composition such as is shown in Table 2 might reasonably be expected to be valid to pressures of 20 atmospheres.

As can be seen from Table 2 the total hydrocarbon content is sufficiently high that the gas will require reforming before it can be efficiently utilized in a methanol synthesis loop.

Table 2

Composition of Product Gas Using Commercial Oxygen

Component	Mole % (dry basis)
H_2	19.4
CO	36.7
CH_4	12.2
C_2H_x	5.0
CO_2/N_2	26.7
Heating Value	384 BTU/s.c.f.

METHANOL SYNTHESIS

To produce methanol from a fluidized bed biomass gasifier requires a
different approach from that of the conventional natural gas fueled route.
Methane is hydrogen rich and it is necessary to add carbon usually in the
form of CO_2 to balance the reaction

$$3CH_4 + 2H_2O + CO_2 \longrightarrow 4CH_3OH \tag{1}$$

Biomass, on the other hand, is hydrogen lean and carbon can be removed
as CO_2 to balance the reaction

$$CH_{1.4}O_{.6} + 0.7H_2O \longrightarrow 0.7CH_3OH + 0.3CO_2 \tag{2}$$

$$(wood)$$

Alternatively, hydrogen can be added, but this is generally more expensive

$$CH_{1.4}O_{.6} + 0.4H_2O + 0.9H_2 \longrightarrow CH_3OH \tag{3}$$

Process Description

A typical process [1] proposed for the production of methanol from wood
is described in Figure 2.

The material flow shown in Figure 2 begins at the wood pile where wood,
in the form of chips or sawdust, is retrieved. The wood is screened
and then dried before being conveyed to the gasifier. In the gasifier
wood is partially oxidized with oxygen to convert the biomass into gas

235

and ash. The latter is separated out by mechanical collectors. Steam is then added to the gas prior to heating in a primary reformer. The gases leaving the reformer, containing principally CO_2, CO, H_2 and H_2O, are cooled and passed through a shift converter to adjust the $H_2 : CO$ ratio to 2:1, the correct value for methanol.

Much of the remaining heat, along with the CO_2, is then removed from the gas in the CO_2 absorption system. From here, the gas is compressed and combined with the recycle from the methanol quench drum before entering the synthesis reactor. After leaving the catalyst vessel, the gases are cooled and methanol separated out. From the separator, the methanol is depressurized, distilled and pumped to storage. The unreacted gases are recycled to the synthesis loop. A small purge is bled from the system to prevent inerts such as N_2 and CH_4 from accumulating in the system.

One of the parameters considered during the preliminary process optimization was the gasifier operating pressure. The effects of increased reactor pressure are: reduced equipment size, lower compression power but increased methane slip in the reformer. There are also certain technological limitations within the wood feed system.

The initial conclusion is that a value of 1700 kPa (17 ata) appears to offer a good compromise.

A demonstration project based on such a gasifier has recently been announced. The project, which has a capacity of 250 B.D.T.P.D. is intended for the Province of Quebec, Canada.

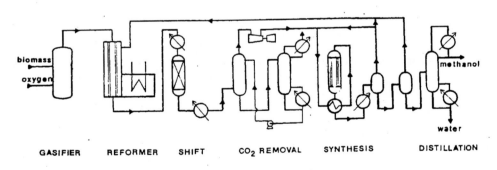

Figure 2. Methanol from Biomass

REFERENCES

1. Black, J.W.; Wedlock, J.C. "Synfuels from Biomass Grow Slowly." Hydrocarbon Processing Vol. 61: (June, 1982) p.89

APPENDIX

Discussion of Gasifier Requirements

As was mentioned above, there are a number of different gasifier systems available. Each of these systems offers different choices to the process designer. Some gasifiers produce almost pure CO and H_2 while others, like the fluidized bed, manufacture a gas with considerable quantities of hydrocarbons. Oxygen is used in certain units while others utilize indirect heat.

A detailed analysis of each of the units requires considerable effort beyond the scope of this presentation. However, a limited discussion of hydrocarbon production in oxygen gasifiers is appropriate to fluidized bed gasification.

Ideally the synthesis gas from a biomass gasifier would be comprised of hydrogen and carbon monoxide in the ratio of 2:1 with sufficient carbon dioxide to satisfy the methanol synthesis loop requirements. This cannot be achieved in a conventional pressurized oxygen fluidized bed gasifier. However, it is possible to conceive of a design that might result in a gas much lower in hydrocarbons than the data presented in Table 2.

For example, if it is assumed that a catalyst be added to the bed then some of the methane would be reformed to CO and H_2. Alternatively, by operating the reactor at a higher temperature, methane is also reformed.

Gas analyses typical of such conditions are presented in Table 3.

Table 3

Alternative Operating Conditions for an
Oxygen Fluidized Bed Gasifier

Temp. °C	760	760	925
Components	Mole %	Mole %	Mole %
CO	26.7	30	28.1
CH_4	8.9	3.7	1.0
H_2	14.1	26.2	35.6
C_2H_4	3.6	1.5	----
CO_2	18.8	16.9	20.4
H_2O	27.3	21.2	15.5
O_2T/T OD Wood	.31	.38	.45
% Increase in O_2 usage	----	+ 25%	+ 45%

It is immediately obvious from Table 3 that there is a trade-off; re-forming can be avoided but at the expense of additional oxygen and carbon dioxide removal capacity. It is implicitly assumed that the overall energy requirements are the same in all cases whether reforming is carried out in the bed or in a separate reformer. This is not strictly true since more heat is required for an externally fired re-former but this is probably offset by the additional energy requirements for oxygen production and compression.

To identify the capital cost differences, it is necessary to review the costs of oxygen production and reforming. An approximate capital cost breakdown for a small methanol plant is shown in Table 4.

Table 4

Capital Cost for small (300 TPD) Methanol Plant

	$ million (1980)
Feed Preparation	7.3
O_2 Plant	8.3*
Gasifier	4.5
Reformer	2.1*
Shift	0.9
CO_2 Removal	1.9*
Syn Loop	10.7
Off Sites	12.9
O/H Burden	15.0
	$63.2

From the table it can be concluded that the elimination of the reformer is approximately equal to about 25% increase in oxygen plant capacity. (The effects of scale savings on the increased size of the oxygen plant is offset by the additional heat exchange area for the extra gas volume and the carbon dioxide removal).

It is concluded, therefore, that at a first pass, the extra methane pro-duced by the fluidized bed gasifier is not necessarily detrimental.

238

METHANOL FROM WOOD AND PEAT

L. Waldheim, E. Rensfelt
STUDSVIK ENERGITEKNIK AB
Fuel Technology Department
S-611 82 NYKÖPING, Sweden

ABSTRACT

Due to the lack of domestic petroleum resources and natural gas in Sweden, the interest for use of biomass as raw material for production of methanol arose soon after the 1973 oil crisis.

Gasification is the missing step for the commercial production of methanol from biomass.

Feasibility studies during 1979 showed that oxygen blown gasification processes working below ash melting point had a distinct advantage over non-oxygen processes or processes working above ash melting point.

Tars and methane from biomass pyrolysis need a higher reaction temperature for conversion than is needed for char gasification in a fluidized bed. The interest have therefore been centralized to two processes, the High Temperature Winkler and MINO, both being pressurized, two stage, oxygen blown processes.

The HTW process has been studied as a short term development, the process operating conditions only needed to be adapted to the biomass fuel.

During 1980 and 1981 a pilot plant atmospheric pressure gasifier was used to determine these conditions together with pressurized bench-scale experiments. The results are used by UHDE for design of a demonstration plant in Sweden.

The other process, MINO, is a longer term development, this process using a high temperature fly ash filter and a catalytic secondary stage for tar and methane conversion.

Currently a pilot plant based on this concept is being built in Studsvik, and bench scale studies continue at the technical universities.

Sweden, having no petroleum or natural gas resources, is heavily dependent on imported oil both for residential and industrial heating and for transportation fuel. In 1979 the net import of oil was roughly 26 million toe, being 70% of the total energy consumption.

An important part of the energy consumption, ∿20% is used for transportation, 97% of this amount being based on oil, equalising ∿7.4 million toe. In a time where oil prices are rising, and political disturbances can both influence prices and the amount available for import, oil substitution and energy saving is one of the aims of Swedish energy policy.

For residential and industrial heating, a combination of saving and oil substitution for coal, wood or peat can be foreseen in the future and several old boiler facilities already have been altered and new ones commissioned for these fuels.

For the transportation sector, the situation is more difficult as the whole sector is designed for the use of liquid fules. In a report (1) by the Swedish Commission for oil substitution, the commission concludes that methanol for the foreseeable future being the most interesting candidate; pointing out the following advantages:

-    improved security of supply. Natural gas, heavy oil, coal, peat and wood can be used

-    time advantages. Distribution of 15% methanol in gasoline blends can be achieved quickly.

-    motor developments possible. 100% methanol motors.

-    environmental benefits. Less lead anti knocking agent needed.

-    better refinery economics. More nafta can be used for gasoline.

The disadvantages, the commission claims, are

-    conversion of vehicles required

-    changes in storage and distribution system

-    uncertainty of developments in other countries.

The group concludes that the short term substitution would be imported methanol based on oil or natural gas, where as a long term development coal or biomass could be used.

A pilot program is now in operation, and a test fleet of 2000 both company and private owned cars can now fill the M15 blend throughout Sweden, Figure 1.

With regard to production, the immediate solution is oil or natural gas based methanol from western Europe but in the longer perspective production will at least partly take place in Sweden.

An energy combinate where methanol is produced together with fuel gas and hot water for residential heating of the Stockholm area is being studied, Figure 2.

Biomass such as wood and peat, being the only domestic fuels available also is considered for methanol production. The amount of wood wastes and peat available have been estimated to 2-6 million tons of oil equivalents, depending on competition from other uses, e.g. residential heating. This amount, taking into account conversion losses being 15-40% of total transportation fuel consumption. Energy forestry on a large scale could contribute the raw material base, the possible amount greatly overriding the peat and wood waste resources.

Basic studies of gasification in Sweden

The oil crisis 1973 started an interest in the utilization of peat and wood in gasification processes.

In the gasifier, the fuel is first heated up and dried, then pyrolyzed to tar, gases and char. The char is then gasified with steam and oxygen the latter generating heat for the overall process.

By secondary reactions, tar and methane, can also be converted to low molecular weight gases, Figure 3.

Laboratory studies showed that the char yields on pyrolysis is low, and that large amounts of tars and methane is formed in this stage, Figure 4,5. Also the formed char is highly reactive on gasification, Figure 6 (2, 3, 4).

For production of synthesis gas, the secondary gas phase reactions are extremely important as these limit the amount of inerts in the gas.

In recent years, several laboratory studies have been performed, showing that high temperatures are necessary for methane conversion whereas tars are more easily broken down, and that catalysts are available, which are able to decrease the required temperature.

In 1979, the Board of Energy Source Development, initialized a feasibility study of biomass gasification for production of methanol, summing up the work performed. This feasibility study, presented more in detail elsewhere (5), showed that oxygen processes, working below ash melting point, was more economical than non-oxygen processes as these used more energy to break down tars and methane, as well as high temperature slagging processes as these use high amounts of oxygen to raise the temperature and have higher fuel quality demands, Figure 7. Also as a result the MINO process was proposed for further development.

The processes that were considered as being both more efficient and more practical were two stage processes, where the fuel is pyrolyzed and gasified in a char fluidized bed at pressure. Due to the high char reactivity, the tendency for dust entrainment and the low ash melting point, especially with peat, this first stage will be run at a lower temperature ensures a stable fluidization than the second stage where temperature is increased and tars and methane are converted.

Two such processes are under development in Sweden, the High Temperature Winkler process and the MINO process.

The HTW process in Sweden

The HTW process developed by UHDE/Rheinbraun in West Germany for lignite gasification has for a long time been considered for development in Sweden, the advantage being that lignite is a fuel of close ressemblance to peat and wood. This makes it possible to use the process only with small adaptions and having the German experience to build on, thereby providing a short cut path to larger size gasification plants.

The HTW process is a two stage process within the same reactor shell. In the bottom of the reactor, a conically section contains the fluidized bed operating at 1.0 MPa, Figure 8. The fuel is fed to the fluidized bed where it is pyrolyzed and gasified with steam and oxygen. From the bottom of the cone, ash is discharged.

The dust ladden gas containing tars and methane, leaving the bed enters a cylindrical shaft where additional oxygen is introduced to increase temperature enough to bring about tar and methane conversion, the dust being burned out at the same time.

The raw synthesis gas passes a cyclone where residual dust is captured and returned to the bottom of the gasifier.

This process has been studied in the so called Demo-plant project ran by the Studsvik subsidiary, Svensk Metanolutveckling AB, aiming to build a 240 tpd demonstration plant in cooperation with UHDE.

In this context subprogrammes have been performed in Sweden, studying the fuel drying system integration with the methanol plant, looking at the suitability of several commercially available drying processes in a methanol plant as well as the utilization of waste heat from the gasification - methanol plant for drying.

Also, the necessary adaptions of the operating parameters to be able to produce a synthesis quality gas has been studied by Studsvik.

During 1980 and 1981 a programme was run in a modified shale gasifier at Ranstad. 10 operating weeks have been performed and the results are presently being evaluated.

The Ranstad pilot plant, Figure 9, operates at atmospheric pressure and contains a cylindrical fluidized bed, designed for $900^{\circ}C$ and a pear shaped secondary zone designed for $1200^{\circ}C$. The throughput is roughly 2.5 ton DS per day.

In this reactor, the temperature necessary for tar and/or methane conversion, the influence of residence time on conversion, the gas yields and oxygen consumption has been studied for the secondary zone, as well as fluidized bed properties, kinetics, oxygen consumption and dust entrainment for both peat and wood.

242

Together with these experiments at atmospheric pressure, a number of runs were performed at various pressures in the bench scale equipment of the Royal Institute of Technology in Stockholm, Figure 10, to indicate the influence of pressure, but also to determine size scale factors. The results of these studies will provide the design basis for the demo-plant.

The schedule for this project is that the full design of a unit based on drying studies and gasification experiments as well as for general facilities together with estimates of investment and operating cost will be reported to the Department of Industry during 1982, to make a go ahead possible in 1982-83.

The MINO process

The MINO process, being a long term development, was proposed in the feasibility study mentioned earlier.

Like the HTW process it is a two stage process, Figure 11, where the first stage is a pressurized, 20-30 atm, fluidized bed where the fuel is pyrolyzed and gasified with oxygen and steam at 700-900°C.

Unlike the HTW, the secondary stage is not directly coupled to the first stage within the same reactor shell.

Instead the gas leaving the gasifier after passing a cyclone, enters a high temperature filter where the last remains of dust are taken away.

This is necessary to avoid plugging of the secondary stage, where additional oxygen is added, the temperature raised and tar and methane catalytically converted to carbon monoxide and hydrogen.

The advantages of this process are;

- low oxygen consumption as the catalysts make the conversion possible at lower temperatures.

- separation of high temperature from solids containing part decreases the risk for sintering the formation of ash deposits.

- the process condensate is free from dust and soot and very clean (<1000 ppm COD).

- heat recovery with less fouling problems.

- high efficiency because of low oxygen consumption, good possibilities for heat recovery and high process pressure.

Based on this concept a pilot plant is at present being built at Studsvik, Figure 12.

This unit has a 0.3 m diameter gasifier which is fed directly from a lock hopper through a full tube or by a screw from the side. The gasi-

fier is designed for 35 atm, 900°C. After passing the filter, the gas
is converted in the secondary stage, containing the catalyst, designed
for 35 atm, 1200°C.

After cooling, the gas is flared. Apart from the gasification section,
the plant also contains fuel storage, milling, screening and drying
facilities and a liquid oxygen and nitrogen storage and supply system.

The cost of this unit is 5 million $ and start-up is scheduled for
August 1982. Figure 13 shows an artist view of the plant area where
the fuel pretreatment stages are shown, Figure 14 is a blow-up of the
"tower" where the process equipment such as gasifier, filter and secondary reactor are located.

ADKNOWLEDGEMENT

Dr Åke Brandberg, Svensk Metanolutveckling AB, Dr Nils Lindman, and
colleagues of the Royal Institute of Technology. Dr Owe Svensson,
Enerchem AB.

REFERENCES

1.   Introduction of Alternative Motor Fuels. Report from the Swedish
     Commission for Oil Substitution.
     Department of Industry Ds I 1980:20 (English unabridged transla-
     tion of Ds I 1980:19).

2.   Erik Rensfelt et al., Basic gasification studies. Energy from bio-
     mass and wastes, Symposium paper 465-494. August 14-18 1978,
     Washington D.C.

3.   Erik Rensfelt et al., New possibilities for gasification of peat
     at low temperatures. 6th International Peat Congress. Symposium
     papers, August 17-23 1980, Duluth, Minnesota.

4.   C Ekström, E Rensfelt, Flash pyrolysis of biomass in Sweden.
     Paper presented at the SERI "Specialist's workshop on fast
     pyrolysis of biomass, October 19-22 1980, Copper Mountain, Colorado.

5.   S Engström, N Lindman, E Rensfelt, L Waldheim, A new synthesis gas
     process for biomass and peat. Energy from biomass and Wastes V.
     January 26-30 1982. Lake Buena Vista, Florida.

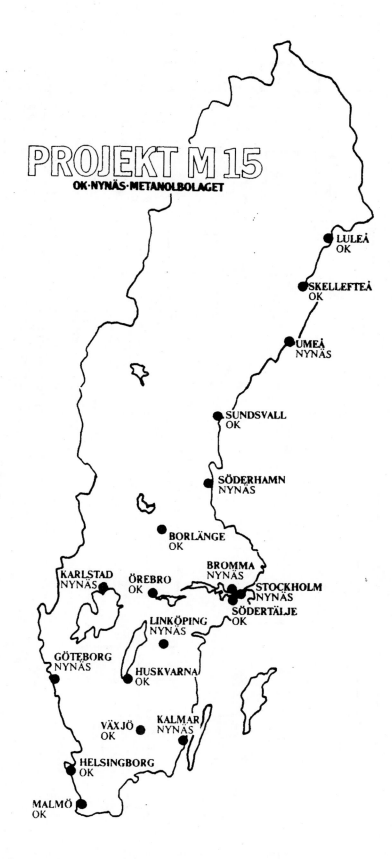

Figure 1: Methanol Fuel Blend Distribution Network

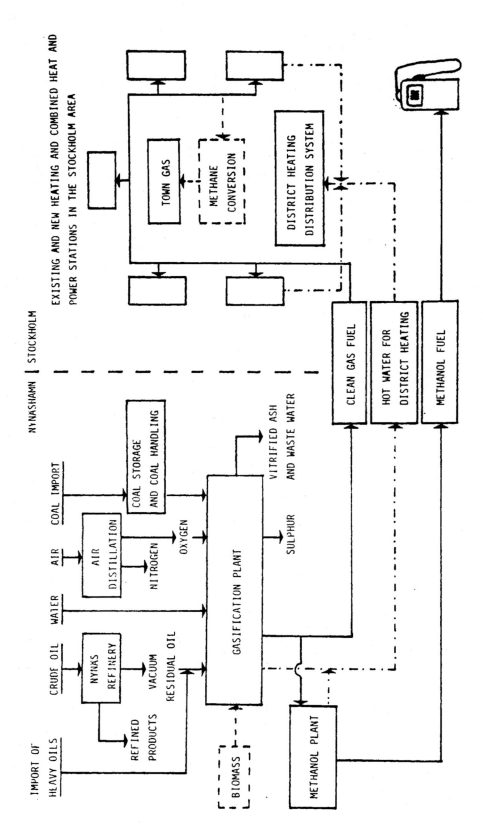

Figure 2: The Nynäs combinate. Fuel gas, methanol and heat from residual oil and coal.

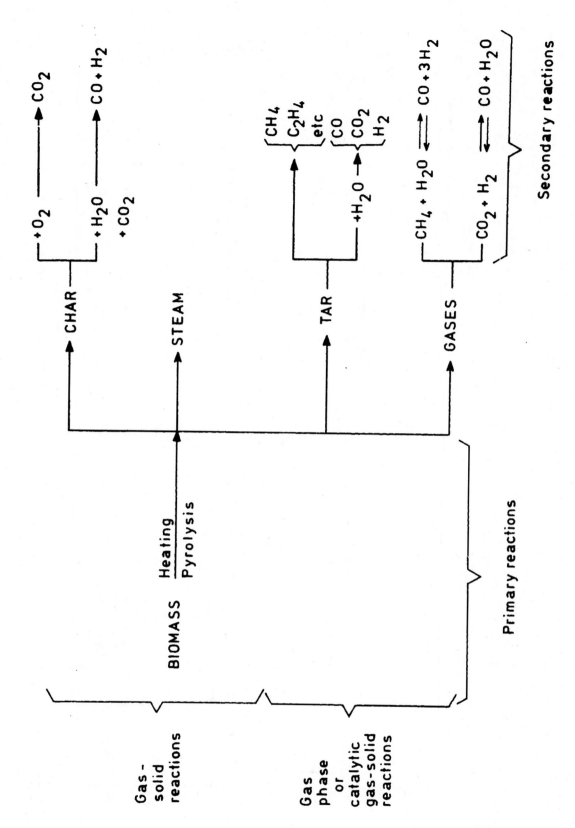

Figure 3: Principle reaction paths in gasification.

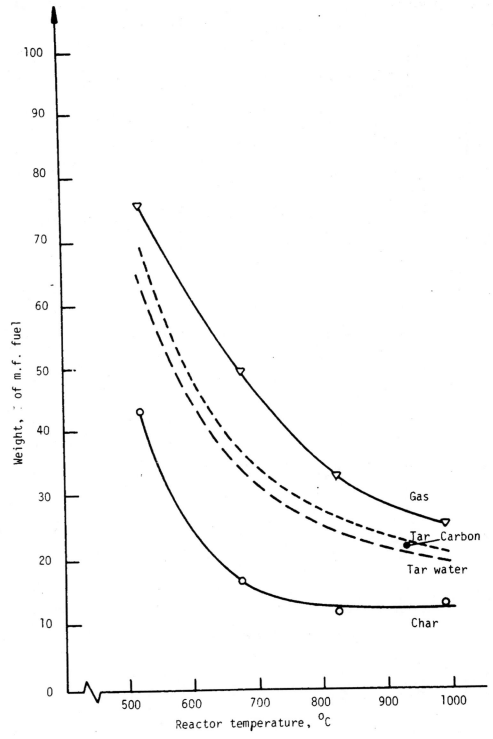

Flash pyrolysis of poplar wood
Product distribution at different reactor
temperature

Particle size: 0.4 - 0.5 mm

Figure 4

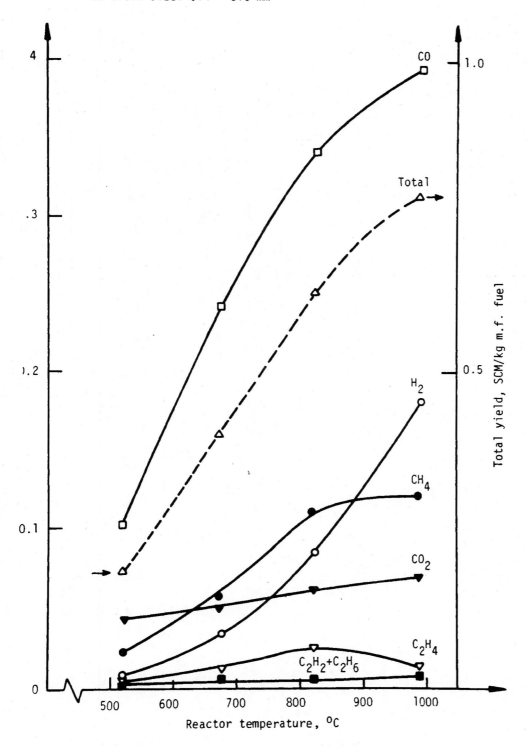

Flash pyrolysis of poplar wood
Gas production at different reactor
temperatures

Particle size: 0.4 - 0.5 mm

Figure 5

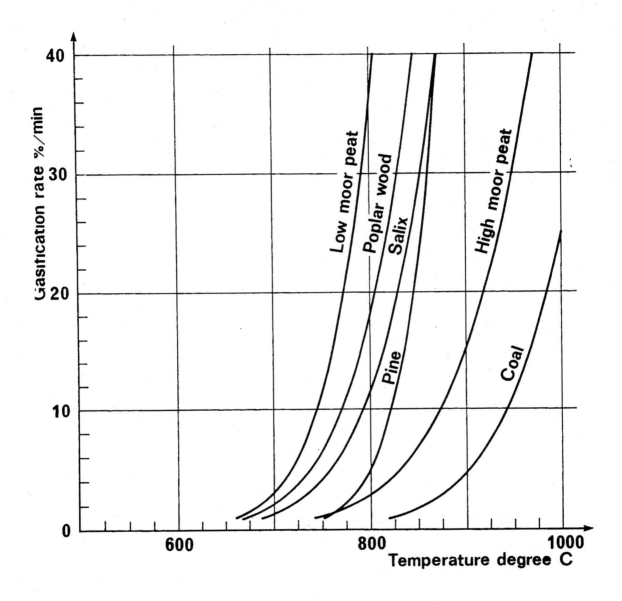

Figure 6:   Reaction rate of chars for steam gasification.

EFFICIENCY OF DIFFERENT WOOD TO METHANOL PROCESSES

LOSSES % HHV

BASE WOOD 50% DRY BASIS TO METHANOL

	OXYGEN	SLAGGING	NON-OXYGEN
CO_2-REMOVAL	5- 7	7- 8	3- 5
COOLING LOSS	18-23	19-24	25-32
FLUE GAS	3- 4	4- 5	7- 8
OXYGEN	3	4	-
DRYING	13	13	13
MILLING	<1	4- 6	<1
	42-50	51-60	48-58

EFFICIENCY % HHV

OXYGEN	SLAGGING	NONOXYGEN
48-55	40-45	45-50

Figure 7

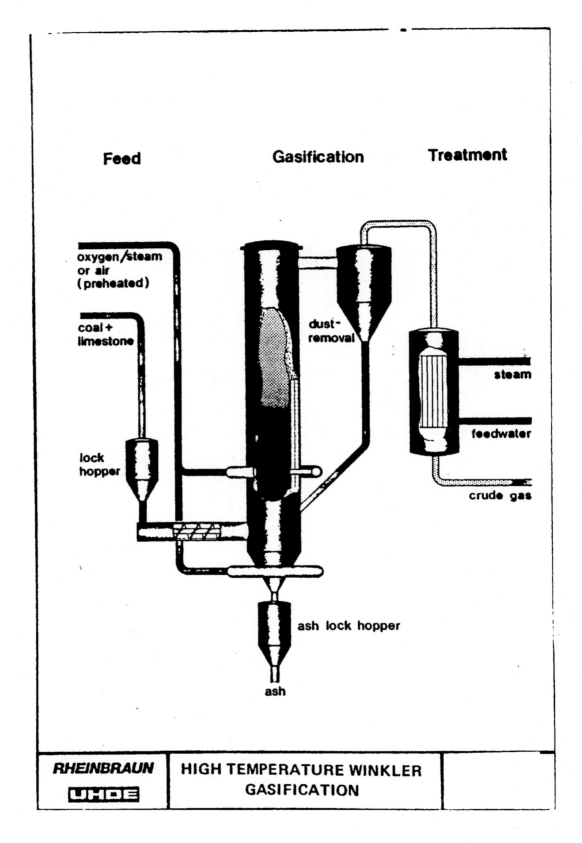

Feed   **Gasification**   **Treatment**

oxygen/steam
or air
(preheated)

coal +
limestone

dust-
removal

steam

feedwater

lock
hopper

crude gas

ash lock hopper

ash

| RHEINBRAUN UHDE | HIGH TEMPERATURE WINKLER GASIFICATION | |

Figure 8: High Temperature Winkler gasifier.

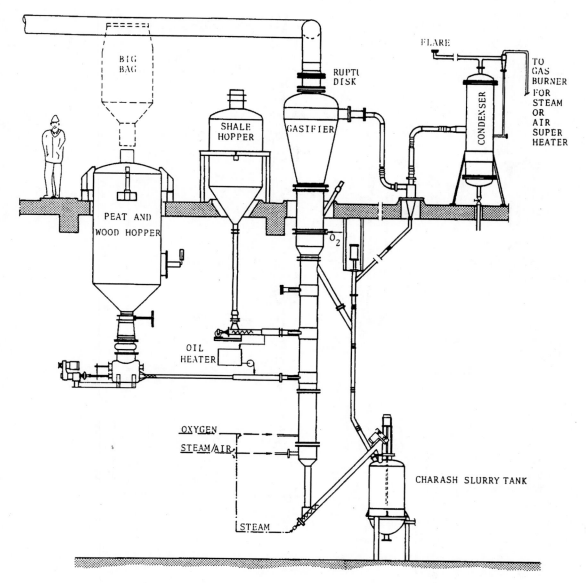

Figure 9:   The Ranstad gasifier

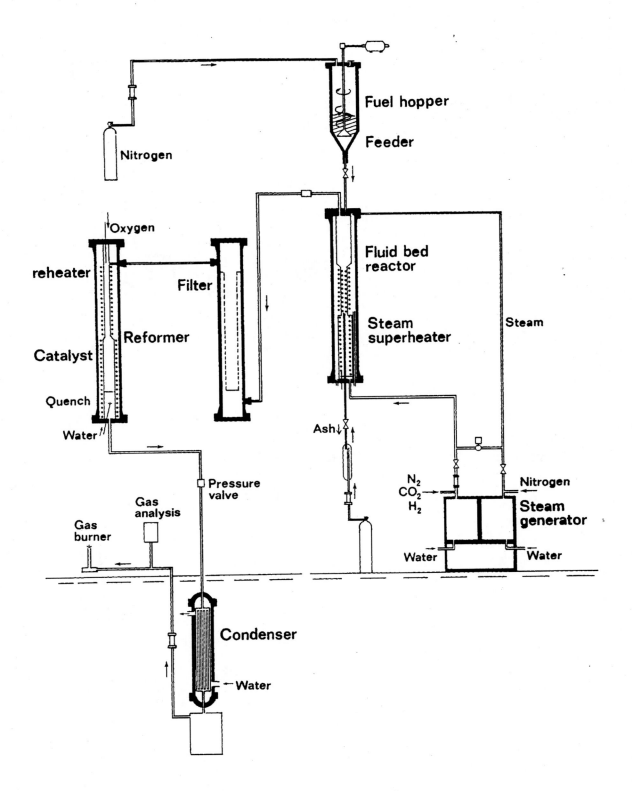

Figure 10: PDU at Royal Institute of Technology.

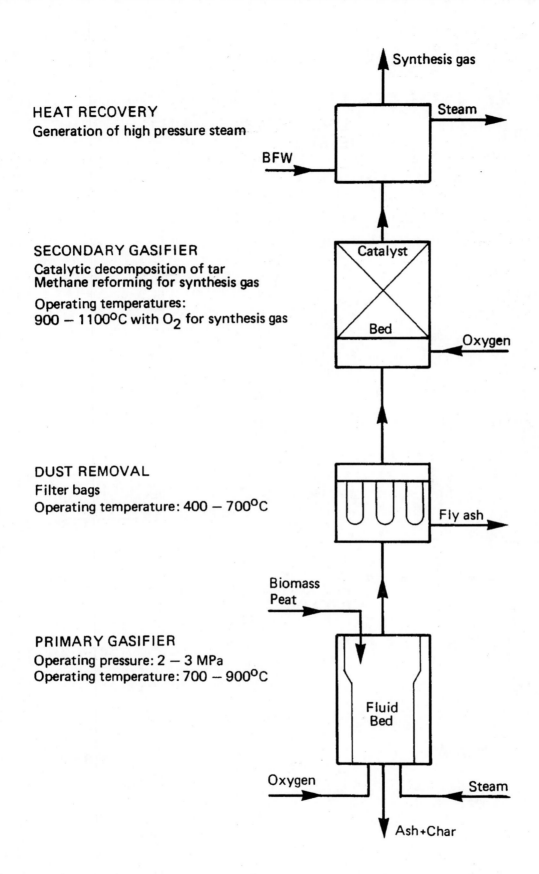

Figure 11: MINO Principle Flow Scheme.

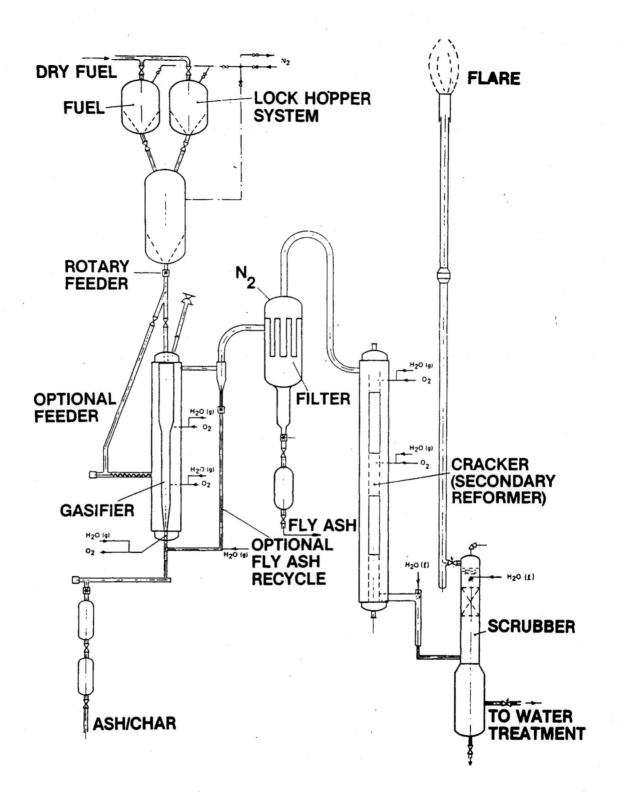

Figure 12: MINO Pilot plant.

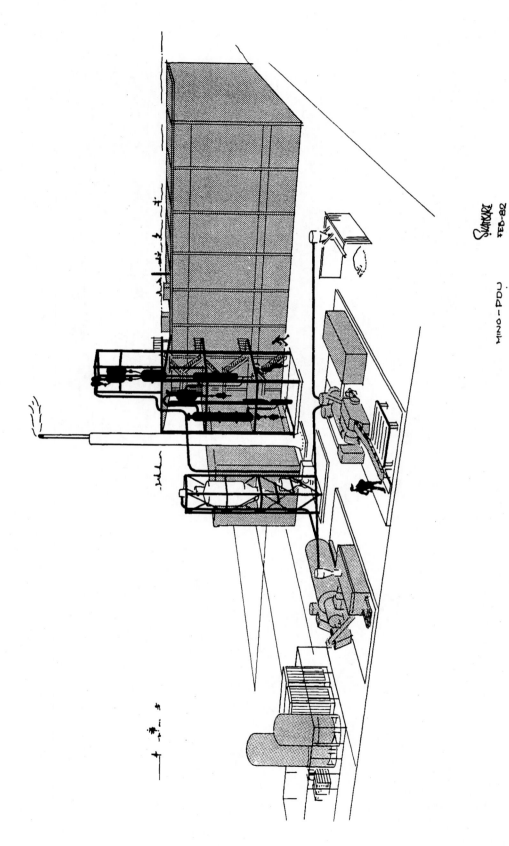

Figure 13: MINO Pilot plant. Artist's view of facility.

257

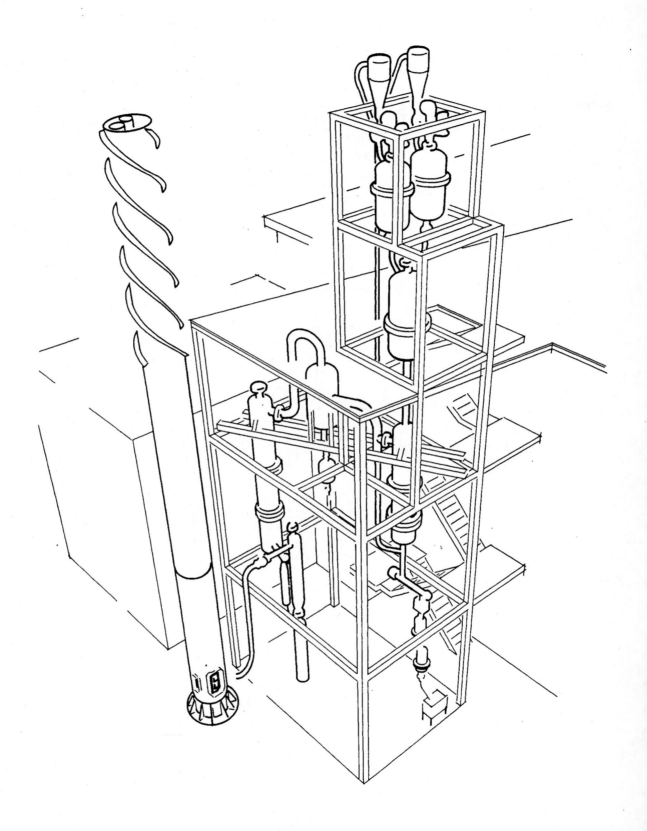

Figure 14: MINO Pilot Plant. Blow up of artist's view. Central process equipment.

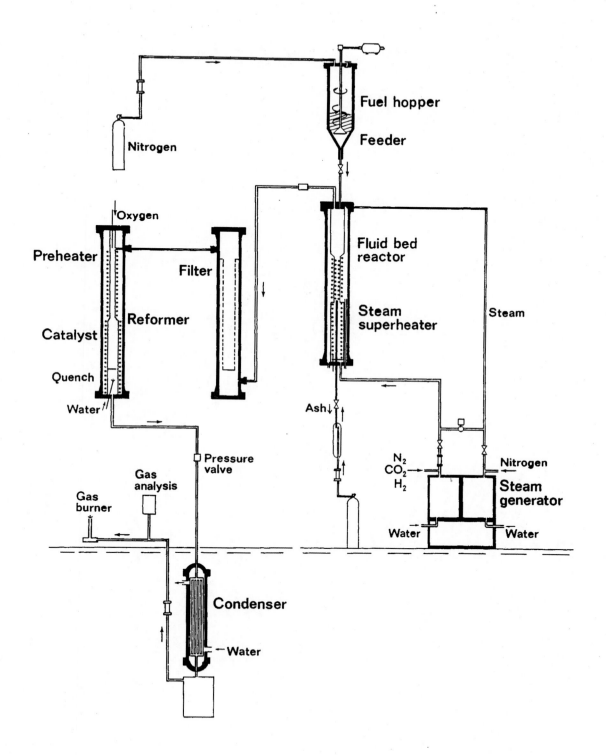

Figure 15

BIOMASS GASIFICATION DEVELOPMENTS

H.T. Wilson   and   J.R. Gibbins

Foster Wheeler Power Products Ltd.
Greater London House, Hampstead Rd.
London, NW1 7QN

SUMMARY

The present Foster Wheeler Power Products Ltd. Work Programme related to Biomass gasification is described. A description of a proposed 20 t/d gasification facility is also presented. Theoretical studies on gasification equilibrium thermodynamics, undertaken to complement and support the practical experimental work, are discussed and reported.

The equilibrium models have been found appropriate for a wide range of gasifier types and have provided valuable insight into fundamental aspects of gasifier design and operation.

INTRODUCTION

The present international interests in Biomass as a source of hydrocarbons for a variety of industrial applications continues to escalate. In particular, for those nations lacking the usual indigenous resources of oil or coal, Biomass conversion to Methanol represents a major investment potential which could reduce dependency on foreign imports and assist trade balance. Recognising the difficulties in implementing new technology it is FWPP's view that the lead into the potentially extensive Biomass market should be on a sound practical and theoretical base.

The special expertise FWPP has developed in the area of Biomass processing - particularly during the last ten years is being consolidated. For this reason a proposal was submitted to the U.K. Department of Energy (ETSU) and the C.E.C. (EEC No. C.24317 - Solar Energy Programme September 1979). The proposal, for a 40 kg/h pressurised Biomass gasification test facility was accepted and the work programme is now well advanced. In April 1980 FWPP submitted a further proposal to the C.E.C. related to the second phase of this programme, i.e. design and construction of a 20 t/d Biomass gasification pilot facility (EEC No. ESE/P/016/UK). Action on this latter programme is presently being discussed in the light of the 40 kg/h test plant objectives. Because of the FWPP interest in progressing active Biomass developments, it is considered timely to summarise the available expertise in the subject area.

This paper provides background to present activity and presents practical and theoretical aspects of the first stages of the FWPP gasification programme.

FWPP GASIFICATION PROGRAMME

Background

FWPP has a broad experience in pilot plant projects and specialised expertise in pyrolysis processes. The 'in-house' studies on thermal waste processing have been proceeding since the late 1960's.

Paper studies were instigated in late 1970 by the U.K. Department of Energy (ETSU), to establish the 'state of the art' in pyrolysis and gasification processes. It was considered that this approach was sufficient to indicate a generic approach to the field but that it was not suitable for design selection. FWPP and ETSU, on review, agreed that the direction of research should be to establish optimum process conditions and reactor design for synthesis gas production from Biomass.

The project objectives specified were to design and operate a test rig in order to gain sufficient insight regarding process conditions and reactor mode to design a Biomass gasification rig. This contrasts : the more generally adopted approach which is to opt for a particular reactor design for sometimes quite arbitrary reasons.

Parallel ETSU studies (supported) have indicated the premier position of wood in the long term. Consequently it was decided that for up-graded fuel processes such as SNG or MeOH, emphasis should be based on wood.

In addition to the main test facility which is presently being commissioned, ETSU are supporting a programme of work at the University of Aston in the U.K. This programme relates to single particle models and experimental studies on single particles using a thermogravimetric approach. The work between FWPP and UAB is closely co-ordinated.

DESIGN - CONSTRUCTION OF THE TEST FACILITY

A simplified 40 kg/h test facility Process Flow diagram is presented in Fig. 1. Due to the need to establish operational experience and because of time constraints for the arrangement and design of the 40 kg/h test facility, the first reactor to be tested was based on the FW Cross-Flow concept, although the chosen reactor shell design allows for a variety of flow configurations through refractory re-structuring and/or shell section replacement, Fig. 2.

The facility now being commissioned has been designed for an operating pressure of 30 bar and a maximum temperature of 1200°C.

Solids feeding and removal for the first reactor selected and super-heater design were identified as the main problem areas, although the operational design considerations have necessitated a continuous active appraisal of all components.

The solids feed equipment allows material to be continuously batched into the reactor via a pressurised lock hopper and triple slide valve lock system. The lock interspaces are selectively pressurised/depressurised with inert gas. Feeding is undertaken on a semi-automatic basis with operator initiation of the cycle from a low feed signal taken from a nuclear level detector mounted on the reactor. Ash/char products will be removed on a batch basis, although provision is made for continuous ash removal. The feed system described is only suitable for operating pressures up to 10 bars; beyond this pressure feed will be added using a batch charge arrangement.

Superheated steam at temperatures up to $900^{\circ}C$ is required for steam-only gasification. The final design selected allows superheated steam to be generated by passing saturated steam through single tubes with direct electric resistance heating in the tube walls. Providing the steam at the high temperatures and pressures entailed the solution of complex heat and mechanical design problems in respect of the super-heater tubes, the inherent difficulties being compounded by the need for variable steam rates.

Facilities on the test facility include an on-line data logger to monitor and process instrumentation signals and give alarms if set operating parameters are exceeded. A dedicated micro-computer will be used to undertake continuous data analysis. The necessary software for the data analysis is under development.

A partial oxidation system to treat the gases emerging from the cross-flow will be evaluated in the second phase of the programme. In this 'add on' reactor, oxygen will be introduced to raise the gas temperature to around $1000^{\circ}C$. Provision has also been made for the introduction of a packed bed of catalyst. Work on the design of this system has been completed and an order has been placed for its manufacture.

A conceptual design for a co-current down-draught reactor has been developed for the third phase of work with the test facility - Fig. 3. The design studies for this reactor have been complemented by the theoretical and experimental work described below.

Experimental programmes for the test facility are now being finalised. The findings of the active experimental programme may lead to reconsideration of the desired reactor configuration for the third phase of work.

Close project co-ordination has been maintained with The University of Aston in Birmingham (UAB) which is undertaking a parallel Biomass programme funded by the U.K. Department of Energy (ETSU).

Theoretical Gasifier Model

Theoretical computer models have been developed to product gas flow-rates, temperatures and other basic rig design parameters and to identify promising areas for investigation in the test programme (2). The models are based on the assumption that the product gases leaving the reactor will be in thermodynamic equilibrium. They deal only with the properties and flowrates of the streams in and out of the gasifier system; the details of processes inside the reactor are not analysed. While aspects such as reaction rates and internal temperature profiles cannot, therefore, be predicted, the models can be applied to a large variety of reactor types.

A high level of correlation has been achieved with published experimental performance figures for coal gasifiers of the fixed bed, fluidised bed and entrained particle type, indicating the validity of the basic assumptions.

C/H/O Equilibrium Calculations

The method described by Baron, Porter and Hammond (1) was used as a basis for calculating equilibrium in the presence of solid carbon, and a similar approach was developed to calculate equilibrium gas composition with no solid carbon. In both cases only five gases will be present at equilibrium in significant quantities under gasification conditions : CO, CO_2, H_2, H_2O and CH_4. Five independent equations are therefore required to calculate the gas composition, and a further one if solid carbon is included. Conservation of each element gives three equations; the remainder can be derived by equilibrium considerations for any suitable combination of reactions.

The reactions and derived equations for the gas partial pressures, where P is the total pressure, are :

Both Cases :

$$CO + H_2O \rightleftharpoons CO_2 + H_2 \quad : \quad K_1 = pCO_2 \ x \ pH_2/(pCO \ x \ pH_2O) \qquad (1)$$

Solid Carbon :

$$C + H_2O \rightleftharpoons CO + H_2 \quad : \quad K_2 = pCO \ x \ pH_2 \ x \ P/pH_2O \qquad (2)$$

$$C + 2H_2 \rightleftharpoons CH_4 \quad : \quad K_3 = pCH_4/(pH_2^2 \ x \ P) \qquad (3)$$

No Solid Carbon :

$$CH_4 + H_2O \rightleftharpoons CO + 3H_2 \quad : \quad K_4 = pH_2^3 \ x \ p^2/(pCO \ x \ pH_2O) \qquad (4)$$

The equilibrium constants ($K_1 - K_4$) for a given temperature are calculated using polynomial expressions derived from tabulated data.

Overall Model

The equilibrium system diagram for the gasifier is shown in Fig. 4. The basic model calculates the product gas composition and the net heat output from the system for given feeds and reaction temperature; this is also extended to give an iterative method to find the products and reaction temperature that will occur for a given heat output. A number of programme versions have been written to investigate the influence of various process parameters. - Table 1.

Typical results from two areas are presented : steam/oxygen gasification, Fig. 5, and the effect of pressure variation, Fig. 6.

Other process variables which have been examined include steam temperature, system heat loss, carbon utilisation rate, CH_4 recycling and prime fuel injection.

Steam/Oxygen Gasification

Most reactors will operate at or near zero heat output (i.e. adiabatically). With steam or oxygen only, neither of the gas compositions predicted would be particularly suitable for Methanol Synthesis. Improved results can be obtained however, by combined steam/oxygen gasification and/or increased steam flows. Fig. 7 shows the effect on CH_4 content and theoretical maximum methanol yield over the range of steam and oxygen flows attainable in the rig.

Effect of Pressure

Le Chatelier's principle predicts that as the pressure is increased, CH_4, CO_2 and H_2O will be produced in preference to CO and H_2. The equilibrium analysis for an adiabatic reactor given in Fig. 5 shows that the change is most pronounced at low pressures; above about 10 bars the gas composition is virtually unaltered. This can be explained by two factors : the lower percentage increase in total pressure at higher pressures for a given absolute increase and the rise in equilibrium temperature with lower gas calorific value as more CO_2 and H_2O are produced, which tends to counteract the effect of the increasing pressure. If the same invariance with changing pressure is confirmed in practice it may be a useful simplifying factor in system optimisation studies.

General Considerations

A number of general computer investigations were undertaken to examine the effect of variation in process parameters such as H/O ratio. These studies are not yet complete, but the preliminary findings already provide valuable process insight regarding optimisation.

PROPOSED 20 t/d DEMONSTRATION PLANT

In the proposed 20 t/d facility sized and dried biomass is converted to charcoal at 500°C and essentially atmospheric pressure, by combustion gases from an inert gas generator. Liquid and gaseous pyrolysis products are cooled, the gas being passed to the inert gas generator, drier or flare and the pyroligneous liquor pumped to a slurry mixer. Product charcoal is passed to the mixer, and the resulting charcoal slurry is pumped to the entrained bed gasifier operating at 55 bar pressure. A mixture of oxygen and steam is introduced to initiate and maintain gasification at approximately 1350°C. Steam for gasification is provided by a gas-fired package boiler with superheat facilities. The product gases pass through a shift chamber/quench cooler, then into a scrubbing system where recirculated condensate is used as the coolant. Excess liquor from the scrubber is passed back to the slurry unit. The product gases from the scrubber are analysed and then combusted in the boiler and/or flare/stack

TABLE 1.

EQUILIBRIUM PROGRAMME OPTIONS

Equilibrium Regime	Equilibrium in the presence of solid carbon (Steam/Oxygen flow rates limited)		Equilibrium in the absence of solid carbon (Steam/Oxygen flow rates from solid carbon equilibrium to stoichiometric combustion).	
INPUT DATA	H/O ratio or steam only/oxygen only Equilibrium temperature.	H/O ratio or steam only/oxygen only heat input/output.	Steam mass flow rate Oxygen mass flow rate Equilibrium temperature.	Steam mass flow rate Oxygen mass flow rate Heat input/output
RESULTS	Heat input/output Steam mass flow rate Oxygen mass flow rate	Equilibrium temperature Steam mass flow rate and/or Oxygen mass flow rate.	Heat input/output	Equilibrium temperature.

facility before discharge to atmosphere. Part of the main product gas from the demonstration plant will be sent through a methanol process route to generate small quantities of methanol for verification and analysis.

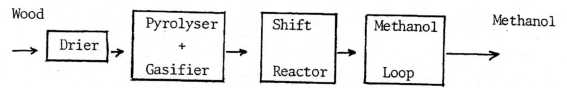

This process is described in more detail in a recent EEC Energy Publication (3).

The process flow diagram for the proposed pilot plant is shown in Fig. 8. A summary heat and mass balance is presented in Table 2.

TABLE 2   MASS AND ENTHALPY BALANCE DATA

Nature of Stream	Mass Flowrate (kg/h)	Temperature (°C)	Total Enthalpy (MJ/h)
Dried Feed (10% H_2O)	463.0	25	7685.8
Air to Inert Gas Generator	68.7	25	-
Char Product	128.2	500	4373.9
Pyrolysis Gas Export	151.3	40	324.4
Cooling Water from Scrubber	-	-	1294.4
Effluent Pryolysis Liquor	252.2	40	1308.8
Char Slurry	387.2	250	5961.9
Oxygen to Gasifier	310.0	150	36.0
Ash from Gasifier	4.6	924	4.3
Steam to Gasifier + Shift Reactor	500.0	270	1342.6
Product Syngas	1,192.6	924	7286.2

Plant Size Considerations

Based on the technical information available to FWPP through extensive analysis, it is considered that a 50% MeOH yield (weight basis - oven dried feed) is a reasonable maximum from a Biomass Gasification process, thus, a 200 t/d module would yield 100 t/d of MeOH. If one assumes a figure of 100 t/ha/y Biomass yield on an 'as received' basis, an 'energy plantation' area of 1460 ha per module (assuming 50% moisture in 'as received' material) is necessary. The Biomass yield figure is highly variable and would have a dramatic effect on processing costs - a point which has not gone unnoticed.

CONCLUSIONS

To support the widening FWPP interests in the Biomass Gasification area, theoretical gasifier models based on equilibrium considerations have been generated. The models have been shown to be appropriate for a wide range of gasifier types and a number of fundamental aspects of gasification technology have been examined using them.

Extending the equilibrium study to cover the relationship between methanol yield and the gasifier operating conditions has generated results which have been used to design a 40 kg/hr test facility and specify a meaningful experimental programme.

The findings to date have also provided an input for the design of a 20 t/d demonstration plant.

REFERENCES

1. Baron, R.E., et alia 'Chemical Equilibrium in Hydrogen/Oxygen Systems', MIT Press, London, 1976

2. Gibbens, J.R.   'General Thermodynamic Models for Gasifier Systems Based on Chemical Equilibria in a C/H/O Mixture in the Presence/Absence of Solid Carbon' (Confidential unpublished RD 695 Foster Wheeler technical notes).

3. Palz, W and Grassi G.,   'Energy from Biomass' Series E, Volume 2, D. Reidel, pp. 89-100.

BIOMASS GASIFICATION PLANT

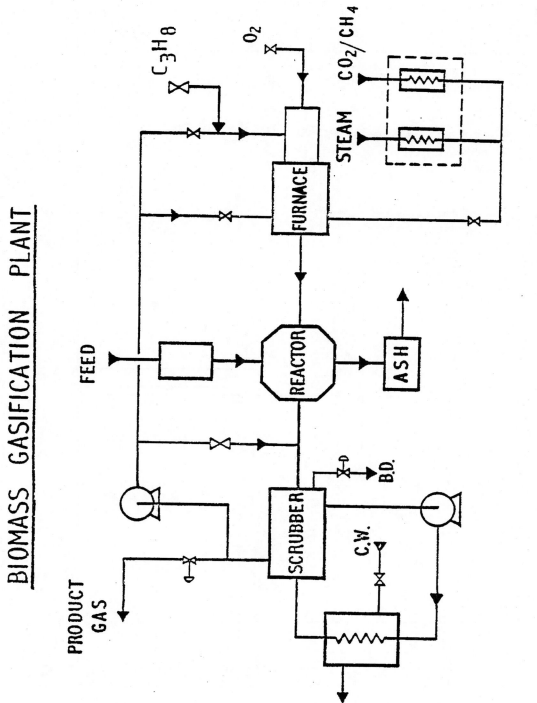

FIG. 1

www.KnowledgePublications.com

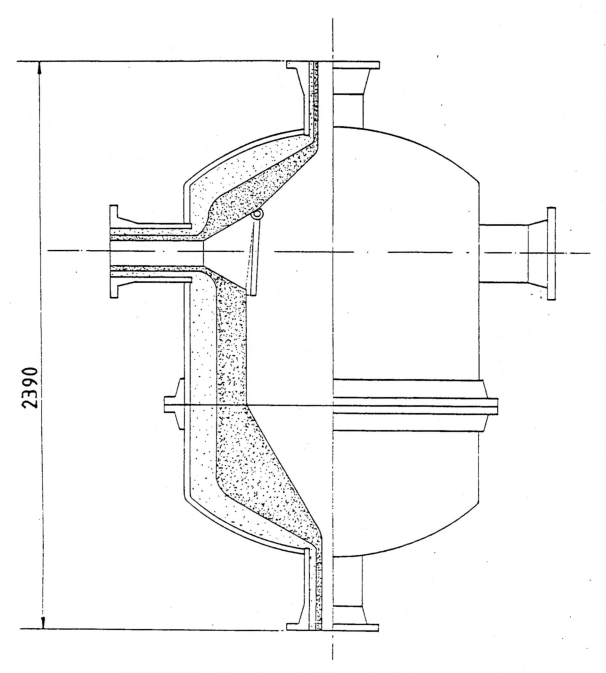

2390

TEST RIG REACTOR VESSEL
CROSSFLOW

FIG. 2

CONCEPTUAL DESIGN OF DOWNDRAUGHT GASIFIER — OPTION 2

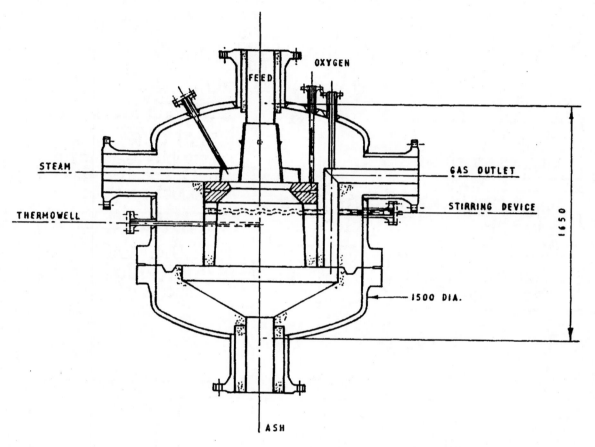

FIG. 3

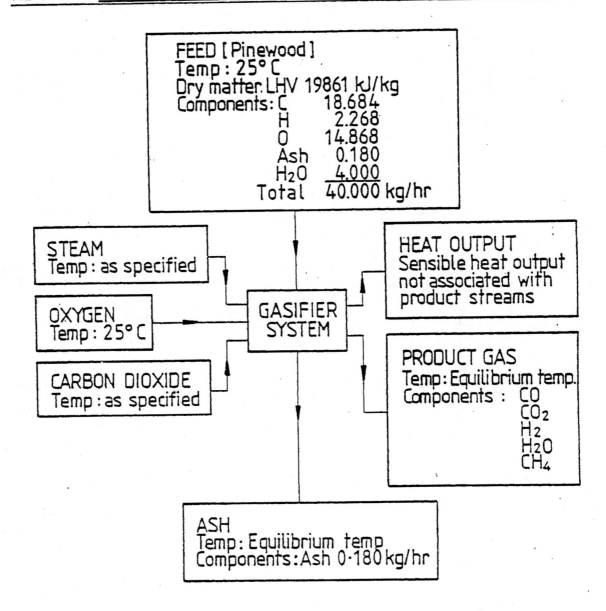

```
FEED [Pinewood]
Temp: 25°C
Dry matter LHV 19861 kJ/kg
Components: C      18.684
            H       2.268
            O      14.868
            Ash     0.180
            H₂O     4.000
            Total  40.000 kg/hr
```

```
STEAM
Temp: as specified
```

```
OXYGEN
Temp: 25°C
```

```
CARBON DIOXIDE
Temp: as specified
```

GASIFIER SYSTEM

```
HEAT OUTPUT
Sensible heat output
not associated with
product streams
```

```
PRODUCT GAS
Temp: Equilibrium temp.
Components :  CO
              CO₂
              H₂
              H₂O
              CH₄
```

```
ASH
Temp: Equilibrium temp
Components: Ash 0·180 kg/hr
```

ATE 30.7.81	REV.			
RAWN BY	REV.			Fig. 4
R. Dowsall	REV.			
APPROVED				

VARIATION IN GASIFIER PERFORMANCE WITH SYSTEM PRESSURE FOR EQUILIBRIUM WITH SOLID CARBON. EQUILIBRIUM TEMP: 700°C   GAS H/O RATIO: 1·7

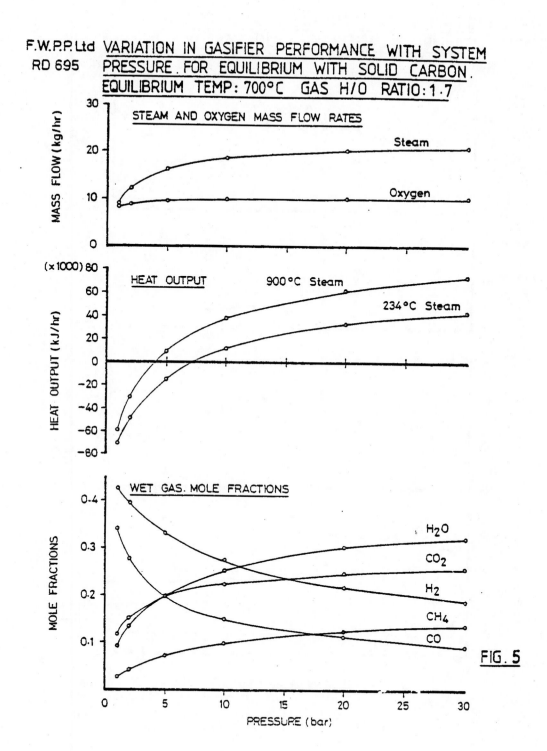

FIG. 5

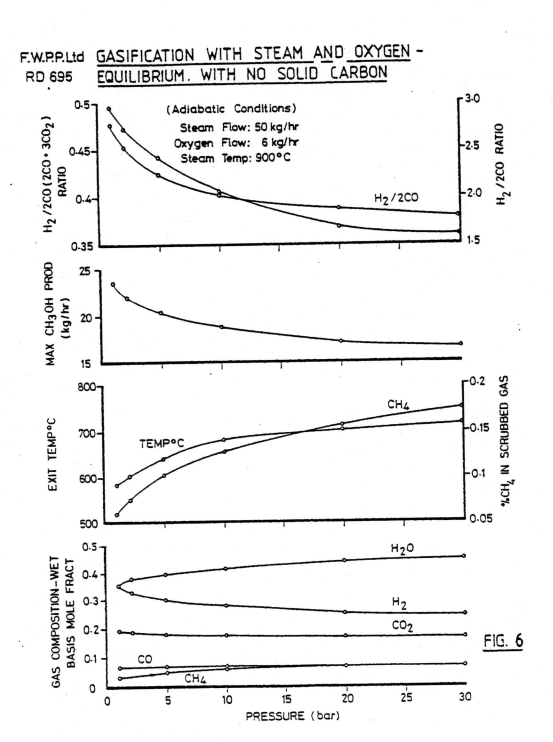

FIG. 6

FACTORS RELATING TO THEORETICAL METHANOL PRODUCTION
FOR VARIOUS STEAM AND OXYGEN FLOWRATES

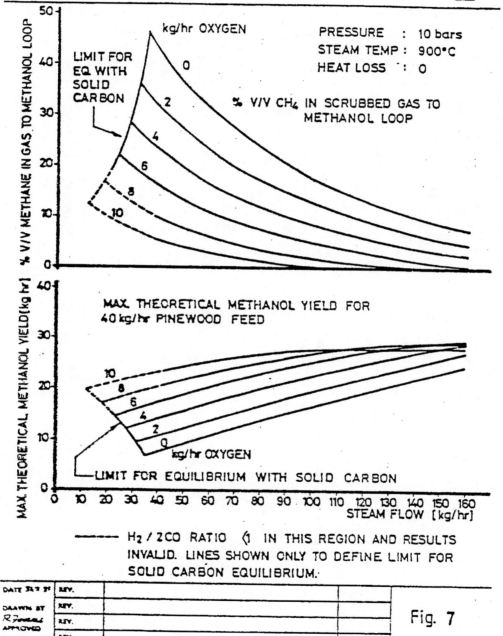

------ H₂ / 2CO RATIO ⟨1 IN THIS REGION AND RESULTS
INVALID. LINES SHOWN ONLY TO DEFINE LIMIT FOR
SOLID CARBON EQUILIBRIUM.

Fig. 7

FLOWSHEET FOR 20 TONNES/DAY BIOMASS TO METHANOL PLANT

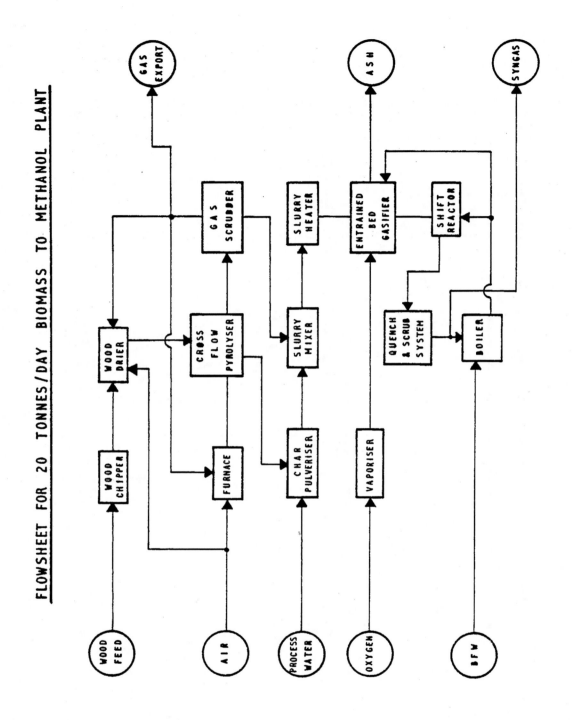

FIG. 8

Fuel Use of Methanol

DISSOCIATED METHANOL TEST RESULTS

Joseph G. Finegold and J. Thomas McKinnon
Solar Energy Research Institute
1617 Cole Boulevard
Golden, CO 80401

ABSTRACT

This paper describes the design and testing of an automotive fuel system that provides hydrogen-rich gases to an internal combustion engine by catalytically cracking, or dissociating, methanol on board the vehicle. The vaporization and dissociation of methanol absorb heat from the engine exhaust and increase the lower heating value of the fuel by approximately 22%. In addition, raising the compression ratio and burning with excess air increase the engine thermal efficiency.

Engine dynamometer test results with dissociated methanol demonstrated improvements in brake thermal efficiency compared to gasoline from 30% to 100% depending on engine speed and torque. Lower speeds and torques produce the largest improvements. This paper presents maps of exhaust temperature and exhaust heat content. The exhaust temperature is almost always high enough for dissociation to occur, but at lower power outputs, there is only enough exhaust energy for partial dissociation of the methanol.

INTRODUCTION

We expect dissociated methanol to offer higher efficiency than conventional liquid fuels because of three factors: (1) the increase in chemical energy due to waste heat recovery, (2) an extended lean misfire limit, and (3) higher allowable compression ratio. Exhaust emissions also are lower.

In the past, many researchers have proposed on-board fuel processing to generate hydrogen for automotive applications [1,2,3,4]. Numerous groups have constructed several experimental automobiles and performed engine tests [5,6,7,8]. Only recently has dissociation of alcohol attracted much serious attention.

Methanol can be dissociated to hydrogen and carbon monoxide or carbon dioxide by strongly endothermic reactions. The reactions occur in the 250°-350°C range, which matches available waste heat in engine exhaust, increasing the enthalpy of the fuels as shown in Table 1. In terms of the energy increase, the dissociation reaction yielding carbon monoxide is more attractive than the steam reforming reaction yielding carbon dioxide. The resultant fuels also have a higher energy density since less, or no, water is required. The steam reforming reaction has the advantage of occurring at a lower temperature (~200°C). Methanol has less tendency to coke (lay down carbon) on dissociation than hydrocarbon fuels do.

277

TABLE 1. COMPARISON OF FUEL PROCESSING REACTIONS

Reaction	Increase in Lower Heating Value
Methanol	
$CH_3OH + heat \rightarrow 2H_2 + CO$	22%
$CH_3OH + H_2O + heat \rightarrow 3H_2 + CO_2$	15%
Ethanol	
$C_2H_5OH + H_2O + heat \rightarrow 4H_2 + 2CO$	20%
$C_2H_5OH + 3H_2O + heat \rightarrow 6H_2 + 2CO_2$	13%

The methanol dissociation reaction is the reverse of the reaction by which methanol is produced. Although it is strongly endothermic, dissociation is thermodynamically favored because of an increase in entropy, as shown by the equation for free energy:

$$\Delta G_{rxn} = \Delta H_{rxn} - T\Delta S_{rxn} = -39.7 \ kJ/gmol \qquad [1]$$

$$\Delta H_{rxn} = 99.6 \ kJ/gmol$$
$$\Delta S_{rxn} = 243 \ J/gmol°C$$
$$T = 300°C \ (573 \ K)$$
$$P = 100 \ kPa$$

Equilibrium favors the reaction going nearly to completion. At 300°C and 150 kPa, equilibrium considerations predict that 99.9% of the methanol will be converted to CO and H_2, discounting side reactions.

In addition to the desired dissociation reaction, many side reactions are possible as shown in Table 2. Most of the side reactions are undesirable. Reactions 2 and 3 consume hydrogen that would have otherwise been available to extend the lean misfire limit. Reaction 5 produces solid carbon that would plug the catalyst bed and destroy the catalyst activity.

The choice of catalyst has a major effect on reaction kinetics and, thus, the composition of the reaction products. A number of catalysts are known to be active for methanol dissociation (e.g., platinum, palladium, copper, zinc). In addition to high activity toward dissociation at low temperatures and low activity toward side reactions, a fuel-reforming catalyst should have a low cost, long life, and be resistant to poisoning by impurities that might be present in fuel-grade methanol.

TABLE 2. METHANOL DISSOCIATION AND SIDE REACTIONS

(1)	CH_3OH	$\rightarrow$	$CO + 2H_2$
(2)	$2CH_3OH$	$\rightarrow$	$CH_3OCH_3 + H_2O$
(3)	$CH_3OH + H_2$	$\rightarrow$	$CH_4 + H_2O$
(4)	$CO + H_2O$	$\rightarrow$	$CO_2 + H_2$
(5)	$2CO$	$\rightarrow$	$C_2 + CO$
(6)	CH_3OH	$\rightarrow$	$CH_2O + H_2$

SYSTEMS DESCRIPTION

The dissociated methanol system comprises a fuel system to dissociate the methanol and a modified internal combustion engine to burn it. They are shown together in a simplified schematic drawing in Fig. 1 and in a comprehensive one in Fig. 2 showing instrumentation locations.

Fuel System

The function of the fuel system is to vaporize and dissociate the methanol and to deliver the hydrogen-rich gases to the engine to be burned. The major components, in order of fuel flow, are the vaporizer, superheater, reactor, and gas cooler. To minimize time and cost, most of the components selected are commercially available, although some were slightly modified. All the components were sized to fit into the engine compartment of a 1980 Chevrolet Citation so the system could be road tested.

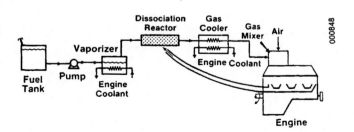

FIGURE 1. CONCEPTUAL DIAGRAM OF AUTOMOTIVE SYSTEM

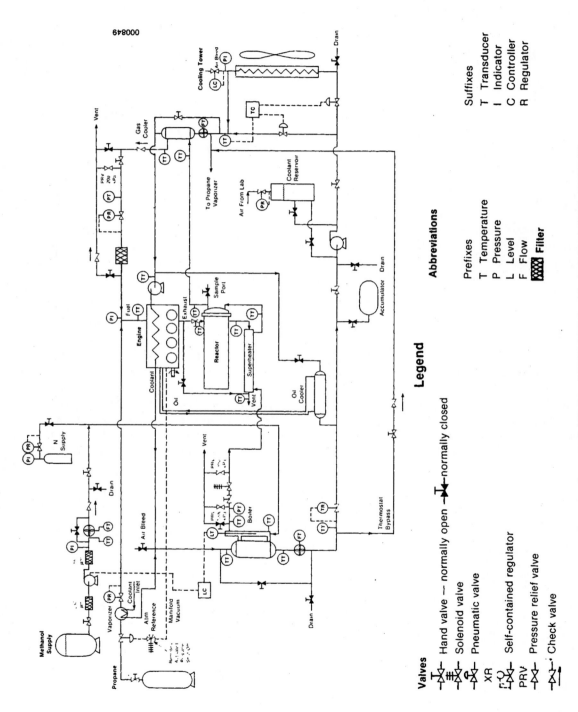

FIGURE 2. DETAILED SCHEMATIC OF AUTOMOTIVE SYSTEM

Legend

Valves

Hand valve — normally open
normally closed

Solenoid valve

Pneumatic valve

XR

Self-contained regulator

PRV
Pressure relief valve

Check valve

Abbreviations

Prefixes
T Temperature
P Pressure
L Level
F Flow

Filter

Suffixes
T Transducer
I Indicator
C Controller
R Regulator

Liquid methanol is pumped by a small electric gear pump from a fuel reservoir. It then is filtered to 7 μm using a series of filters. From here the methanol passes through a solenoid valve and into the vaporizer, a vertically-mounted, shell-and-tube heat exchanger with 2200 cm^2 of heat transfer area. Engine coolant, which provides heat for the vaporization, flows through the tubes, and the methanol is vaporized in the shell. A cylinder is mounted directly above the vaporizer and serves as a vapor-liquid separation chamber. A level probe, operating on an electrical capacitance principle, monitors the methanol level in the vaporizer. Cycling the liquid methanol solenoid valve controls the liquid level. The engine coolant temperature and, to a lesser extent, the vaporization rate determine the vaporization pressure. Most of the testing was conducted with the engine coolant in the 90°-100°C range, producing a methanol vapor pressure of 180-200 kPa.

Methanol leaves the vaporizer as saturated vapor at approximately 80°C. It passes through a solenoid valve and into the superheater, a double-pipe heat exchanger with 880 cm^2 heat transfer area that heats the methanol to approximately 250°C using engine exhaust after it leaves the catalytic reactor. Upon leaving the superheater, the methanol vapor enters the dissociation reactor, where the methanol vapor makes contact with the catalyst and where heat from the engine exhaust drives the endothermic reaction. The reactor was designed, built, and tested by Cerini, Houseman, and Voecks [9] at the Jet Propulsion Laboratory under contract with the Solar Energy Research Institute (SERI). The reactor is a stainless steel, shell-and-tube heat exchanger, 100 cm long and 18 cm in diameter with 4.0 m^2 of heat transfer area. The 0.8-cm ID tubes are packed with catalyst pellets over which the fuel flows. The engine exhaust flows directly from the exhaust manifold to the reactor. Both fuel and the exhaust sides are two pass flow, and the flow is counter-current. The reaction occurs on the surface of a Cu-ZnO catalyst supported on alumina pellets, United Catalysts #T2107RS.

The gaseous fuel, which consists of hydrogen and carbon monoxide in approximately a 2:1 ratio with small amounts of methanol, methane, and dimethyl ether, leaves the reactor at approximately 300°C. Before entering the engine, the gaseous fuel is cooled to 100°C to improve the volumetric efficiency, lower NO_x emissions, and increase resistance to preignition. The cooling is done using engine coolant from the radiator in a small shell-and-tube heat exchanger (heat transfer area = 1200 cm^2). The decrease in temperature increases the energy density of the fuel from 5.4 kJ/ℓ to 8.3 kJ/ℓ (methane at STP is 34.0 kJ/ℓ). The higher energy density of the fuel allows increased engine power output because the fractional volume required for fuel in the air-fuel mixture is reduced.

A conventional gas regulator upstream of the carburetor controls pressure of this gaseous fuel. The final step in fuel processing is to filter any catalyst fines from the fuel stream to protect the engine. At this point, the carburetor can draw on a supply of cool synthesis gas at a regulated pressure.

Since the fuel processing system requires engine heat to function, a separate start-up system is required. For the test stand, propane was plumbed to the fuel line directly upstream of the carburetor. After the engine is adequately warmed up, the methanol flow is started and the propane flow shut off. A liquid methanol fuel injection system is being installed in the vehicle for startup.

Engine

We used a General Motors 2.5-ℓ, in-line, four-cylinder engine rated at 65 kW from a 1980 Chevrolet Citation. The block and cross-flow head are cast iron. The GM high energy ignition system was used. The engine was modified only slightly to operate on dissociated methanol. The compression ratio was increased from the stock 8.3:1 to approximately 14:1 by installing flat-top pistons with greater compression height and by milling 1.5 mm from the cylinder head. The original carburetor was replaced with an Impco air-valve carburetor, Model 225, designed for propane. No changes were made to valve timing, but we removed the exhaust gas recirculation, exhaust air injection equipment, and the exhaust catalyst.

RESULTS

Figures 3 and 4 show the engine maps for the baseline gasoline engine and the dissociated methanol system, respectively. Note that the peak efficiency for the gasoline system is 27% and for the methanol system, 35%. The peak efficiency for methanol occurs at a lower speed.

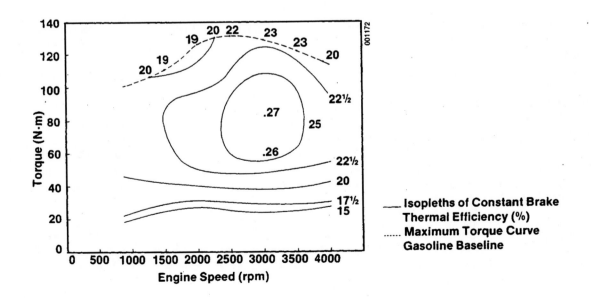

FIGURE 3. GASOLINE ENGINE MAP

Figures 5 and 6 present brake thermal efficiency compared to torque at 1000 and 2000 rpm, respectively, for both the gasoline system and the dissociated methanol system. The improvement is in the range of 31% to 48% at 1000 rpm and from 38% to 49% at 2000 rpm.

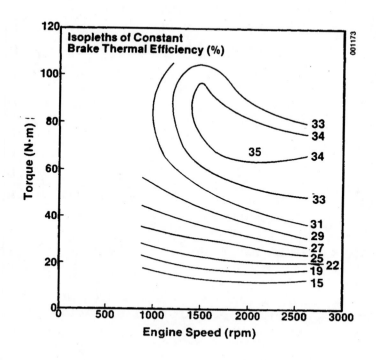

FIGURE 4. DISSOCIATED METHANOL ENGINE MAP

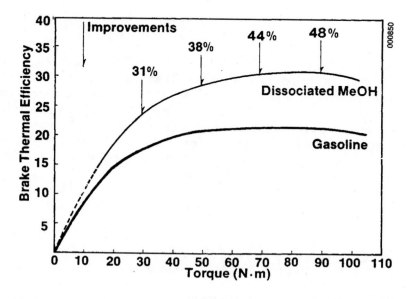

FIGURE 5. BRAKE THERMAL EFFICIENCY VS. TORQUE AT 1000 rpm

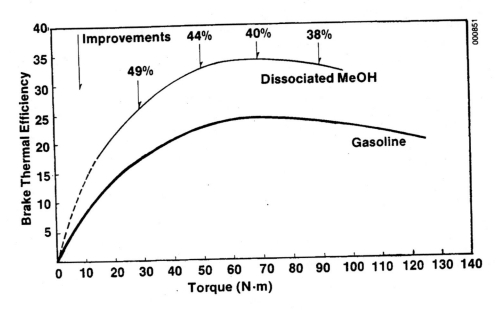

FIGURE 6. BRAKE THERMAL EFFICIENCY VS. TORQUE AT 2000 rpm

Figures 7 and 8 show maps of exhaust temperature and exhaust heat content relative to that required for 100% dissociation of the inlet methanol. With the Cu/ZnO catalyst, the effective lower temperature limit for reaction is 250°-300°C. At the lower power points, the exhaust temperature and heat content are only high enough to dissociate part of the methanol. In practice, this is not a problem. Even with a small fraction of the methanol dissociated, there is enough hydrogen generated to gain the desired lean-burn advantages. Some of the possible chemical energy gain, however, is not realized.

DISCUSSION

The data presented in the previous section shows substantial improvements in brake thermal efficiency for the dissociated methanol system when compared to the gasoline system. We attribute the improvements to three basic differences: (1) the chemical energy increase of the fuel resulting from the vaporization and subsequent catalytic dissociation of methanol into hydrogen and carbon monoxide; (2) the increase in engine efficiency resulting from the use of a very high compression ratio; and (3) the use of very low equivalence ratios.*

---

*Equivalence ratio (ϕ) is the actual fuel/air ratio divided by the stoichiometric fuel/air ratio. It is the inverse of the excess air ratio (λ).

The chemical energy increase of the fuel is greatest under high loads when the most thermal energy is present in the exhaust. Despite this, the improvements relative to gasoline are greatest under low loads.

The increased compression ratio is made possible by the high resistance to preignition of the hydrogen-rich fuel. High compression ratios (expansion ratios) allow more work to be extracted from a given charge on the expansion stroke, thus increasing the thermodynamic efficiency. The magnitude of the increase may be estimated from the equation for air-standard cycle efficiency:

$$\eta = 1 - \left(\frac{1}{CR}\right)^{\gamma-1} \tag{2}$$

where

η = thermal efficiency
CR = compression ratio
γ = ratio of specific heats (C_p/C_v).

Excess air combustion causes higher thermal efficiency for several reasons: reduced throttling losses, cooler combustion temperatures, and decreased heat capacity of the combustion products. Excess air combustion is possible because of the wide flammability limits of hydrogen, the major constituent of the fuel. The optimum equivalence ratio was as low as $\phi = 0.3$ ($\lambda = 3.3$) depending on engine speed and load.

Throttling losses are reduced in a lean-burn engine because manifold pressures are much higher for a given power output; thus, the engine does not need to expend as much shaft power in pumping the air/fuel mixture into the cylinders. For example, a 2.5-ℓ engine operating at 2500 rpm with a manifold pressure of 70 kPa (9-in. Hg vacuum) wastes approximately 1 kW of shaft power pumping air across the partially closed throttle. An engine fueled with hydrogen or hydrogen-rich gases can operate under most conditions with the throttle almost or completely wide open. Power is modulated by controlling fuel flow once wide-open throttle at low equivalence ratios is attained.

Low equivalence ratios reduce peak combustion temperatures because of the diluent effect of the excess air. The most obvious effect is that heat losses to the cylinder walls are lowered, allowing more heat to be converted to work. Two more subtle effects are changes in heat capacity with temperature and dissociation of water and carbon dioxide at high temperature. For example, from 100° to 2500°C the C_v of water vapor increases 55%. The result is that a given amount of heat increases combustion temperatures more at a lower temperature and, thus, is more effective. High combustion temperatures cause a fraction of the water vapor and carbon dioxide to endothermically dissociate at the start of the expansion stroke, absorbing some of the energy of combustion. The water vapor and carbon dioxide recombine and release the energy, but it

285

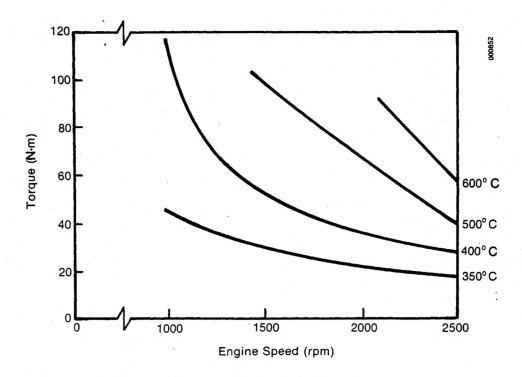

FIGURE 7. EXHAUST TEMPERATURE MAP

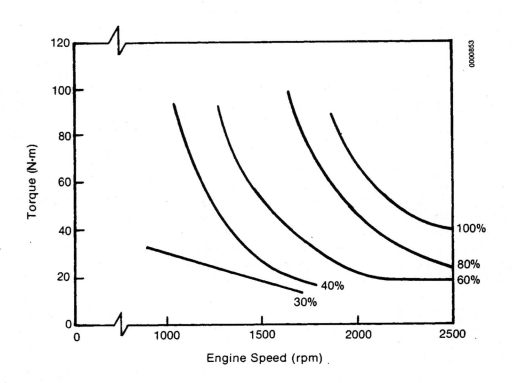

FIGURE 8. PERCENTAGE OF FUEL METHANOL THAT CAN BE DISSOCIATED WITH EXHAUST HEAT

is released later in the expansion stroke where it is less effective. The dissociation is a very strong function of temperature and pressure.

The heat capacity of the combustion products of a lean-burn engine is further reduced because air has a lower heat capacity than water and carbon dioxide. This allows higher combustion temperatures for a given heat input. Equation 2 also shows this effect since γ increases as C_v decreases.

The power of the dissociated methanol engine was comparable to the gasoline engine at low engine speeds. The energy density of the fuel is approximately one-fourth that of methane and one-tenth that of propane, but less air is required to burn the dissociated methanol. Thus, the energy density of the air/fuel mixture is approximately the same for all these gaseous fuels and is about 10% less than gasoline/air mixtures. The increased compression ratio brings the power of gasoline and dissociated methanol engines to about the same level.

VEHICLE INSTALLATION

The entire system was installed in the engine compartment of the Citation for road testing and EPA emissions testing. The methanol vaporizer was replaced with a shell-and-tube heat exchanger with 3300 cm^2 of heat transfer area, 50% larger than the original one, allowing the coolant thermostat setting to be lowered to ~85°C. The methanol vaporizes in the shell, and the coolant flows in a two-pass configuration in the tubes. The heat exchanger is mounted vertically as was the one on the test stand. A larger capacity filter with a more favorable shape for vehicle installation was used. The fuel regulator was replaced with a larger capacity one to allow more precise pressure regulation. No muffler is used on the vehicle as the reactor adequately silenced exhaust noise.

SUMMARY

A dissociated methanol fuel system was designed, built, and tested. Improvements in the brake thermal efficiency of 30%-100% over gasoline were obtained from engine dynamometer tests even though the fuel generally did not completely dissociate. Vehicle tests are currently underway, and we are designing a second generation system to solve the problems encountered in the first system and to explore the benefits of design improvements.

ACKNOWLEDGMENTS

Many people at SERI performed the work on this project. We especially want to thank current team members: Mark Sorency, Gerard Glinsky, Steve Rummel, Ed Gostling, Mike Karpuk, Mark Blakeslee, and Dan Schell for their contributions. Dr. R. Passamaneck was responsible for the engine dynamometer testing of the dissociated methanol system.

Dr. C. S. Smith is acknowledged for providing the management environment that stimulated this work. This work was funded by the Office of Alcohol Fuels, U.S. Department of Energy.

REFERENCES

1. Breshears, R., H. Cotrill, and J. Rupe. Hydrogen Injection for Internal Combustion Engines. Presented to Council on Environmental Quality Advisory Committee on Alternative Power Systems. Ann Arbor, Mich. 1974.

2. Houseman, J. and G. E. Voecks. "Hydrogen Engines Based on Liquid Fuels: a Review." Third World Hydrogen Energy Conference Proceedings. Tokyo, Japan. 1980.

3. Kester, F. L., A. J. Konopta, and E. H. Camara. "On-Board Steam-Reforming of Methanol to Fuel the Automotive Hydrogen Engine." IECEC 1975 Record. 1975. pp. 1176-1183.

4. Sjostrom, K., S. Eriksson, and B. Lindner. "Hydrogen-Fuel for Tomorrow Today." First International Automotive Fuel Economy Research Conference Proceedings. Arlington, Va. 1979.

5. Noguchi, M., T. Bunda, M. Sumiyoshi, J. Kageyama, and S. Yamaguchi. "A Study on Reformed Fuel for an Automotive Gasoline Engine." NATO/CCMS 4th International Symposium on Automotive Propulsion Systems. Washington, D.C. 1977.

6. Inagaki, T., T. Hirota, and Z. Ueno. "Combustion and Emission of Gaseous Fuel from Reformed Methanol in Automotive Engines." Alcohol Fuels Technology 3rd International Symposium Proceedings. Asilomar, Calif. 1979.

7. MacDonald, J. S. Evaluation of the Hydrogen-Supplemented Fuel Concept with an Experimental Multicylinder Engine. SAE No. 760101. 1976.

8. Finegold, J. G. Hydrogen: Primary or Supplementary Fuel for Automotive Engines. SAE #760609, Society of Automotive Engineers West Coast Meeting. 1976.

9. Cerini, D., J. Houseman, and G. Voecks. "Operation of a Catalytic Methanol Decomposition Reactor for Vehicular Use." Proceedings of the 4th International Symposium on Alcohol Fuels Technology. Guaruja, Brazil.

METHANOL BLENDS - THE IMMEDIATE MARKET

Garvin De Shazer

ENERGOS CORP.,
Denver, CO

In spite of the present oil and gas "glut", a great deal of methanol is now being used as blends in gasoline because there is also a "methanol glut" due to excess production capacity now coming on stream. With methanol being traded at as low as $0.50/gal in bulk it is a very attractive octane improver for refineries, distributers and jobbers.

Nevertheless there are several obstacles to wide use of methanol blends. Phase separation and possible attack on certain parts require careful blending of methanol with additives at the refinery level. In addition the EPA waivers for methanol addition set certain limits depending on the total additive used. The present situtation of methanol blending will be discussed along with trends now developing.

PAPER UNAVAILABLE AT TIME OF PRINT

FUTURE OF METHANOL FUEL

CHUCK STONE
FUTURE FUELS OF AMERICA

PAPER UNAVAILABLE AT TIME OF PRINT

SPEAKERS WHO WERE UNABLE TO ATTEND,
BUT WERE KIND ENOUGH TO SEND THEIR PAPER
FOR INCLUSION IN THE PROCEEDINGS

OXYGEN-BLOWN ENTRAINED-FLOW GASIFICATION OF WOOD

W. J. Cousins

Physics and Engineering Laboratory, DSIR, Lower Hutt, New Zealand

A 5 kg/h oxygen-blown entrained-flow gasifier for wood has been operated. From a feed of dry sawdust it gave a gas that consisted mostly of CO, H_2, and CO_2 in the volume ration 1.8:1:1. The most important operating variables were the oxygen/wood input ratio and the wood moisture content, but neither variable caused rapid change in either gas quality or quantity. There was, however, considerable variation in the gasifier internal temperature which increased with the oxygen/wood ratio. Water-gas shift equilibrium did not seem to be reached except possibly when the gasifier temperature was high.

Keywords: Gasification; wood; oxygen; synthesis gas (carbon monoxide, hydrogen); carbon dioxide; steam; biomass.

INTRODUCTION

With the coming of the oil and gas crises the generation of liquid and gaseous fuels from solid fuels has reassumed importance. In many countries coal forms the most significant solid fuel reserve, but wood is an alternative feedstock that has great potential in some countries. New Zealand, for example, could provide its entire transport fuel requirements from less than one million hectares of forest if the wood were converted to a more or less conventional transport fuel (Cousins 1978; Troughton & Cousins 1976).

Complex conversion processes are involved. One of the most versatile is based on gasification and has much in common with technology already in use for the conversion of coal and natural gas as shown below.

Graphic

Of the several steps involved in the conversion of wood, only the initial oxygen-blast gasification requires development (Cousins 1978). Even that process is not completely unknown because during the 1940s the Distibois company in France gasified wood in a cocurrent, moving-bed gasifier and synthesized 130 kg/h of methanol from the product gas (A. de Lacotte, President, Distibois, pers. comm. 1978). A much larger version of the Distibois gasifier and one based on the German Winkler design are currently being evaluated for an 80,000 kg/h wood-methanol plant in Brazil (G.J. Lins, Companhia Energetica de São Paulo, pers. comm. 1978).

Although the Distibois gasifier has several desirable features, it is based on a moving-bed principle which has limited scale-up potential. It also requires a dry feedstock in the form of relatively large blocks to avoid clogging at the grate. If it can be assumed that there will be a parallel between wood and coal gasification technologies then a fluid bed wood gasifier should be easier to scale up and should accept a more finely divided feedstock that would be comparatively easy to dry and handle. However, there do not seem to be any published data on the performance of oxygen-blown, fluid-bed gasifiers for wood, and so a laboratory-scale unit was constructed and evaluated.

MATERIALS AND METHODS

Pinus radiata D. Don sawdust was used for the trials. It was oven dried, sieved to remove particles larger than 6 mm diameter, and if necessary remoistened. Three moisture contents were used, ovendry (<1.5%), 10% and 20% (of ovendry weight). The rate of delivery of sawdust was controlled by a reciprocating feeder that could be preset to deliver 2-15 kg/h.

The gasifier (Fig. 1) consisted of a 300 mm diameter, 1.00 m high steel shell lined with castable refractory. Internal dimensions were 150 x 50 mm in cross section. Both the wood and oxygen inlets were located near the bottom of the gasifier, the wood feeder being a 22 mm diameter screw, and the oxygen inlet a single copper tube.

The product gas flowed from the top of the gasifier to a simple impingement trap; which collected any entrained charcoal, and then via a short flue to a burner. Gas samples for analysis were taken either from the flue or from the side of the gasifier opposite the outlet pipe. From the flue sampling point the gas was pumped at a rate of 0.06 scm (standard of cubic metre)/h through a condenser, soot filter, and flowmeter. All of the water and most of the soot from the gas were collected in the condenser which consisted of a coil of polythene tubing immersed in a water bath. The small amount of soot remaining was removed in a filter, leaving a clean gas that burned with a nearly colourless blue flame. Samples for gas chromatographic analysis were collected in 60 cm^3 syringes at times of 15, 30, and 45 min after ignition of the gasifier.

Ignition of the gasifier was straightforward. The procedure was to start the wood feed, then the oxygen flow, and then to drop a lighted match into the gasifier. After about 10s the first greyish-white gas would emerge from the flue and could be ignited safely after 30s. It would then burn steadily for the duration of the trial. Generally the flame was luminous and yellow in colour, indicating the presence of soot particulates. After a warm-up period of about 20 min the product gas composition did not vary significantly with time and so most of the trials were limited to 50 min duration. Measurements taken were:

Inputs: wood mass and moisture content; oxygen, carbon dioxide, and steam flow rates;

Outputs: charcoal mass, gas composition; and for about half of the trials, the masses of water and soot (or tar) per volume of product gas.

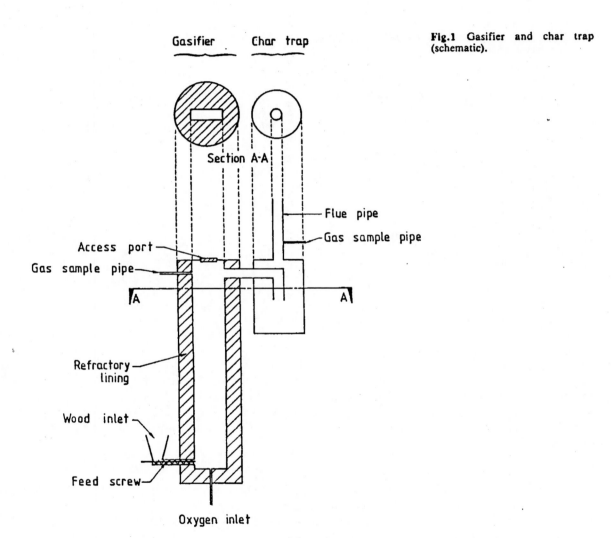

Fig.1 Gasifier and char trap (schematic).

The gas output volume was not measured directly but was calculated from the hydrogen and oxygen balances for those trials in which the water content of the output gas was determined. Usually the "volume" given by the hydrogen balance was higher than that from the oxygen balance, but the discrepancies were not large and ranged from a maximum of 12% at low oxygen input levels to 0% at high oxygen levels. As a first approximation the average of the two values was taken to the correct value.

The procedure was then extended to those trials in which water yields were not measured by the use of assumed water yields. The justification for this was the observation that the yield of water appeared to be constant provided that the inputs of water and CO_2 were not altered (see Fig. 2).

Although only 4 results are shown in Fig. 2 the observation was supported by two other series of trials, one involving the gasification of moist wood and the other an input of CO_2 with the oxygen. In both cases the yield of water was independent of the oxygen input.

Table 1 Ultimate analyses of the wood used in the gasifier trials and the carbonaceous outputs from the gasifier.

Material	C	H	O	Ash
Pinus radiata wood	0.499	0.062	0.435	0.004
Charcoal + soot	0.910	0.010	0.003	0.077

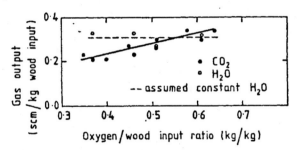

Fig.2 Effect of oxygen input on the yields of non-combustible gases and vapours.

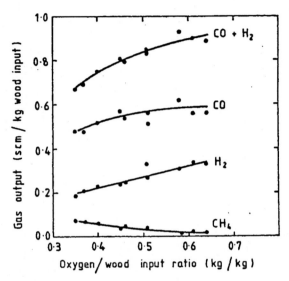

Fig.3 Effect of oxygen input on the yields of combustible gases.

The above procedure ignored any oxygen and hydrogen present in the carbonaceous outputs, but should not have introduced serious error as the amounts of O and H involved were generally small (see Table 1). An alternative procedure could have been based on the carbon balance but was avoided because of uncertainties in the measurements of tar yields at low oxygen input levels.

Table 1. Ultimate analyses of the wood used
in the gasifier trials and the
carbonaceous outputs from the gasifier

Material	C	H	O	Ash
Pinus radiata wood	0.499	0.062	0.435	0.004
Charcoal + soot	0.910	0.010	0.003	0.077

Gasifier internal temperatures were monitored with chromel-alumel thermocouples located 10 mm in from the refractory wall at heights above the oxygen inlet of 100, 200, 300, 400, 600, and 900 mm. Temperatures were recorded continuously on a multipoint recorder.

RESULTS AND DISCUSSION

Preliminary trails soon showed that a dense-phase fluidised bed could not be maintained in the gasifier, probably because of its small size, but that consistent and reliable performance could be obtained if the specific throughput was increased so that the bed was maintained in a highly expanded, or entrained, state. At a throughput of 300 kg/h m^2 the product charcoal was not entrained in the gas stream but formed an unstable plug at the bottom of the gasifier, and most of the gas flowed through a blowhole in the plug. From 600 to 1700 kg/h m^2 the charcoal was mostly entrained in the gas stream. A throughput of 750 kg/h m^2 was chosen for the tests reported below to ensure stable operation of the gasifier with minimum consumption of wood.

Gas Production

The main outputs from the gasifier were CO, H_2, CO_2, and water vapour in the approximate volume ratio of 1.8:1:1:1. Some methane, charcoal, soot, and at low oxygen inputs some tar were also produced. Most of the yields varied with the oxygen/wood input ratio (hereafter referred to as oxygen imput) as shown in Figs. 2 and 3, the most significant changes being the increases in CO and H_2 and decrease in CH_4 with increasing oxygen input. For syngas generation the yield of $CO + H_2$ should be as high as possible, and this is shown by Fig. 3 to require a high oxygen input. Extrapolating the trends of Fig. 3 suggests, however, that any further increase in O_2 input will not give a very large increase in the yield of $CO + H_2$. Only at the lowest oxygen inputs was any ethane detected, and then only trace amounts.

Charcoal and Soot Formation

The yield of charcoal decreased with increasing oxygen input. Although there was considerable scatter in the data, there seemed to be a uniform reduction from 0.06 kg/kg of wood input at an oxygen input of 0.35 kg/kg to 0.045 at an oxygen input of 0.66. The charcoal was relatively coarse, with less than 3% of it passing through a 100 µm screen. Consequently it was easily removed from the gas stream in a simple impingement trap. Material passing through the trap was mostly submicron in size and seemed to be soot.

It was possible to lower the net yield of charcoal by returning some of the product to the gasifier inlet. A single trail in which 0.06 kg of char was mixed with each kilogram of wood showed that approximately one-third of the recycled char could be consumed in a single recycle step.

Repeated recycling is used in some entrained flow coal gasifiers to eliminte char production. In the Babcock and Wilcox (BiGas) reactor, for example, the recycle char stream amounts to 20% of the fresh coal feed (Kimmel et al. 1976). However, ash in the BiGas system is removed as a liquid slag, whereas ash in the entrained-flow wood gasifier is recovered as a solid mixed with the entrained charcoal, and some purging of charcoal will, therefore, always be necessary.

Measurements of soot and tar production were not accurate, but were adequate to give qualitative information on variations. Only at the lowest oxygen inputs was there any tar in the gas stream, and even then only about 0.03 kg/kg of wood. As the oxygen input, and hence gasifier temperature, were increased the yield of tar rapidly decreased and became negligible for oxygen inputs above 0.45 kg/kg.

At higher oxygen levels the product gas contained tar-free soot. The quantity varied from 3 to 9g/scm of gas and did not seem to bear any consistent relationship to oxygen input. However, increases in both wood moisture and CO_2 input seemed to reduce the amount produced.

The production of soot is undesirable because it can lead to clogging of gas pipelines and poisoning of catalysts, but is to be expected in a cocurrent gasifier in which the partial combustion of high molecular weight primary pyrolysis products occurs in any oxygen-deficient atmosphere. Because the soot is tar-free it should not be difficult to remove from the gas in conventional equipment. For comparison, the particulate loadings of coal gases range from 0.5-6g/scm for stirred bed and fixed bed gasifiers to 27-55g/scm for a Koppers-Totzek gasifier (Becker & Murthy 1976).

Gasifier Temperatures

In a 2h trial the temperatures at the three lowest measurement sites reached steady values approximately 45 min after ignition, but the temperatures at the higher sites required nearly 90 min to stabilize. At 45 min, however, all temperature readings were within 15% of the steady value.

Fig. 4 shows the steady state temperature variation along the length of the gasifier for an oxygen input of 0.5. The temperature seemed to reach its maximum value about 250 mm above the oxygen inlet and then decreased at higher levels. Such a variation is consistent with the sequence of gasification reactions given by Cousins (1978); i.e., pyrolysis of the incoming feed at low levels in the gasifier, followed by the exothermic combustion of some of the volatile products to give a temperature maximum some distance from the gasifier inlets, and finally endothermic reactions between the hot charcoal, CO_2, and H_2O with consequent heat absorption.

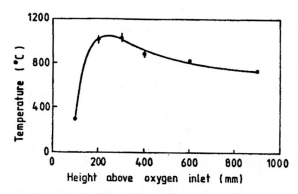

Fig.4 Variation in the gasifier internal temperature with distance from the oxygen inlet.

Fig. 5 shows the effect of oxygen ratio on the temperature at three levels in the gasifier. For clarity only the best-fit straight lines to the data are shown. Their equations are:

$$T = 170 + 1600x \qquad r^2 = 0.84 \qquad \text{(height 200 mm)}$$
$$T = 130 + 1300x \qquad r^2 = 0.84 \qquad \text{(height 400 mm)}$$
$$T = 100 + 1000x \qquad r^2 = 0.89 \qquad \text{(height 900 mm)}$$

where T is the temperature in $^{\circ}C$, and x is the oxygen/wood ratio in kg/kg. The temperature readings on which Fig. 5 was based were all taken 45 min after ignition of the gasifier, and so the temperatures shown for heights of 400 and 900 mm are approximately 15% below the steady state values. Nevertheless, the effect of oxygen input is clearly demonstrated and is considerable.

Effects of Water and Carbon Dioxide

Addition of moisture to the feedstock tended to degrade the performance of the gasifier. Increase of the wood moisture content from ovendry to 20% caused the yields of CO and H_2 to decrease by 14 and 6% respectively and the yield of CO_2 to increase. There were no significant changes in the yields of CH_4, or charcoal, the net yield of water, or to the gasifier internal temperature. A possible beneficial change, however, was an apparent reduction in the output of soot.

An input of steam to the gasifier also was not beneficial. At a steam rate of 0.5 kg/kg of wood the production of combustible gases was reduced, and the production of CO_2 increased when compared to results with the zero steam input.

Addition of CO_2 to the oxygen input tended to degrade the gasifier's performance. Increase of the CO_2 level from 0 to 0.25 kg/kg of wood caused the CO and H_2 yields to decrease by 6 and 20% respectively, the net yield of CO_2 to decrease by 17%, and the yield of water to increase by 23%. There were no significant changes to the production of CH_4, and charcoal or to the gasifier temperature. Somewhat surprisingly, the yield of soot was reduced, especially when the oxygen input was high.

Energy Balance

Energy balance computations for the gasifier are summarized in Fig. 1. To reduce experimental scatter the data have been divided into two groups, low oxygen input and high oxygen input, and averaged. Variations due to change in oxygen input are, therefore, somewhat masked, but variations due to change in moisture content are displayed reliably. From Fig. 6 it appears that the total output of combustibles is relatively independent of both oxygen input and wood moisture content. Changes in the two inputs seem to cause an exchange of char and CH_4 for CO and H_2. If CO and H_2 are the desired products then clearly a high oxygen input and low moisture content are to be preferred, although variations in the range 0-10% for moisture content and (from Fig. 3) 0.55-0.65 for oxygen input do not seem to be very important.

As the oxygen input, and hence internal temperature, increase both the heat lost by conduction through the gasifier walls and the sensible heat carried away by the hot exiting gas increase, as would be expected. Together, the two heat losses amount to a rather large 20% of the wood energy input, but the situation could be improved in a bigger plant where there is scope for (a) reduction of the conduction heat loss by reduction of surface to volume ratio of the gasifier and (b) recovery of the gas sensible heat in the form of process steam or hot air for drying the incoming wood feed.

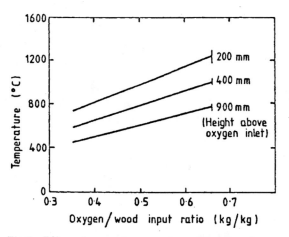

Fig.5 Effect of oxygen input on the gasifier internal temperature. The error bars indicate the standard deviations in the data at the positions shown.

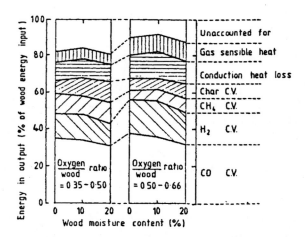

Fig.6 Variations in energy outputs with oxygen input and wood moisture content.

Gas Shift Equilibrium

An assumption that is commonly used in thermodynamic studies of gasification (with considerable success) is that water gas shift equilibrium is reached and partially determines the output gas composition (Batchelder et al. 1953). To check the validity of such an assumption for the entrained flow gasifier an apparent gas shift equilibrium temperature was determined from the output gas composition and is plotted against the peak temperature measured inside the gasifier in Fig. 7. Clearly the apparent gas shift equilibrium temperature decreases as the gasifier internal temperature increases, and so the assumption that gas shift equilibrium is always reached does not seem to be realistic.

Two characteristic features of the entrained-flow gasifier that may inhibit gas shift equilibrium are (1) residence times of gases are short, typically less than 1s, and (2) the charcoal "bed" in the gasifier is in a highly expanded state which precludes adequate gas-carbon contact.

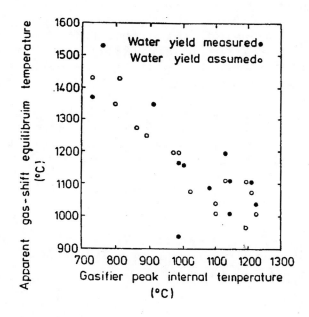

CONCLUSIONS

Wood can be gasified in an oxygen-blown, entrained-flow gasifier to give a gas containing CO, H_2, and CO_2 in the volume ratios 1.8:1:1. Removal of the CO_2 would leave a carbon monoxide-rich synthesis gas.

The gas also contains small quantities of CH_4, entrained charcoal, and soot. At oxygen inputs of 0.45-0.65 kg/kg of wood the char and soot are tar-free and should be relatively easy to separate from the gas in conventional gas cleaning systems. At lower oxygen inputs the gas is contaminated with tar.

Inputs of moisture, steam, and CO_2 all seem to degrade the performance of the gasifier and therefore are not recommended; at least, not for small-scale ambient pressure entrained-flow gasifiers. Although an input of CO_2 does seem to reduce the yield of soot it is unlikely to be cost effective because CO_2 is more costly than soot to remove from the gas.

Operating conditions are not critical. The gasifier functions at specific rates from 300 to 1700 kg/h m^2, but best at rates above 600. The upper limit to throughput is not known. Changes in oxygen/wood ratio, wood moisture content, steam input, and CO_2 input all cause changes in both the quality and the quantity of the product gas, but not rapid changes. For a high yield of synthesis gas ($CO + H_2$), the optimum conditions seem to be an oxygen/wood ratio of about 0.55-0.65 kg/kg and a wood moisture content of less than about 10%.

Probably the most dramatic variation is in the internal temperature of the gasifier. Over the recommended oxygen input range of 0.55-0.65 kg/kg the peak temperature near the gasifier wall varies from 1100 to 1200°C. However, other than providing a guide for the selection of refractory linings the value of the temperature measurements is debatable. According to Batchelder et al. (1953) there can be large variations in gas temperature across the gasifier, as well as along the gasifier as observed in the above trials.

Under most operating conditions water gas shift equilibrium is not reached in the gasifier. There may well be equilibrium, or close approach to equilibrium, at high oxygen inputs, but the simple assumption of equilibrium at all oxygen inputs is not valid.

REFERENCES

Batchelder, H. R.; Busche, R. M.; Armstrong, W. P. 1953: Kinetics of Coal Gasification: Proposed Mechanism of Gasification. Industrial Engineering Chemistry 45(2): 1856-78.

Becker, D. F.; Murthy, B. N. 1976: Feasibility of Reducing Fuel Gas Clean-up Needs, Survey of the Effect of Gasification Process Conditions on the Entrainment of Impurities in the Fuel Gas. ERDA Contract No. (49-18)-1236.

Cousins, W. J. 1978: Transport Fuels from Wood by Gasification. Proceedings 1st Biotechnology Conference on Biomass and Energy, 24-26 May 1978 Massey University: 290-301.

Kimmel, S.; Neben, E. W.; Pack, G. E. 1976: Economics of Current and Advanced Gasification Processes for Fuel Gas Generation. NTIS No. EPRI-AF-244.

Troughton, J. H.; Cousins, W. J. 1976: Prospects for Energy Farming. New Zealand Energy Journal 4(12): 190-4.

PRESSURIZED OXYGEN BLOWN FLUIDIZED BED GASIFICATION OF WOOD

Gérard Chrysostome
Jean-Michel Lemasle
Creusot-Loire
Division Energie
BP 31
F 71208 Le Creusot

SUMMARY

Pressurized Oxygen Blown Fluidized Bed Gasification of Wood

The Energy Division of the Creusot-Loire Company undertook three years ago studies for the creation of new processes in the way of new energies valorization. Among these figures biomass gasification. The research covers fluidized bed wood gasification with oxygen.

It is supported by an experimental unit, the implementation of which is at the "Laboratoire d'Essais Energetiques" of LE CREUSOT (Fr). Its principle is the atmospheric oxygen blown fluidized bed wood gasifier, allowing to gasify 100-150 kg/h of dry substance. Tests on that pilot began in early 1981. Today, about 25 experiments with pure oxygen have been conducted, representing 10 tons of wood and also 2 tons of straw pellets.

Results so far obtained on the LeCreusot's atmospheric pilot reactor demonstrated the opportunity to undertake studies for the erection of a pressurized oxygen blown fluidized bed gasifier for wood. The intended reactor will make it possible to gasify 60 tons/day of dry wood under a 15 bar pressure. The unit should be operated in early 1983. The equipment is dimensioned so that it can operate under pressures between 10 and 30 bar. That demonstration plant will include all the facilities permitting to operate it under industrial conditions: biomass drying; feeding biomass into the gasifier with help of an uninterruptedly operating machine; heat recovery; dust removal; recycling of unburnt carbon, if any. Different kinds of biomass can be tested: wood, wastes from farming or from forestry activities.

Extrapolation of our atmospheric present results, in case of a wood to methanol configuration, should give about 28 ton/day methanol for 65 ton/day dry wood in an energetically completely integrated unit; which leads to an approximate 54% thermal yield.

1.   Introduction

Presently, the methanol synthesis is industrially conducted with natural gas or oil fractions as raw materials. Industrial units, producing up to 1500 TPD methanol generally include:

- production of a raw synthesis gas (CO + H2)

- cleaning and composition adjustment of the synthesis gas (H2/CO=2)

- methanol synthesis itself, most of time realized between 50 and 100 bar.

The biomass gasification, which produces a carbon monoxyde and hydrogen mixture should contribute to a significant amount of methanol in the near future.

The methanol synthesis which is industrially carried out with an as pure as possible gas imposes to gasify with pure oxygen. Taking in account the pressure at which synthesis of methanol is achieved, gasification itself has to be conducted under pressure.

The Creusot-Loire French Company is presently testing in its "Laboratoire d'Essais Energetiques" of LE CREUSOT a reactor which allows the atmospheric gasification in an oxygen blow fluidized bed of 100-150 kg/h of dry wood. With the help of results up to now obtained on that pilot reactor, we decided to undertake the studies for the implementation of a demonstration unit which permit to gasify 60 TPD of dry wood under a 15 bar pressure.

2.   Description of the Laboratory Experimental Unit

A schematic diagram of the gasifier is drawn on figure 1.

A drawing of the complete installation "gasifier + post-combustion chamber" is shown on figure 2.

The pilot unit is mainly composed of a 400 mm diameter fluidized bed gasifier and an 800 mm diameter post combustion chamber for gases produced in the gasifier. A low thermal inertia reactor has been chosen. So, it is composed of a stainless steel casing with an outside insulation; at its bottom is a perforated grid for the fluidizing reagent distribution.

Wood is fed in a 0.7 m^3 hopper before being conveyed into the reactor by an endless screw. The fluidized bed itself is made of an inert material (extrasilica sand), the granulometry of which comprises between 0.1 and 0.6 mm; the quantity of sand used for each test is 50 to 60 kgs.

The solution of an inert material for the fluid bed allows to gasify biomass of a rather wide range in dimensions.

Gasification is performed around 800°C. Preheating of the reactor is achieved by natural gas combustion.

Temperatures are controlled by use of thermocouples.

Produced gas is analyzed by means of infra-red analyzers for CO-CO_2, paramagnetic analyses for residual O_2 and chromatography for H_2, CH_4, N_2 and Ar. Flow rate of produced gas is measured by injection of a controlled quantity of argon in the reactor which is analyzed by gas chromatography.

The main part of produced gas is burnt in the special burner of the refractory lined post-combustion chamber. Then, combustion gases are diluted, filtered and sent to the stack.

3.   Experimental Results

About 20 tests have been so far conducted with paper mill wood chips under pure oxygen conditions. Characteristics of these tests are summarized below.

3.1   Operational Conditions

- Wood: pine chips: 3 to 40 mm
                 moisture: 20 to 40%
                 capacity: 80 to 100 kg/h (dry)

- Oxygen: purity: 99.5%
                 flow rate: 18 to 22 Nm3/h

- Temperature: fluidized bed: 800°C
                 top of the reactor: 700°C

3.2   Results

The typical dry gas composition and characteristics are the following.

CO = 33.5%
CO2 = 30.3%
H2 = 18.7%
CH4 = 10.0%
N2 = 1.8%

small amount of oil and tars
small amount of light hydrocarbons
(probably 2-3% O_2 hydrocarbons)
Carbon conversion: 85%
Thermal gas yield: 60% (based on CO-H2-CH4)

4. Pressurized Gasifier: Project Contents

Based on results and observations obtained on the atmospheric gasifier described before, the process development unit project is composed of the following sections (shown on figure 3):

1) Wood reception and storage
2) Wood sizing and drying
3) Production of utilities
4) Oxygen production
5) Wood feeding under pressure by use of a "special machine"
6) Pressurized oxygen blown fluidized bed gasification (15 bar)
7) Methane conversion in an oxygen blown reformer furnace
8) Gas cleaning and scrubbing
9) Treatment and recycling of unburnt char, if any.

The project doesn't include at present the methanol synthesis.

The overall demonstration unit is self conducted and regulated in order to:

- obtain a reliable working, perfectly controlled and secured

- be representative of an industrial unit.

The main characteristics of that demonstration plant are a 60 TPD dry wood capacity under a 15 bar pressure. The flexibility of the unit has been foreseen so that it can be possible to work between 10 and 30 bar, leading to a wood consumption comprised between 40 and 120 TPD.

Based part on experimental results and part on theoretical values calculated under pressure, the expected results on that unit are, for the gasifier exit gas:

$CO = 29\%$
$CO2 = 22\%$
$H2 = 21\%$
$H2O = 20\%$
$CH4 = 8\%$

In order to go into details regarding the wood to methanol configuration, a simplified process flow diagram (figure 4) and material and heat balances have been set-up. They lead to the following values, in case of a completely integrated plant in an energetic point of view.

Wood consumption = 66 TPD d.a.f. (including 6 TPD for feeding a boiler)

Methanol production = 28 TPD

Thermal yield = 54%

The energetic autonomy of the plant is provided by heat recovery at different steps of the process. A supply is necessary to cover the complete demand of energy; this is obtained by burning part of the wood in a boiler generating steam. In that boiler is also burnt the purge gas produced in the methanol sythesis loop.

Such a wood supply represents about 10% of gasified wood.

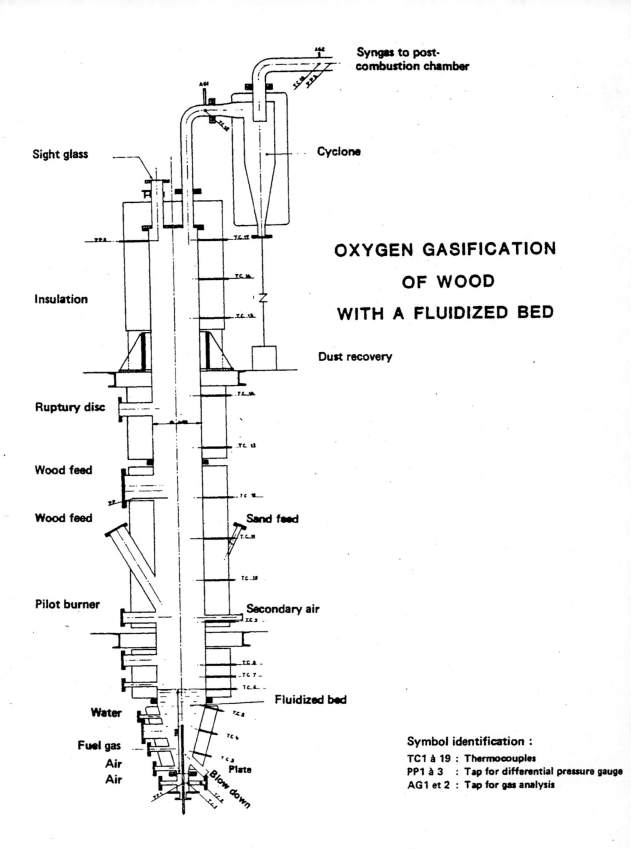

Sight glass

Insulation

Ruptury disc

Wood feed

Wood feed

Pilot burner

Water

Fuel gas

Air

Air

Syngas to post-combustion chamber

Cyclone

OXYGEN GASIFICATION
OF WOOD
WITH A FLUIDIZED BED

Dust recovery

Sand feed

Secondary air

Fluidized bed

Plate

Blow down

Symbol identification :

TC1 à 19 : Thermocouples
PP1 à 3 : Tap for differential pressure gauge
AG1 et 2 : Tap for gas analysis

FIGURE 1

FIGURE 2

LE CREUSOT'S EXPERIMENTAL UNIT OF FLUIDISED BED WOOD GASIFICATION

CREUSOT-LOIRE
DIVISION ÉNERGIE
USINE DU CREUSOT

PRESSURIZED OXYGEN BLOWN
FLUIDIZED BED GASIFIER

PROJECT CONTENTS

Capacity = 60 T P D Dry Wood

Pressure = 15 Atm

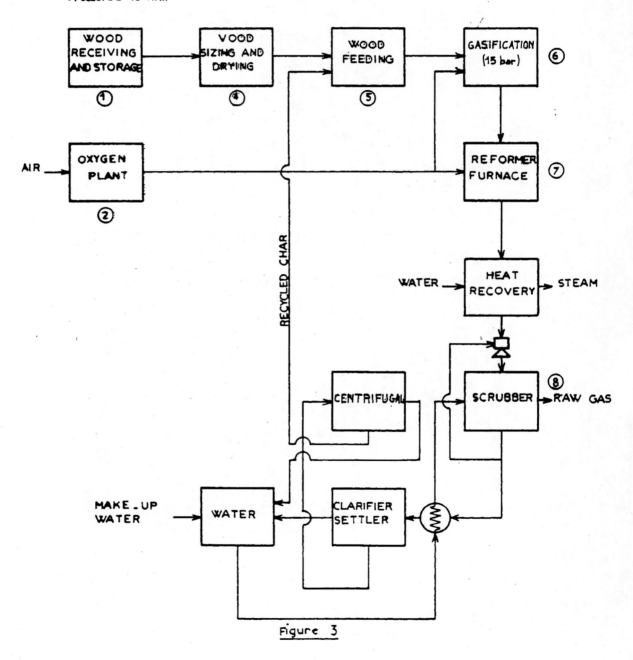

Figure 3

PRESSURIZED OXYGEN BLOWN
FLUIDIZED BED GASIFIER

WOOD TO METHANOL CONFIGURATION

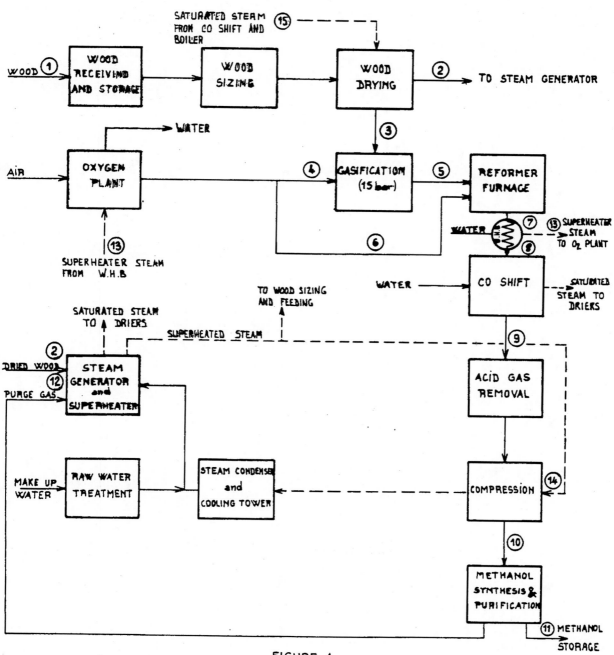

PRODUCTION OF FUEL GRADE PEAT
AT FIRST COLONY FARMS, INC.

A. B. Allen
Manager, Peat Research and Development
First Colony Farms, Inc.
Creswell, N.C.

ABSTRACT

The surface peat deposits found along the coastal plain in eastern North Carolina contain high quality fuel grade peat that can be used as a feed stock for gasification processes, methanol production, chemical extraction or electric power generation. However, before the peat can be effectively utilized, the high natural moisture content must be reduced and the peat must be harvested and stockpiled.

The present peat production program at First Colony Farms is aimed at developing and evaluating various methods of harvesting and stockpiling commercial quantities of high grade fuel peat at or around 30% moisture.

The following paper discusses the peat production technology developed during First Colony Farm's peat program.

INTRODUCTION

The peat deposits found along the coastal plain of North Carolina contain high quality fuel grade peat with an average heating value of more than 10,000 BTU's per dry pound and low sulphur and ash content. The deposits differ from some of the other peats found in the United States in that they contain large quantities of large, sound Atlantic White Cedar and Cypress logs, stumps and roots which may extend throughout the full depth of the deposit. A second difference is that these deposits are much more highly decomposed and, in the raw state, have the appearance and feel of a heavy, reddish brown grease. These two factors make it impractical to utilize production equipment available from other areas of the world. It is necessary to develop a new line of equipment suited to these conditions, and to modify techniques to facilitate production.

First Colony Farms has developed and evaluated both a milled peat and a sod peat program. Equipment for both production methods was designed, built, production rates established from actual field operations, drying rates established, weather data analyzed and a total cost in dollars per million BTU's determined.

FIELD OPERATIONS

Both the milled and sod peat production methods depend upon the sun and wind for drying the peat to the desired moisture content, in this case, around 30%. Therefore, the preparation of the bog is actually the construction of a large solar collector used to collect energy from the sun and dry the peat so that it can be harvested and stockpiled. It is essential that this collector be properly profiled initially and maintained during production to prevent any ponding of precipitation that would deter drying.

Initial Bog Preparation

The initial bog preparation phase includes the construction of adequate canals, ditches and water control structures for proper drainage of the site, adequate roads for access to the site, removal of surface vegetation and proper profiling and sloping of the fields. These activities can become extensive depending upon the existing conditions of the bog and may require as much as four years to complete satisfactorily.

The bog has been designed so as to be divided into 320 acre blocks approximately one mile in length and one-half mile in width. This is accomplished by constructing main outfall canals with adjacent roads built from canal spoil at one mile intervals. Intermediate canals that feed into

314

the main outfall canals are constructed perpendicular to main outfall canals at one-half mile intervals. Along each side of each intermediate canal, headland roads are constructed from canal spoil (see Figure 1). This 320 acre block is then divided into thirty-two harvest strips by small V-ditches, constructed at 165 foot intervals, that drain into the intermediate canals. At the end of the field with the lowest elevation, corrugated steel pipe culverts are installed under the headland road in each V-ditch to allow for field drainage into the intermediate canals (see Figures 2 and 3).

After the drainage system has been installed, the harvest strips are ready for the grinding and sloping operations. The surface vegetation found on deep peat lands is made up of small, waxy leafed shrubs such as Gallberry, Bayberry, Magnolia and scattered pond pine. This surface vegetation can be effectively ground and incorporated into the upper surface of the peat layer where it will rapidly decompose and have little effect on the overall quality of the peat, thus eliminating the standard practice of pushing the vegetation and upper wood layer into long windrows with bulldozers and hauling this debris from the fields. This incorporation of vegetation into the upper surface is known as the initial 4" surface vegetation grind and is accomplished by the use of a modified Bros Rotor Mixer. Following this operation, and by use of the same unit, a second grind with a depth of 8" to 10" is made. This reduces the debris to a finer consistency, mixes it with the upper layer and grinds any wood found in the upper 8" to 10".

Now that the initial grinding operations have been completed, the augering or sloping operations can be accomplished with little or no hindrance from buried wood. A large screw auger attached to a 310 HP base unit is used to laterally convey the initially ground layer from the ditch to the center of the field, thus creating a rough slope on the surface of the field. A modified, high flotation motor grader is then used to rough grade the entire surface of the field and build a slope from the ditch to the center of the field of approximately 1%.

At this time any V-ditches that may have become plugged by debris from the augering-sloping operations should be cleaned out by use of the ditch cleaning unit attached to the 450 HP base.

Additional wood exposed by the augering-sloping and ditching operations should be ground by a second 8" to 10" grind with the Bros Rotor Mixer, followed by a final fine grading operation with the motor grader. As described above, it is absolutely essential to maintain a well-graded and sloped profile on the field surface so that precipitation will not pond. The colloidal peats will not absorb water very readily, therefore ponded water must evaporate or run off to the ditch.

315

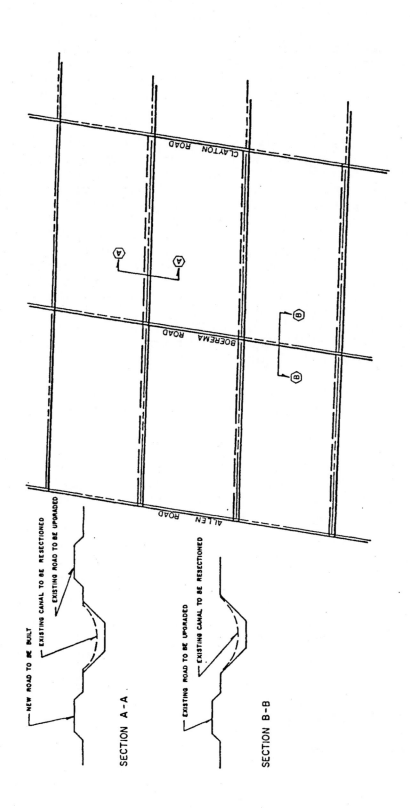

FIRST COLONY FARMS , INC.
CRESWELL, N. C.
INITIAL 1920 GROSS ACRE PEAT BOG

NEW HEADLAND ROAD
EXISTING ROAD
EXISTING CANAL

FIGURE 1

FIRST COLONY FARMS, INC.
CRESWELL,   N. C.

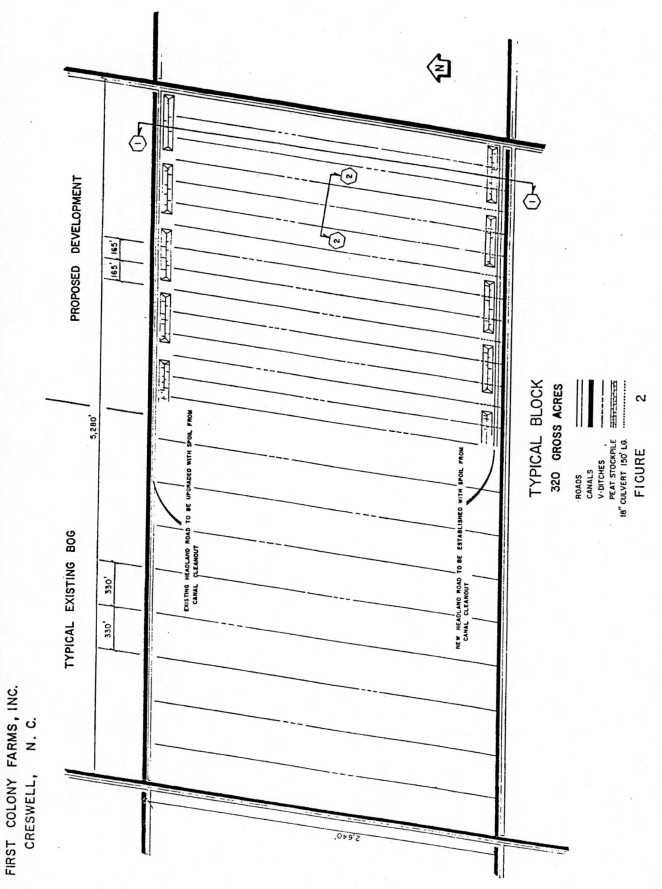

PROPOSED DEVELOPMENT

TYPICAL EXISTING BOG

5,280'

165' 165'

330' 330'

EXISTING HEADLAND ROAD TO BE UPGRADED WITH SPOIL FROM
CANAL CLEANOUT

NEW HEADLAND ROAD TO BE ESTABLISHED WITH SPOIL FROM
CANAL CLEANOUT

2,640'

N

TYPICAL BLOCK
320 GROSS ACRES

ROADS
CANALS
V-DITCHES
PEAT STOCKPILE
18" CULVERT 150' LG.

FIGURE 2

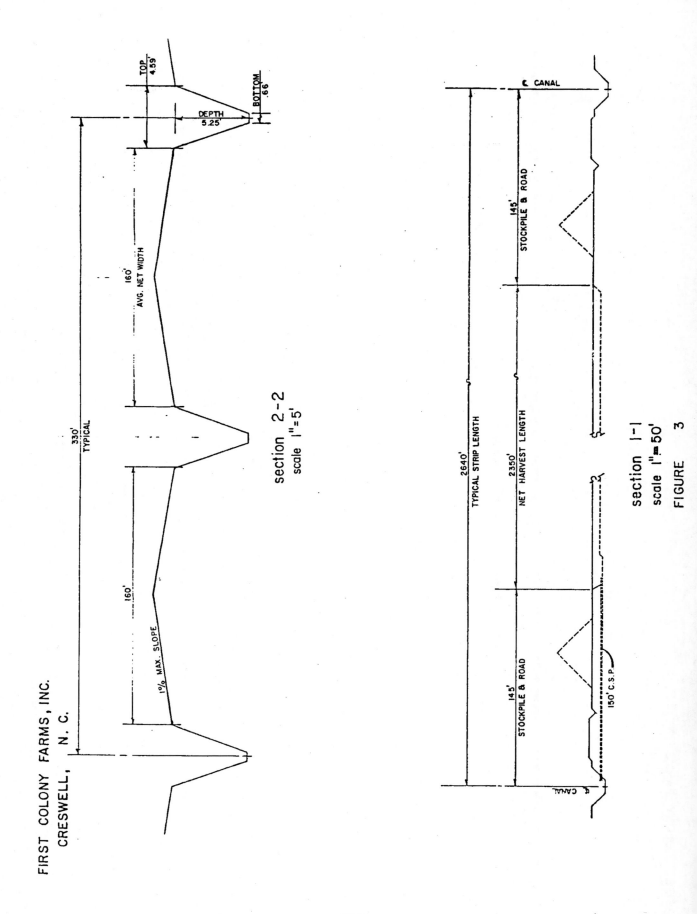

FIRST COLONY FARMS, INC.
CRESWELL, N. C.

section 2-2
scale 1" = 5'

section 1-1
scale 1" = 50'

FIGURE 3

318

If the weather conditions are favorable, production can begin after the previously described bog preparation operations have been completed. If the weather is unfavorable, the fields should be rolled with a heavy roller to reduce the possibility of saturation of the upper milled surface by precipitation. See Table 1 for equipment and production rates.

Peat Production

Following the completion of the initial bog preparation phase and upon the advent of favorable weather conditions, the bog is ready for production. The production methods utilized at First Colony Farms are based upon modified versions of European milled and sod peat production methods.

Milled Peat Production. The first step in the production of milled peat is to mill or fluff a thin layer of the surface of the fields by using a shallow milling unit attached to a tractor (this layer is approximately 1 to 1 1/2 inches thick). The shallow milling unit is not designed to mill or grind wood and will perform only in areas that have been deep milled with the heavier wood grinding units. The upper portions of this fluffed layer will dry very quickly by solar energy. However, in order to dry the entire layer, a second operation called "turning" must now take place.

Turning is accomplished with a spoon harrower attached to a small tractor. The spoons actually sink down into the thin milled peat layer and flip the loose peat over, exposing a new surface to the sun for drying. In North Carolina, during the hotter summer months, turning can reduce the moisture content of the peat approximately seven percentage points for each turn. During this period, turns can take place as often as each half hour.

Once the peat has been turned and dried to the desired moisture content, it is then windrowed or ridged. A windrower attached to a small tractor is designed to scrape and collect the dryer peat into a long ridge from an area 24 feet wide. From a 165 foot wide harvest strip, seven windrows or ridges, each with approximately 26 to 36 tons of dried 30% moisture peat, will be collected.

The windrows are loaded into carts by use of a modified Athey Force Feed Loader with a side discharge conveyor. Each cart has a capacity of approximately 10 tons of 30% moisture peat. The cart carries the loaded peat to the stockpile area where it is side dumped at the base of the stockpile. The peat is later stacked into a stockpile with approximately 1:1 side slopes where it is stored until transported to a user.

After approximately 4 inches of peat has been removed, the heavy solid wood begins to create production problems for the shallow milling and windrowing equipment. When this happens, a deep production miller, which is attached to the

319

TABLE I

FIRST COLONY FARMS, INC.
CRESWELL, N.C.
PEAT PRODUCTION PROGRAM

INITIAL BOG PREPERATION
EQUIPMENT PRODUCTION SCHEDULE

OPERATION	TYPE EQUIP.	Ft / Hr	FUEL CONSMP.
1. CONSTRUCT NEW V-DITCHES & INSTALL NECESSARY CULVERTS	SCREW DITCHER w/450 BASE	750 Ft/Hr	15 GPH
2. INITIAL 4" VEGETATION GRIND OF ENTIRE FIELD	BROS ROTOR MIXER	6000 Ft/Hr	14 GPH
3. 8"-10" REGRIND OF ENTIRE FIELD	BROS ROTOR MIXER	5000 Ft/Hr	14 GPH
4. ROUGH AUGER ENTIRE FIELD	AUGER PLANER w/310 BASE	4000 Ft/Hr	14 GPH
5. ROUGH GRADE ENTIRE FIELD	CAT 12-14 MOTOR GRADER	4.68 Acres/Hr	10 GPH
6. CLEAN OUT EXISTING V-DITCH AND/OR CUT NEW V-DITCH	WHEEL DITCHER w/450 BASE	1500 Ft/Hr	15 GPH
7. LEVEL CENTER WINDROWS AND 8"-10" REGRIND OF ENTIRE FIELD	BROS ROTOR.MIXER w/450 BASE	5000 Ft/Hr	14 GPH
8. FINE GRADE ENTIRE FIELD	MOTOR GRADER	6 Acres/Hr	10 GPH
9. ROLL AND SEAL ENTIRE FIELD	ROLLER DRUM w/1066 TRACTOR	10 Acres/Hr	7 GPH

320

310 HP base and is designed to grind heavy wood, performs a milling and grinding operation at around 4 inches of depth. The 4 inch depth provides not only a new milled layer free from large wood for the shallow milling and windrowing equipment to operate on, but is also shallow enough not to deter the overall drying operations by mixing wetter peat from below with the upper dryer peat.

The above steps are repeated throughout the production season. The season typically extends from mid-March to mid-November and yields an average of 155 drying days. It is estimated that, in a commercial production operation, approximately sixteen inches of peat will be depleted annually. This depletion will yield just over 650 tons of 30% moisture peat per net acre of production area.

See Table 2 for equipment and production rates.

Sod Peat Production. The bog is prepared in the same manner for both milled and sod peat production. However, the production of sod peat differs from milled peat production in that it entails the mechanical removal of wet peat from the bog and its extrusion of approximately 4 inch diameter cylinders or sods, onto the bog surface where it is left to air dry. Production is accomplished by the operation of the Quadruple Head Sod Extruder attached to the 450 HP base unit. This unit cuts four 1 3/4 inch wide slots approximately fourteen inches deep into the bog surface. The wet raw peat and wood fiber removed from the slots are thrown up into the extruder chambers and pushed out through orifices 4 inches in diameter. The ideal moisture content of the sod at the time of extrusion is around 65%. This can be accomplished by varying the depth of cut of the cutting wheels in the bog surface, thus varying the moisture content of the raw peat. The sods break off in various lengths ranging from about 8 to 12 inches and fall to the bog surface where they are left to air dry to approximately 30% moisture.

After the sods have dried, typically for seven to twelve days, they are windrowed into long ridges with the sod peat windrowing unit pulled by a tractor. This allows for additional drying, especially the portions that have been in contact with the ground, and arranges the sods for easy pick up with the loading unit.

The sod loading operation utilizes the modified Athey Force Feed Loader that travels down the windrow picking the sods up and conveying them to the side dumping carts. The carts, with a rate capacity of 10 tons, transport the harvested sod peat to the stockpile area for storage. Stacking units are used to stack the sods into a properly shaped stockpile, having approximatley 1:1 side slopes.

See Table 3 for equipment and production rates.

TABLE 2

FIRST COLONY FARMS, INC.
CRESWELL, N.C.
PEAT PRODUCTION PROGRAM
MILLED PEAT PRODUCTION
EQUIPMENT PRODUCTION SCHEDULE

OPERATION	TYPE EQUIPMENT	Ft/Hr	FUEL CONSMP.
1. SHALLOW MILL	SHALLOW MILLER w/1066 I.H. TRACTOR	11500 Ft/Hr	8 GPH
2. TURN	TURNING SPOONS w/1066 I.H. TRACTOR	30000 Ft/Hr	8 GPH
3. WINDROW	WINDROWER w/1066 I.H. TRACTOR	25000 Ft/Hr	8 GPH
4. LOAD & TRANSPORT	ATHEY LOADER w/A TWO CART TRANSPORT SYSTEM	13000 Ft/Hr	10 GPH

TABLE   3

FIRST COLONY FARMS, INC.
CRESWELL, N.C.
PEAT PRODUCTION PROGRAM

SOD PEAT PRODUCTION
EQUIPMENT PRODUCTION SCHEDULE

OPERATION	TYPE EQUIPMENT	Ft/Hr	FUEL CONSMP.
1. SOD PRODUCTION	QUADRUPLE HEAD SOD UNIT ; 450 SUOKKONE BASE	3600 Ft/Hr 32 Tons/Hr a 30% M.C.	15 GPH
2. SOD PEAT WINDROWING	SOD PEAT WINDROWER UNIT ; MODIFIED I.H. FARM TRACTOR	13000 Ft/Hr	10 GPH
3. SOD PEAT LOADING	MODIFIED ATHEY FORCE FEED LOADER ; 10 TON TRANSPORT CARTS ; MODIFIED I.H. FARM TRACTOR	13000 Ft/Hr	10 GPH 8 GPH

TABLE 4

FIRST COLONY FARMS, INC.
CRESWELL, N.C.
PEAT PRODUCTION PROGRAM
ANNUAL BOG PREPERATION
EQUIPMENT PRODUCTION SCHEDULE

OPERATION	TYPE EQUIPMENT	Ft / Hr	FUEL CONSUMP.
1. CLEAN OUT EXISTING V-DITCH	WHEEL DITCHER w/450 BASE	1500 Ft/Hr	15 GPH
2. 8"-10" REGRIND OF ENTIRE FIELD	BROS ROTOR MIXER	5000 Ft/Hr	14 GPH
3. FINE GRADE ENTIRE FIELD	MOTOR GRADER	6 Acres/Hr	10 GPH
4. ROLL AND SEAL ENTIRE FIELD	ROLLER DRUM	10 Acres/Hr	7 GPH

Annual Bog Preparation

Following the production season's depletion of the harvest strips, the fields are left excessively out-of-shape, with heavy wood and stumps exposed on the surface and the ditches blocked or filled with eroded peat. The ditch cleaning, regrinding, shaping and fine grading operations are repeated as in the initial bog preparation phases to correct this situation.

See Table 4 for equipment and production rates.

RECLAMATION

Attempts over the years to develop the deep peat lands of eastern North Carolina for agricultural purposes have had only marginal success. First Colony has attempted to convert some of its deep peat acreage into permanent pasture for a cattle program but found that the problem of heavy wood and its removal, plus the high acidity of the peat, made it an expensive endeavor.

However, once the peat has been removed down to the transition layer, which is a mixture of organic and mineral

EFFECTS OF WEATHER CONDITIONS ON PEAT PRODUCTION

Because solar energy is used to dry peat produced at First Colony Farms, weather becomes one of the most important production factors. Weather data collected from First Colony Farms and nearby weather stations has been used to determine the extent that production is likely to be affected by weather. Results show that there is an expected average of 155.5 harvesting days per year and a 99.5% chance of at least 130 harvesting days per year.

Drying rate studies of the milled peat turning operations show a variance of moisture loss. Four percentage points of moisture are lost per turn, with an optimum turning time interval of two hours, in mid to late-March. Seven percentage points of moisture are lost per turn, with an optimum turning time interval of one-half hour, in July. And four percentage points of moisture are lost per turn, with an optimum turning time interval of 3 hours, in late October and early November. These drying rates, along with a 3 day production cycle and allowance for deep production milling, will result in an average of 26 to 40 harvests per year.

Studies of sod peat drying rates indicate that, in an average year, there will be sixteen production cycles with an average of sixteen days per cycle.

Tables 5 and 6 show the projected production and harvest days of a milled and sod peat production operation for a typical year.

FIRST COLONY FARMS, INC.
CRESWELL, N.C.

MILLED PEAT PRODUCTION
PRODUCTION vs. HARVEST CYCLES

TABLE 5

Legend:
- X - TOO WET
- P - PRODUCE ONLY
- S - SINGLE HARVEST POTENTIAL
- M - MULTIPLE HARVEST POTENTIAL

Key: H&P = Harvest & Produce · PO = Produce Only · TW = Too Wet to Work

Day	Mar H&P	Mar PO	Mar TW	Apr H&P	Apr PO	Apr TW	May H&P	May PO	May TW	Jun H&P	Jun PO	Jun TW	Jul H&P	Jul PO	Jul TW	Aug H&P	Aug PO	Aug TW	Sep H&P	Sep PO	Sep TW	Oct H&P	Oct PO	Oct TW	Nov H&P	Nov PO	Nov TW
1			X	S			M					X			X	M			M					X	S		
2		P		S			M					X	S			M				P				X	S		
3	S				P							X			X	S			S					X			X
4	S					X	M					X	M			M					X	M			S		
5	S				P				X			X	S			M					X		P		S		
6			X		P			P			P		M			M					X	M			S		
7			X	S				P			P		M			M				P		M			S		
8		P		S			M			S			M			M			M			M			S		
9	S			M					X			X	M			M			M			M			S		
10	S			M				P				X	M			M					X	S			S		
11		P		M			S					X	M					X	M			M				P	
12	S					X			X	M			S					X	M			M					X
13	S					X			X	M			S			M			S				P			P	
14	S					X			X	M					X		P			P		M				P	
15	S				P				X			X	M			M			S			M				P	
16	S			M					X			X	M			M			M			M				P	
17	S			M					X	S					X	M			M			M				P	
18	S			M					X	M			M			M			M			M				P	
19	S					X			X	M					X	M			M			M				P	
20	S					X			X			X			X			X	M					X		P	
21	S					X			X			X			X	M			S			M				P	
22	S					X			X			X	S				P		S			S				P	
23	S				P				X			X		P		S			S			M				P	
24			X		P				X	S				P				X			X	M				P	
25		P		M				P			P			P			P				X	M					X
26		P		M				P			P		S			M				P		M					X
27	S			M					X	M			S			M				P		M				P	
28	S			M					X	M			S			M			S			M				P	
29	S			M					X	M			M			M					X	M				P	
30	S			M					X	M			M			M					X	M					X
31	S								X				M			M						M					
TOTAL DAYS OF HARVEST & PRODUCE	**22**			**16**			**6**			**12**			**21.5**			**24.5**			**17**			**25**			**9**		
TOTAL DAYS OF PRODUCE ONLY		**5**			**6**			**5**			**4**			**3**			**3**			**5**			**2**			**16**	
TOTAL DAYS OF NO WORK			**4**			**8**			**20**			**14**			**6.5**			**3.5**			**8**			**4**			**5**

TOTALS: Harvest & Produce = 153 · Produce Only = 49 · No Work = 73

326

SOD PEAT PRODUCTION
PRODUCTION vs. HARVEST CYCLES

TABLE 6

DAY OF MONTH	MARCH TOO WET TO WORK	MARCH PRODUCE ONLY	MARCH PRODUCE & HARVEST	APRIL TOO WET TO WORK	APRIL PRODUCE ONLY	APRIL PRODUCE & HARVEST	MAY TOO WET TO WORK	MAY PRODUCE ONLY	MAY PRODUCE & HARVEST	JUNE TOO WET TO WORK	JUNE PRODUCE ONLY	JUNE PRODUCE & HARVEST	JULY TOO WET TO WORK	JULY PRODUCE ONLY	JULY PRODUCE & HARVEST	AUGUST TOO WET TO WORK	AUGUST PRODUCE ONLY	AUGUST PRODUCE & HARVEST	SEPTEMBER TOO WET TO WORK	SEPTEMBER PRODUCE ONLY	SEPTEMBER PRODUCE & HARVEST	OCTOBER TOO WET TO WORK	OCTOBER PRODUCE ONLY	OCTOBER PRODUCE & HARVEST	NOVEMBER TOO WET TO WORK	NOVEMBER PRODUCE ONLY	NOVEMBER PRODUCE & HARVEST
1	x				P28	H18		P50	H39	x			x				P100	H90		P128	H115	x					H162
2		P1			P29	H19		P51	H40	x				P75			P101	H91,92		P129		x					H163
3		P2		x				P52		x				P76	H68		P102	H93		P130	H116,117	x			x		
4		P3		x				P53	H42,43	x				P77			P103		x				P147	H139			H164
5		P4		x			x			x				P78	H69		P104	H94	x				P148	H140			H165
6	x				P30		x			x				P79	H70		P105	H95	x				P149	H141			
7	x				P31			P54			P61	H52-58		P80			P106	H96	x				P150	H142			H166
8		P5			P32	H20		P55			P62	H59		P81			P107	H97		P131			P151	H143			H167
9		P6			P33	H21		P56			P63	H60		P82	H71		P108	H98		P132			P152				H168
10		P7			P34	H22	x				P64			P83	H72		P109	H99		P133		x					
11		P8			P35	H23	x			x				P84	H73		P110	H100,101		P134		x					
12		P9			P36	H24		P57	H44,45	x				P85	H74,75	x				P135			P153	H144,146			
13		P10		x				P58	H47	x				P86		x				P136			P154				
14		P11		x			x				P65			P87	H76,77		P111			P137			P155	H147			
15		P12			P37		x				P66	-		P88	H78		P112			P138			P156	H148			
16		P13			P38		x			x				P89	H79		P113			P139	H118		P157	H149			
17		P14	H1		P39	H25	x			x				P90	H80		P114	H102,103		P140	H119,120		P158	H150			
18		P15	H2,5		P40	H26	x				P67			P91			P115	H104		P141	H121,131		P159	H151			
19		P16	H3,6		P41	H27,30	x				P68		x				P116	H105		P142	H122,123 125,132		P160	H152			
20		P17	H4		P42	H28,31	x				P69		x				P117	H106		P143	H124 126,133		P161				
21		P18	H7,8		P43	H29,32	x				P70	H61	x				P118	H107	x				P162				
22		P19	H8,10		P44	H35	x			x			x				P119	H108	x				P163	H153			
23		P20	H11		P45	H34	x			x				P92			P120		x				P164				
24	x			x			x			x				P93	H81		P121	H109	x			x					
25		P21			P46	H35-38	x			x							P122	H110,111					P165	H154,155			
26		P22	H12	x				P59	H46,48	x				P94	H82,83		P123	H112		P144			P166	H156			
27		P23	H13	x				P60	H49-51		P71	H62,64		P95	H84		P124	H113,114		P145	H127-129 134-136		P167	H157			
28		P24	H14		P47						P72	H65		P96	H85	x				P146	H130 137,138		P168	H158			
29		P25	H15		P48		x				P73	H66		P97	H86		P125		x					H159			
30		P26	H16		P49		x				P74	H67		P98	H87		P126		x					H160			
31		P27	H17				x							P99	H88,89		P127							H161			TOTALS

	MARCH	APRIL	MAY	JUNE	JULY	AUGUST	SEPTEMBER	OCTOBER	NOVEMBER	
TOTAL DAYS OF HARVEST & PRODUCE	13	15	7	8	18	20	9	(3) 17	HARVEST ONLY (10) 7	107
TOTAL DAYS OF PRODUCE ONLY	14	7	4	6	7	8	10	5	—	61
TOTAL DAYS OF NO WORK	4	8	20	16	6	3	11	6		74

P1- "P" INDICATES SOD PRODUCTION,
H1- "H" INDICATES SOD HARVEST,

#- INDICATES FIRST PRODUCTION RUN
&- INDICATES HARVEST OF FIRST PRODUCTION RUN

16 days per cycle =

$\frac{2,698 \text{ accumulative drying days}}{168 \text{ potential production-harvest cycles}}$

327

soils, it can be easily converted to highly productive agricultural land that has the drainage installed, the wood removed, the fields sloped and a high natural pH.

In 1977 First Colony Farms removed five and one-half
feet of peat from an area approximately 60 feet wide and
1,700 feet long exposing the transition layer. This layer
was disked into the underlying mineral soils, the land limed,
fertilized and prepared for planting the same as any other
first year land. One-half of the strip was planted in soybeans and one-half in milo which produced yields of 38
bushels per acre of beans and 76 bushels per acre of milo.

Two additional strips have since been developed in
other areas of the Phelps Bog. Crop yields for all three
strips are averaging between 40 and 50 bushels of soybeans
per acre and 150 to 160 bushels of corn per acre.

SUMMARY

The program at First Colony Farms has deomonstrated that
a high grade fuel peat can be economically produced by both
the milled peat and sod peat methods from the highly
decomposed and woody bogs found along the coastal plain of
eastern North Carolina.

BIOMASS-TO-METHANOL SPECIALISTS' WORKSHOP

March 3-5, 1982

Tamarron
Durango, Colorado

LIST OF ATTENDEES

Suresh Babu
Institute of Gas Technology
342A South State Street
Chicago, IL 60616
312/567-5758

Michel Bernon
French Scientific Mission
Scientific Attaché
2011 Eye Street N.W.
Washington, DC 20006
202/659-3550

Charles J. Bishop
A.O. Smith Corporation
P.O. Box 584
Milwaukee, WI 53201
414/447-4226

John Black
Omnifuel Gasification Systems Limited
3284 Yonge Street, Suite 501
Toronto, Ontario, Canada M4N 3M7
416/485-0701

Paul B. Boyd
United Catalysts, Inc.
P.O. Box 32370
Louisville, KY 40232
502/637-9751

Oliver Brandon
Energy Technology Support Unit
Building 156, AERE Harwell
Oxfordshire OX11 ORA, England
Tel: Abingdon (0235) 834621
Telex: 83135

Paul Danish
Rocky Mountain Business Journal
Box 4522
Boulder, CO 80306
303/934-2411 or 303/443-6518

Garvin De Shazer
Energos Systems, Inc.
11000 E. Yale Ave., Suite 103
Aurora, CO 80014

Joseph G. Finegold
Solar Energy Research Institute
1617 Cole Blvd.
Golden, CO 80401
303/231-1016   FTS 327-1016

Marshall E. Frank
Chem Systems, Inc.
303 S. Broadway
Tarrytown, NY 10591
914/631-2828

Simon Friedrich
Biomass Energy Technology Division
Dapartment of Energy
Forrestal Building
1000 Independence Avenue
Washington, DC 21085

Steve Gage
International Harvester
16 W. 160 83rd Street
Burr Ridge, IL 60521
312/887-5490

Michael Graboski
Colorado School of Mines
Golden, CO 80401
303/279-0300, 2764

Robert Graham
Forintek Canada Corporation
800 Montreal Road
Ottawa, Canada K1G 3Z5
519/679-2416, 3176

Adi R. Guzdar
Foster-Miller, Inc.
35D Second Avenue
Waltham, MA 02154
617/890-3200

Joseph H.S. Haggin
Chemical & Engineering News
176 W. Adams Street, Suite 1433
Chicago, IL 60603
312/236-7325

D. Andrew Himmelblau
Sone and Webster Engineering Corp.
245 Summer Street
Boston, MA 02107
617/973-0390

Arthur Hornig
Thagard Systems, Inc.
2712 Kelvin Avenue
Irvine, CA 92705
617/276-6110

Donald L. Klass
IGT
3424 South State Street
Chicago, IL 60616
312/567-3783

Kamil Klier
Department of Chemistry
Lehigh University
Bethlehem, PA 18015
215/861-3577

Stephen M. Kohan
Electric Power Research Institute
P.O. Box 10412
Palo Alto, CA 94303
415/855-2679

Kevin J. Lally
Colorado School of Mines
Golden, CO 80401
303/279-0300, 2764

Nils Lindman
Royal Institute of Technology
Department of Chemical Technology
S-10044 Stockholm, Sweden
Tel : Stockholm 7878248

Thomas R. and Pam Miles
Thomas R. Miles Consulting Design
            Engineers
5475 S.W. Arrowwood Lane
Portland, OR 97225
503/292-0107

Thomas Milne
Solar Energy Research Institute
1617 Cole Blvd.
Golden, CO 80401
303/231-1440 FTS 327-1440

Lyle K. Mudge
Battelle Northwest Laboratory
P.O. Box 999
Richland, WA 99352
509/375-2268

Charles R. Nelson
Gas Research Institute
8600 W. Bryn Mawr
Chicago, IL 60631
312/399-8214

Thomas O'Connell
International Harvester
16 W. 160 83rd Street
Burr Ridge, IL 60521
312/887-2372

Michael Onischak
Manager, Gasification Development
Institute of Gas Technology
3424 South State Street
IIT Center
Chicago, IL 60616
312/567-5830

Leslie A. Oster
KBW Gasification Systems, Inc.
1403 Chamber of Commerce Bldg.
Pittsburgh, PA 15219
412/227-3188

Thomas B. Reed
Solar Energy Research Institute
1617 Cole Blvd.
Golden, CO 80401
303/231-1437 FTS 327-1437

Phil Rich
JPR Associates, Inc.
P.O. Box 280
Stowe, VT 05672
802/253-7220

David Salisbury
Christian Science Monitor
2991 Folsom
Boulder, CO 80302
303/447-0168

Gary F. Schiefelbein
Pacific Northwest Laboratory
Box 999
Richalnd, WA 99352
509/375-2140

Clayton S. Smith
Solar Energy Research Institute
1617 Cole Blvd.
Golden, CO 80401
303/231-1372 FTS 327-1372

William Stevenson
Evergreen Energy Corporation
200 Fifth Avenue
Waltham, MA 02254
617/890-1646

Chuck Stone
Future Fuels of America
1127 11th Street, Suite 318
Sacramento, CA 95814
916/447-2991

Lars P. Waldheim
Studsvik Energiteknik AB
S-61182 Nyköping
Sweden
Tel: + 46 155 80000

Henry T. Wilson
Foster Wheeler Power Products, LTD.
Greater London House
Hampstead Road
London, United Kingdom NW1 7QN
Tel: 01 388 1212 Ext. 569

Victor Yang
Senior Engineer, Systems Division
CTP - Centro De Tecnologio Promon
Avenida Nove de Julho 4939, Bloco A-11
Jardim Paulista, São Paulo
Brasil 01407
011/280-8044 Ext. 602